D1289957

THE
UNIVERSITY OF WINNIPEG
PORTAGE & BALMORAL
WINNIPEG 2. MAN.   CANADA

DISCARDED

THE SHREWSBURY EDITION OF THE WORKS OF
SAMUEL BUTLER.   EDITED BY HENRY FESTING JONES
AND A. T. BARTHOLOMEW.   IN TWENTY VOLUMES.
VOLUME FIFTEEN: THE ODYSSEY

" From some points of view it is impossible to take the Odyssey seriously enough; from others, it is impossible to take it seriously at all; but from whichever point of view it be regarded, its beauty is alike unsurpassable."—*Private letter to the translator.*

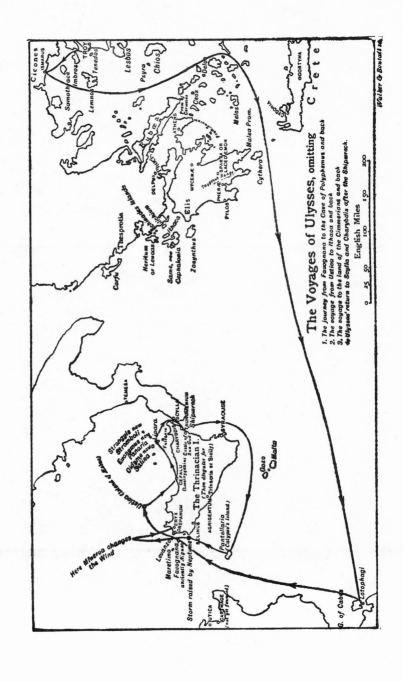

The Voyages of Ulysses, omitting

1. The journey from Favognana to the Cave of Polyphemus and back
2. The voyage from Ustica to Ithaca and back
3. The voyage to the land of the Cimmerians and back
4. Ulysses' return to Scylla and Charybdis after the Shipwreck.

English Miles

0   25   50   100   150   200

Walker & Boutall sc.

PR
4349
.B7
1968
v.15

THE ODYSSEY

RENDERED INTO ENGLISH PROSE

by

SAMUEL BUTLER

AMS PRESS
NEW YORK

All rights reserved
Reprinted with permission
From the edition of 1925, London & New York
First AMS EDITION published 1968
Manufactured in the United States of America

AMS PRESS, INC.
New York, N.Y. 10003

AL PROFESSORE
CAV. BIAGIO INGROIA
PREZIOSO ALLEATO
L'AUTORE RICONOSCENTE

Contents

The Odyssey

Contents

Illustrations

THE *ODYSSEY RENDERED INTO ENGLISH* *prose for the use of those who cannot read the original* appeared in 1900. In 1922 a new edition appeared simultaneously with a new edition of *The Authoress* *of the Odyssey*. The present edition is a reprint of that of 1922, as to which the reader is referred to pp. xix, xx, *post*, with a few minor corrections and alterations. Some account of the genesis of the two books and of their subsequent history will be found in the Introduction to the Shrewsbury Edition of *The Authoress*.

New collotypes have been substituted for the old half-tones, Butler's own negatives (some of which have been kindly lent by the Master and Fellows of St. John's College, Cambridge) being used for the purpose.

An additional illustration appears opposite p. 97.

1925.   H.F.J.
                                         A.T.B.

BUTLER'S TRANSLATION OF THE ODYS-
SEY appeared originally in 1900, and *The Authoress of the Odyssey* in 1897. In the preface[1] to the
new edition of *The Authoress* I have given some
account of the genesis of the two books.

*

With the exception of a few minor alterations and
re-arrangements now to be enumerated so far as they
affect the Translation, the new editions are faithful
reprints of the original editions, with misprints and
obvious errors corrected—no attempt having been
made to edit them or to bring them up to date.

(*a*) It has been necessary to shorten some of the headlines, and here advantage has been taken of various
corrections of and additions to the headlines made by
Butler in his own copies of the two books.

(*b*) For the most part each of the illustrations now
occupies a page, whereas in the original editions they
generally appeared two on one page. It has been
necessary to reduce the plan of the House of Ulysses
and the map of the voyages of Ulysses.

On page 161 of *The Authoress* Butler says: "No
great poet would compare his hero to a paunch full of
blood and fat, cooking before the fire (xx, 24-28)."
This passage is not given in full in the abridged Story
of the Odyssey at the beginning of the book, but in
the Translation it occurs in these words:

" Thus he chided with his heart, and checked it into
endurance, but he tossed about as one who turns a
paunch full of blood and fat in front of a hot fire, doing
it first on one side then on the other, that he may get it
cooked as soon as possible; even so did he turn himself

[1] This preface has been re-written and enlarged for the
Shrewsbury Edition.–H.F.J.

about from side to side, thinking all the time how, single-handed as he was, he should contrive to kill so large a body of men as the wicked suitors."

It looks as though in the interval between the publication of *The Authoress* (1897) and of the Translation (1900) Butler had changed his mind; for in the first case the comparison is between Ulysses and a paunch full, etc., and in the second it is between Ulysses and a man who turns a paunch full, etc. The second comparison is perhaps one which a great poet might make.

In seeing the works through the press I have had the invaluable assistance of Mr. A. T. Bartholomew of the University Library, Cambridge, and of Mr. Donald S. Robertson, Fellow of Trinity College, Cambridge. To both these friends I give my most cordial thanks for the care and skill exercised by them. Mr. Robertson has found time for the labour of checking and correcting all the quotations from and references to the Iliad and Odyssey, and I believe that it could not have been better performed. It was, I know, a pleasure for him; and it would have been a pleasure also for Butler if he could have known that his work was being shepherded by the son of his old friend, Mr. H. R. Robertson, who more than half a century ago was a fellow-student with him at Cary's School of Art in Streatham Street, Bloomsbury.

4th December 1921.   H.F.J.

THIS TRANSLATION IS INTENDED TO supplement a work entitled *The Authoress of the Odyssey*, which I published in 1897. I could not give the whole Odyssey in that book without making it unwieldy, I therefore epitomized my translation, which was already completed and which I now publish in full.

I shall not here argue the two main points dealt with in the work just mentioned; I have nothing either to add to, or to withdraw from, what I have there written. The points in question are:

(1) that the Odyssey was written entirely at, and drawn entirely from, the place now called Trapani on the West Coast of Sicily, alike as regards the Phaeacian and the Ithaca scenes; while the voyages of Ulysses, when once he is within easy reach of Sicily, resolve themselves into a periplus of the island, practically from Trapani back to Trapani, via the Lipari islands, the Straits of Messina, and the island of Pantellaria;

(2) that the poem was entirely written by a very young woman, who lived at the place now called Trapani, and introduced herself into her work under the name of Nausicaa.

The main arguments on which I base the first of these somewhat startling contentions, have been prominently and repeatedly before the English and Italian public ever since they appeared (without rejoinder) in the *Athenaeum* for 30th January and 20th February 1892. Both contentions were urged (also without rejoinder) in the Johnian *Eagle* for the Lent and October Terms of the same year. Nothing to which I should reply has reached me from any quarter, and knowing how anxiously I have endeavoured to learn the existence of any flaws in my argument, I begin to feel some confidence that, did such flaws exist, I should have heard, at any rate about some of them, before now. Without, therefore, for a moment pretending to think that scholars generally acquiesce in my conclusions, I shall act as thinking them little likely so to gainsay me as that it will be incumbent upon me to reply, and shall confine myself to translating the Odyssey for English readers, with such notes as I think will be found useful. Among these I would especially call attention to one on xxii, 465-473, which Lord Grimthorpe has kindly allowed me to make public.

I have repeated several of the illustrations used in *The Authoress of the Odyssey*, and have added two which I hope may bring the outer court of Ulysses' house more vividly before the reader. I should like to explain that the presence of a man and a dog in one illustration is accidental, and was not observed by me till I developed the negative. In an appendix I have also reprinted the paragraphs explanatory of the plan of Ulysses' house, together with the plan itself. The reader is recommended to study this plan with some attention.

In the preface to my translation of the Iliad I have given my views as to the main principles by which a translator should be guided, and need not repeat them here, beyond pointing out that the initial liberty of translating poetry into prose involves the continual taking of more or less liberty throughout the translation; for much that is right in poetry is wrong in prose, and the exigencies of readable prose are the first things to be considered in a prose translation. That the reader, however, may see how far I have departed from strict construe, I will print here Messrs. Butcher and Lang's translation of the first sixty lines or so of the Odyssey. Their translation runs:

" Tell me, Muse, of that man, so ready at need, who

wandered far and wide, after he had sacked the sacred [1] citadel of Troy, and many were the men whose towns he saw and whose mind he learnt, yea, and many the woes he suffered in his heart on the deep, striving to win his own life and the return of his company. Nay, but even so he saved not his company, though he desired it sore. For through the blindness of their own hearts they perished, fools, who devoured the oxen of Helios Hyperion: but the god took from them their day of returning. Of these things, goddess, daughter of Zeus, whencesoever thou hast heard thereof, declare thou even unto us.

" Now all the rest, as many as fled from sheer destruction, were at home, and had escaped both war and sea, but Odysseus only, craving for his wife and for his homeward path, the lady nymph Calypso held, that [2] fair goddess, in her hollow caves, longing to have him for her lord. But when now the year had come in the courses of the seasons, wherein the gods had ordained that he should return home to Ithaca, not even there was he quit of labours, not even among his own; but all the gods had pity on him save Poseidon, who raged continually against god-like Odysseus, till he came to his own country. Howbeit Poseidon had now departed for the distant Ethiopians, the Ethiopians that are sundered in twain, the uttermost of men, abiding some where Hyperion sinks and some where he rises. There he looked to receive his hecatomb of bulls and rams, there he made merry, sitting at the feast, but the other gods were gathered in the halls of Olympian Zeus. Then among them the father of men and gods began to speak, for he bethought him in his heart of

[1] I omit Messrs. Butcher and Lang's note on this word, the Greek for which admits of more than one interpretation.

[2] I again omit Messrs. Butcher and Lang's note.

noble Aegisthus, whom the son of Agamemnon, far-famed Orestes, slew. Thinking upon him he spake out among the Immortals:

" ' Lo you now, how vainly mortal men do blame the gods! For of us they say comes evil, whereas they even of themselves, through the blindness of their own hearts, have sorrows beyond that which is ordained. Even as of late Aegisthus, beyond that which was ordained, took to him the wedded wife of the son of Atreus and killed her lord on his return, and that with sheer doom before his eyes, since we had warned him by the embassy of Hermes the keen-sighted, the slayer of Argos, that he should neither kill the man, nor woo his wife. For the son of Atreus shall be avenged at the hand of Orestes, as soon as he shall come to man's estate and long for his own country. So spake Hermes, yet he prevailed not on the heart of Aegisthus, for all his good will; but now hath he paid one price for all.'

" And the goddess, grey-eyed Athene, answered him, saying: ' O father, our father Cronides, throned in the highest; that man assuredly lies in a death that is his due; so perish likewise all who work such deeds! But my heart is rent for wise Odysseus, the hapless one, who far from his friends this long while suffereth affliction in a sea-girt isle, where is the navel of the sea, a woodland isle, and therein a goddess hath her habitation, the daughter of the wizard Atlas, who knows the depths of every sea, and himself upholds the tall pillars which keep earth and sky asunder. His daughter it is that holds the hapless man in sorrow: and ever with soft and guileful tales she is wooing him to forgetfulness of Ithaca. But Odysseus yearning to see if it were but the smoke leap upwards from his own land, hath a desire to die. As for thee, thine heart regardeth it not at all, Olympian! What! Did not Odysseus by the

ships of the Argives make thee free offering of sacrifice
in the wide Trojan land? Wherefore wast thou then so
wroth with him, O Zeus?'"

The Odyssey (as every one knows) abounds in
passages borrowed from the Iliad; I had wished to
print these in a slightly different type, with marginal
references to the Iliad, and had marked them to this end
in my MS. I found, however, that the translation would
be thus hopelessly scholasticized, and abandoned my
intention. I would nevertheless again urge on those
who have the management of our University presses,
that they would render a great service to students if they
would publish a Greek text of the Odyssey with the
Iliadic passages printed in a different type, and with
marginal references. I have given the British Museum
a copy of the Odyssey with the Iliadic passages under-
lined and referred to in MS.; I have also given an Iliad
marked with all the Odyssean passages, and their
references;[1] but copies of both the Iliad and Odyssey
so marked ought to be within easy reach of all students.

Any one who at the present day discusses the questions that have arisen round the Iliad since Wolf's time,
without keeping it well before his reader's mind that
the Odyssey was demonstrably written from one single
neighbourhood, and hence (even though nothing else
pointed to this conclusion) presumably by one person
only – that it was written certainly before 750, and in all
probability before 1000 B.C. – that the writer of this
very early poem was demonstrably familiar with the
Iliad as we now have it, borrowing as freely from those
books whose genuineness has been most impugned, as
from those which are admitted to be by Homer – any
one who fails to keep these points well before his

[1] The press-marks of these books are, for the Odyssey, Bks. 3.
c. 2 ; and, for the Iliad, Bks. 3. c. 3.

readers, is hardly dealing equitably by them. Any one on the other hand, who will mark his Iliad and his Odyssey from the copies in the British Museum above referred to, and who will draw the only inference that common sense can draw from the presence of so many identical passages in both poems, will, I believe, find no difficulty in assigning their proper value to a large number of books here and on the Continent that at present enjoy considerable reputations. Furthermore, and this perhaps is an advantage better worth securing, he will find many puzzles of the Odyssey cease to puzzle him on the discovery that they arise from over-saturation with the Iliad.

Other difficulties will also disappear as soon as the development of the poem in the writer's mind is understood. I have dealt with this at some length in pp. 261-272 [1] of *The Authoress of the Odyssey*. Briefly, the Odyssey consists of two distinct poems: (1) The Return of Ulysses, which alone the Muse is asked to sing in the opening lines of the poem. This poem includes the Phaeacian episode, and the account of Ulysses' adventures as told by himself in Books ix-xii. It consists of lines 1-79 (roughly) of Book i, of line 28 of Book v, and thence without intermission to the middle of line 187 of Book xiii, at which point the original scheme was abandoned.

(2) The story of Penelope and the suitors, with the episode of Telemachus's voyage to Pylos. This poem begins with line 80 (roughly) of Book i, is continued to the end of Book iv, and not resumed till Ulysses wakes in the middle of line 187, Book xiii, from whence it continues to the end of Book xxiv.

In *The Authoress of the Odyssey* I wrote:

[1] The references to *The Authoress* have been adapted throughout to the Shrewsbury Edition of that work.–A.T.B.

Preface to the First Edition

" The introduction of lines xi, 115-137, and of line ix, 535, with the writing a new council of the gods at the beginning of Book v, to take the place of the one that was removed to Book i, 1-79, were the only things that were done to give even a semblance of unity to the old scheme and the new, and to conceal the fact that the Muse, after being asked to sing of one subject, spent two-thirds of her time in singing a very different one, with a climax for which no one has asked her. For roughly the Return occupies eight Books, and Penelope and the Suitors sixteen."

I believe this to be substantially correct.

Lastly, to deal with a very unimportant point, I observe that the Leipsic Teubner edition of 1894 makes Books ii and iii end with a comma. Stops are things of such far more recent date than the Odyssey, that there does not seem much use in adhering to the text in so small a matter; still, from a spirit of mere conservatism, I have preferred to do so. Why ᾿Ημος at the beginnings of Books ii and viii, and ῾Ωc at the beginning of Book vii should have initial capitals in an edition far too careful to admit a supposition of inadvertence, when ὡc at the beginning of Books vi and xiii, and ημος at the beginning of Book xvii have no initial capitals, I cannot determine. No other Books of the Odyssey have initial capitals except the three above mentioned, unless the first word of the Book is a proper name.

25th July 1900.   S. BUTLER.

BOOK ONE: THE GODS IN COUNCIL, MINERVA'S VISIT TO ITHACA, THE CHALLENGE FROM TELEMACHUS TO THE SUITORS

TELL ME, O MUSE, OF THAT INGENIOUS hero who travelled far and wide after he had sacked the famous town of Troy. Many cities did he visit, and many were the nations with whose manners and customs he was acquainted; moreover he suffered much by sea while trying to save his own life and bring his men safely home; but do what he might he could not save his men, for they perished through their own sheer folly in eating the cattle of the Sun-god Hyperion; so the god prevented them from ever reaching home. Tell me, too, about all these things, O daughter of Jove, from whatsoever source you may know them.

So now all who escaped death in battle or by ship- 11 wreck had got safely home except Ulysses, and he, though he was longing to return to his wife and country, was detained by the goddess Calypso, who had got him into a large cave and wanted to marry him. But as years went by, there came a time when the gods settled that he should go back to Ithaca; even then, however, when he was among his own people, his troubles were not yet over; nevertheless all the gods had now begun to pity him except Neptune, who still persecuted him without ceasing and would not let him get home.

Now Neptune had gone off to the Ethiopians, who 22 are at the world's end, and lie in two halves, the one looking West and the other East.[1] He had gone there to accept a hecatomb of sheep and oxen, and was enjoy-

[1] Black races are evidently known to the writer as stretching all across Africa, one half looking West on to the Atlantic, and the other East on to the Indian Ocean.

ing himself at his festival; but the other gods met in the house of Olympian Jove, and the sire of gods and men spoke first. At that moment he was thinking of Aegisthus, who had been killed by Agamemnon's son Orestes; so he said to the other gods:

32 "See now, how men lay blame upon us gods for what is after all nothing but their own folly. Look at Aegisthus; he must needs make love to Agamemnon's wife unrighteously and then kill Agamemnon, though he knew it would be the death of him; for I sent Mercury to warn him not to do either of these things, inasmuch as Orestes would be sure to take his revenge when he grew up and wanted to return home. Mercury told him this in all good will but he would not listen, and now he has paid for everything in full."

44 Then Minerva said, "Father, son of Saturn, King of kings, it served Aegisthus right, and so it would any one else who does as he did; but Aegisthus is neither here nor there; it is for Ulysses that my heart bleeds, when I think of his sufferings in that lonely sea-girt island, far away, poor man, from all his friends. It is an island covered with forest, in the very middle of the sea, and a goddess lives there, daughter of the magician Atlas, who looks after the bottom of the ocean, and carries the great columns that keep heaven and earth asunder. This daughter of Atlas has got hold of poor unhappy Ulysses, and keeps trying by every kind of blandishment to make him forget his home, so that he is tired of life, and thinks of nothing but how he may once more see the smoke of his own chimneys. You, sir, take no heed of this, and yet when Ulysses was before Troy did he not propitiate you with many a burnt sacrifice? Why then should you keep on being so angry with him?"

63 And Jove said, "My child, what are you talking

2

about? How can I forget Ulysses than whom there is
no more capable man on earth, nor more liberal in his
offerings to the immortal gods that live in heaven?
Bear in mind, however, that Neptune is still furious
with Ulysses for having blinded an eye of Polyphemus
king of the Cyclopes. Polyphemus is son to Neptune
by the nymph Thoosa, daughter to the sea-king Phorcys;
therefore though he will not kill Ulysses outright, he
torments him by preventing him from getting home.
Still, let us lay our heads together and see how we can
help him to return; Neptune will then be pacified, for
if we are all of a mind he can hardly stand out against
us."

And Minerva said, " Father, son of Saturn, King of 80
kings, if, then, the gods now mean that Ulysses should
get home, we should first send Mercury to the Ogygian
island to tell Calypso that we have made up our minds
and that he is to return. In the meantime I will go to
Ithaca, to put heart into Ulysses' son Telemachus; I
will embolden him to call the Achaeans in assembly, and
speak out to the suitors of his mother Penelope, who
persist in eating up any number of his sheep and oxen;
I will also conduct him to Sparta and to Pylos, to see if
he can hear anything about the return of his dear father
–for this will make people speak well of him."

So saying she bound on her glittering golden sandals, 96
imperishable, with which she can fly like the wind over
land or sea; she grasped the redoubtable bronze-shod
spear, so stout and sturdy and strong, wherewith she
quells the ranks of heroes who have displeased her, and
down she darted from the topmost summits of Olympus,
whereon forthwith she was in Ithaca, at the gateway of
Ulysses' house, disguised as a visitor, Mentes, chief of
the Taphians, and she held a bronze spear in her hand.
There she found the lordly suitors seated on hides of

3

the oxen which they had killed and eaten, and playing draughts in front of the house. Men-servants and pages were bustling about to wait upon them, some mixing wine with water in the mixing-bowls, some cleaning down the tables with wet sponges and laying them out again, and some cutting up great quantities of meat.

113 Telemachus saw her long before any one else did. He was sitting moodily among the suitors thinking about his brave father, and how he would send them flying out of the house, if he were to come to his own again and be honoured as in days gone by. Thus brooding as he sat among them, he caught sight of Minerva and went straight to the gate, for he was vexed that a stranger should be kept waiting for admittance. He took her right hand in his own, and bade her give him her spear. " Welcome," said he, " to our house, and when you have partaken of food you shall tell us what you have come for."

125 He led the way as he spoke, and Minerva followed him. When they were within he took her spear and set it in the spear-stand against a strong bearing-post along with the many other spears of his unhappy father, and he conducted her to a richly decorated seat under which he threw a cloth of damask. There was a foot-stool also for her feet,[1] and he set another seat near her for himself, away from the suitors, that she might not be annoyed while eating by their noise and insolence, and that he might ask her more freely about his father.

136 A maid servant then brought them water in a beautiful golden ewer and poured it into a silver basin for them to wash their hands, and she drew a clean table beside them. An upper servant brought them bread,

[1] The original use of the footstool was probably less to rest the feet than to keep them (especially when bare) from a floor which was often wet and dirty.

and offered them many good things of what there was
in the house, the carver fetched them plates of all manner
of meats and set cups of gold by their side, and a man-
servant brought them wine and poured it out for them.

Then the suitors came in and took their places on the 144
benches and seats.[1] Forthwith men servants poured
water over their hands, maids went round with the
bread-baskets, pages filled the mixing-bowls with wine
and water, and they laid their hands upon the good
things that were before them. As soon as they had had
enough to eat and drink they wanted music and
dancing, which are the crowning embellishments of
a banquet, so a servant brought a lyre to Phemius,
whom they compelled perforce to sing to them. As
soon as he touched his lyre and began to sing Telemachus spoke low to Minerva, with his head close to
hers that no man might hear.

" I hope, sir," said he, " that you will not be offended 158
with what I am going to say. Singing comes cheap to
those who do not pay for it, and all this is done at the
cost of one whose bones lie rotting in some wilderness
or grinding to powder in the surf. If these men were
to see my father come back to Ithaca they would pray
for longer legs rather than a longer purse, for money
would not serve them; but he, alas, has fallen on an ill
fate, and even when people do sometimes say that he is
coming, we no longer heed them; we shall never see
him again. And now, sir, tell me and tell me true, who
you are and where you come from. Tell me of your
town and parents, what manner of ship you came in,
how your crew brought you to Ithaca, and of what

---

[1] The θρόΝοc or seat, is occasionally called " high," as being
higher than the θρᾶΝΥc or low footstool. It was probably no
higher than an ordinary chair is now, and seems to have had no
back.

nation they declared themselves to be–for you cannot have come by land. Tell me also truly, for I want to know, are you a stranger to this house, or have you been here in my father's time? In the old days we had many visitors for my father went about much himself."

178   And Minerva answered, " I will tell you truly and particularly all about it. I am Mentes, son of Anchialus, and I am King of the Taphians. I have come here with my ship and crew, on a voyage to men of a foreign tongue being bound for Temesa[1] with a cargo of iron, and I shall bring back copper. As for my ship, it lies over yonder off the open country away from the town, in the harbour Rheithron [2] under the wooded mountain Neritum.[3] Our fathers were friends before us, as old Laertes will tell you, if you will go and ask him. They say, however, that he never comes to town now, and lives by himself in the country, faring hardly, with an old woman to look after him and get his dinner for him, when he comes in tired from pottering about his vineyard. They told me your father was at home again, and that was why I came, but it seems the gods are still keeping him back, for he is not dead yet–not on the mainland. It is more likely he is on some sea-girt island in mid ocean, or a prisoner among savages who are detaining him against his will. I am no prophet, and know very little about omens, but I speak as it is

[1] Temesa was on the West Coast of the toe of Italy, in what is now the gulf of Sta Eufemia. It was famous in remote times for its copper mines, which, however, were worked out when Strabo wrote.

[2] *I.e.,* " with a current in it "–see illustrations and map near the end of bks. v and vi respectively.

[3] Reading Nηρίτῳ for Nηίῳ, *cf.* Od., iii, 81, where the same mistake is made, and xiii, 351, where the mountain is called Neritum, the same place being intended both here and in book xiii.

6

borne in upon me from heaven, and assure you that he
will not be away much longer; for he is a man of such
resource that even though he were in chains of iron he
would find some means of getting home again.   But
tell me, and tell me true, can Ulysses really have such a
fine looking fellow for a son?   You are indeed wonderfully like him about the head and eyes, for we were close
friends before he set sail for Troy where the flower of all
the Argives went also.   Since that time we have never
either of us seen the other."

"My mother," answered Telemachus, "tells me I 214
am son to Ulysses, but it is a wise child that knows his
own father.   Would that I were son to one who had
grown old upon his own estates, for, since you ask me,
there is no more ill-starred man under heaven than he
who they tell me is my father."

And Minerva said, "There is no fear of your race 223
dying out yet, while Penelope has such a fine son as you
are.   But tell me, and tell me true, what is the meaning
of all this feasting, and who are these people?   What is
it all about?   Have you some banquet, or is there a
wedding in the family—for no one seems to be bringing
any provisions of his own?   And the guests—how
atrociously they are behaving; what riot they make
over the whole house; it is enough to disgust any
respectable person who comes near them."

"Sir," said Telemachus, "as regards your question, 230
so long as my father was here it was well with us and
with the house, but the gods in their displeasure have
willed it otherwise, and have hidden him away more
closely than mortal man was ever yet hidden.   I could
have borne it better even though he were dead, if he
had fallen with his men before Troy, or had died with
friends around him when the days of his fighting were
done; for then the Achaeans would have built a mound

7

over his ashes, and I should myself have been heir to his renown; but now the storm-winds have spirited him away we know not whither; he is gone without leaving so much as a trace behind him, and I inherit nothing but dismay. Nor does the matter end simply with grief for the loss of my father; heaven has laid sorrows upon me of yet another kind; for the chiefs from all our islands, Dulichium, Same, and the woodland island of Zacynthus, as also all the principal men of Ithaca itself, are eating up my house under the pretext of paying their court to my mother, who will neither point blank say that she will not marry,[1] nor yet bring matters to an end; so they are making havoc of my estate, and before long will do so also with myself."

252 " Is that so? " exclaimed Minerva, " then you do indeed want Ulysses home again. Give him his helmet, shield, and a couple of lances, and if he is the man he was when I first knew him in our house, drinking and making merry, he would soon lay his hands about these rascally suitors, were he to stand once more upon his own threshold. He was then coming from Ephyra, where he had been to beg poison for his arrows from Ilus, son of Mermerus. Ilus feared the ever-living gods and would not give him any, but my father let him have some, for he was very fond of him. If Ulysses is the man he then was these suitors will have a short shrift and a sorry wedding.

267 " But there! It rests with heaven to determine whether he is to return, and take his revenge in his own house or no; I would, however, urge you to set about

[1] It is never plausibly explained why Penelope cannot do this, and from bk. ii, it is clear that she kept on deliberately encouraging the suitors, though we are asked to believe that she was only fooling them.

trying to get rid of these suitors at once. Take my advice, call the Achaean heroes in assembly to-morrow morning–lay your case before them, and call heaven to bear you witness. Bid the suitors take themselves off, each to his own place, and if your mother's mind is set on marrying again, let her go back to her father, who will find her a husband and provide her with all the marriage gifts that so dear a daughter may expect. As for yourself, let me prevail upon you to take the best ship you can get, with a crew of twenty men, and go in quest of your father who has so long been missing. Some one may tell you something, or (and people often hear things in this way) some heaven-sent message may direct you. First go to Pylos and ask Nestor; thence go on to Sparta and visit Menelaus, for he got home last of all the Achaeans; if you hear that your father is alive and on his way home, you can put up with the waste these suitors will make for yet another twelve months. If on the other hand you hear of his death, come home at once, celebrate his funeral rites with all due pomp, build a barrow to his memory, and make your mother marry again. Then, having done all this, think it well over in your mind how, by fair means or foul, you may kill these suitors in your own house. You are too old to plead infancy any longer; have you not heard how people are singing Orestes' praises for having killed his father's murderer Aegisthus? You are a fine, smart looking fellow; show your mettle, then, and make yourself a name in story. Now, however, I must go back to my ship and to my crew, who will be impatient if I keep them waiting longer; think the matter over for yourself, and remember what I have said to you."

" Sir," answered Telemachus, " it has been very kind 306 of you to talk to me in this way, as though I were your

9

own son, and I will do all you tell me; I know you want to be getting on with your voyage, but stay a little longer till you have taken a bath and refreshed yourself. I will then give you a present, and you shall go on your way rejoicing; I will give you one of great beauty and value—a keepsake such as only dear friends give to one another."

314 Minerva answered, "Do not try to keep me, for I would be on my way at once. As for any present you may be disposed to make me, keep it till I come again, and I will take it home with me. You shall give me a very good one, and I will give you one of no less value in return."

319 With these words she flew away like a bird into the air, but she had given Telemachus courage, and had made him think more than ever about his father. He felt the change, wondered at it, and knew that the stranger had been a god, so he went straight to where the suitors were sitting.

325 Phemius was still singing, and his hearers sat rapt in silence as he told the sad tale of the return from Troy, and the ills Minerva had laid upon the Achaeans. Penelope, daughter of Icarius, heard his song from her room upstairs, and came down by the great staircase, not alone, but attended by two of her handmaids. When she reached the suitors she stood by one of the bearing posts that supported the roof of the cloisters [1] with a staid maiden on either side of her. She held a veil, moreover, before her face, and was weeping bitterly.

337 "Phemius," she cried, "you know many another feat of gods and heroes, such as poets love to celebrate. Sing the suitors some one of these, and let them drink their wine in silence, but cease this sad tale, for it breaks

[1] See note on Od., i, 365.

my sorrowful heart, and reminds me of my lost husband whom I mourn ever without ceasing, and whose name was great over all Hellas and middle Argos."[1]

"Mother," answered Telemachus, "let the bard sing 345 what he has a mind to; bards do not make the ills they sing of; it is Jove, not they, who makes them, and who sends weal or woe upon mankind according to his own good pleasure. This fellow means no harm by singing the ill-fated return of the Danaans, for people always applaud the latest songs most warmly. Make up your mind to it and bear it; Ulysses is not the only man who never came back from Troy, but many another went down as well as he. Go, then, within the house and busy yourself with your daily duties, your loom, your distaff, and the ordering of your servants; for speech is man's matter, and mine above all others[2]—for it is I who am master here."

She went wondering back into the house, and laid 360 her son's saying in her heart. Then, going upstairs with her handmaids into her room, she mourned her dear husband till Minerva shed sweet sleep over her eyes. But the suitors were clamorous throughout the

---

[1] Middle Argos means the Peloponnese which, however, is never so called in the Iliad. I presume "middle" means "middle between the two Greek-speaking countries of Asia Minor and Sicily, with South Italy"; for that parts of Sicily and also large parts, though not the whole of South Italy, were inhabited by Greek-speaking races centuries before the Dorian colonizations can hardly be doubted. The Sicans, and also the Sicels, both of them probably spoke Greek.

[2] *Cf.* Il., vi, 490-495. In the Iliad it is "war," not "speech," that is a man's matter. It argues a certain hardness, or at any rate dislike of the Iliad, on the part of the writer of the Odyssey, that she should have adopted Hector's farewell to Andromache here, as elsewhere in the poem, for a scene of such inferior pathos.

covered cloisters,[1] and prayed each one that he might be her bed fellow.

368 Then Telemachus spoke, "Shameless," he cried, " and insolent suitors, let us feast at our pleasure now, and let there be no brawling, for it is a rare thing to hear a man with such a divine voice as Phemius has; but in the morning meet me in full assembly that I may give you formal notice to depart, and feast at one another's houses, turn and turn about, at your own cost. If on the other hand you choose to persist in spunging upon one man, heaven help me, but Jove shall reckon with you in full, and when you fall in my father's house there shall be no man to avenge you."

381 The suitors bit their lips as they heard him, and marvelled at the boldness of his speech. Then, Antinous, son of Eupeithes, said, " The gods seem to have given you lessons in bluster and tall talking; may Jove never grant you to be chief in Ithaca as your father was before you."

388 Telemachus answered, " Antinous, do not chide with me, but, god willing, I will be chief too if I can. Is this the worst fate you can think of for me? It is no bad thing to be a chief, for it brings both riches and honour. Still, now that Ulysses is dead there are many great men in Ithaca both old and young, and some other may take the lead among them; nevertheless I

---

[1] ΜέΓΑΡΑ ϲΚΙΟέΝΤΑ. The whole open court with the covered cloister running round it was called ΜέΓΑΡΟΝ, or ΜέΓΑΡΑ, but the covered part was distinguished by being called " shady " or " shadow-giving." It was in this part that the tables for the suitors were laid. The Fountain Court at Hampton Court may serve as an illustration (save as regards the use of arches instead of wooden supports and rafters) and the arrangement is still common in Sicily. The usual translation " shadowy " or " dusky " halls, gives a false idea of the scene.

will be chief in my own house, and will rule those
whom Ulysses has won for me."

Then Eurymachus, son of Polybus, answered, " It 399
rests with heaven to decide who shall be chief among us,
but you shall be master in your own house and over
your own possessions; no one while there is a man in
Ithaca shall do you violence nor rob you.   And now,
my good fellow, I want to know about this stranger.
What country does he come from?   Of what family is
he, and where is his estate?   Has he brought you news
about the return of your father, or was he on business
of his own?   He seemed a well-to-do man, but he
hurried off so suddenly that he was gone in a moment
before we could get to know him."

" My father is dead and gone," answered Telemachus, 412
" and even if some rumour reaches me I put no more
faith in it now.   My mother does indeed sometimes
send for a soothsayer and question him, but I give his
prophecyings no heed.   As for the stranger, he was
Mentes, son of Anchialus, chief of the Taphians, an old
friend of my father's."   But in his heart he knew that it
had been the goddess.

The suitors then returned to their singing and danc- 421
ing until the evening; but when night fell upon their
pleasuring they went home to bed each in his own
abode.¹   Telemachus's room was high up in a tower²
that looked on to the outer court; hither, then, he hied,
brooding and full of thought.   A good old woman,
Euryclea, daughter of Ops, the son of Pisenor, went
before him with a couple of blazing torches.   Laertes
had bought her with his own money when she was

¹ The reader will note the extreme care which the writer takes
to make it clear that none of the suitors were allowed to sleep in
Ulysses' house.
² See Appendix ; g, in plan of Ulysses' house.

13

quite young; he gave the worth of twenty oxen for her, and shewed as much respect to her in his household as he did to his own wedded wife, but he did not take her to his bed for he feared his wife's resentment.[1]   She it was who now lighted Telemachus to his room, and she loved him better than any of the other women in the house did, for she had nursed him when he was a baby. He opened the door of his bed room and sat down upon the bed; as he took off his shirt[2] he gave it to the good old woman, who folded it tidily up, and hung it for him over a peg by his bed side, after which she went out, pulled the door to by a silver catch, and drew the bolt home by means of the strap.[3]   But Telemachus as he lay covered with a woollen fleece kept thinking all night through of his intended voyage and of the 444 counsel that Minerva had given him.

---

[1] I imagine this passage to be a rejoinder to Il., xxiii, 702-705, in which a tripod is valued at twelve oxen, and a good useful maid-of-all-work at only four.   The scrupulous regard of Laertes for his wife's feelings is of a piece with the extreme jealousy for the honour of woman, which is manifest throughout the Odyssey.

[2] χιτῶνα. " The χιτών, or *tunica*, was a shirt or shift, and served as the chief under garment of the Greeks and Romans, whether men or women."   Smith's *Dictionary of Greek and Roman Antiquities*, under " Tunica."

[3] Doors fastened to all intents and purposes as here described may be seen in the older houses at Trapani.   There is a slot on the outer side of the door by means of which a person who has left the room can shoot the bolt.   My bedroom at the Albergo Centrale was fastened in this way.

N OW WHEN THE CHILD OF MORNING, rosy-fingered Dawn, appeared, Telemachus rose and dressed himself. He bound his sandals on to his comely feet, girded his sword about his shoulder, and left his room looking like an immortal god. He at once sent the criers round to call the people in assembly, so they called them and the people gathered thereon; then, when they were got together, he went to the place of assembly spear in hand—not alone, for his two hounds went with him. Minerva endowed him with a presence of such divine comeliness that all marvelled at him as he went by, and when he took his place in his father's seat even the oldest councillors made way for him.

Aegyptius, a man bent double with age, and of infinite experience, was the first to speak. His son Antiphus had gone with Ulysses to Ilius, land of noble steeds, but the savage Cyclops had killed him when they were all shut up in the cave, and had cooked his last dinner for him.[1] He had three sons left, of whom two still worked on their father's land, while the third, Eurynomus, was one of the suitors; nevertheless their father could not get over the loss of Antiphus, and was still weeping for him when he began his speech.

" Men of Ithaca," he said, " hear my words. From the day Ulysses left us there has been no meeting of our councillors until now; who then can it be, whether old or young, that finds it so necessary to convene us? Has

---

[1] πύματον δ' ὡπλίσσατο δόρπον. So we vulgarly say " had cooked his goose," or " had settled his hash." Aegyptius can-not of course know of the fate Antiphus had met with, for there had as yet been no news of or from Ulysses.

he got wind of some host approaching, and does he
wish to warn us, or would he speak upon some other
matter of public moment? I am sure he is an excellent
person, and I hope Jove will grant him his heart's
desire."

35   Telemachus took this speech as of good omen and
rose at once, for he was bursting with what he had to
say. He stood in the middle of the assembly and the
good herald Pisenor brought him his staff. Then,
turning to Aegyptius, " Sir," said he, " it is I, as you
will shortly learn, who have convened you, for it is I
who am the most aggrieved. I have not got wind of
any host approaching about which I would warn you,
nor is there any matter of public moment on which I
would speak. My grievance is purely personal, and
turns on two great misfortunes which have fallen upon
my house. The first of these is the loss of my excellent
father, who was chief among all you here present, and
was like a father to every one of you; the second is
much more serious, and ere long will be the utter ruin
of my estate. The sons of all the chief men among you
are pestering my mother to marry them against her will.
They are afraid to go to her father Icarius, asking him
to choose the one he likes best, and to provide marriage
gifts for his daughter, but day by day they keep hanging
about my father's house, sacrificing our oxen, sheep,
and fat goats for their banquets, and never giving so
much as a thought to the quantity of wine they drink.
No estate can stand such recklessness; we have now no
Ulysses to ward off harm from our doors, and I cannot
hold my own against them. I shall never all my days
be as good a man as he was, still I would indeed defend
myself if I had power to do so, for I cannot stand such
treatment any longer; my house is being disgraced
and ruined. Have respect, therefore, to your own

16

consciences and to public opinion. Fear, too, the
wrath of heaven, lest the gods should be displeased and
turn upon you. I pray you by Jove and Themis, who
is the beginning and the end of councils, [do not] hold
back, my friends, and leave me singlehanded[1]—unless
it be that my brave father Ulysses did some wrong to
the Achaeans which you would now avenge on me, by
aiding and abetting these suitors. Moreover, if I am
to be eaten out of house and home at all, I had rather
you did the eating yourselves, for I could then take
action against you to some purpose, and serve you with
notices from house to house till I got paid in full,
whereas now I have no remedy." [2]

With this Telemachus dashed his staff to the ground
and burst into tears. Every one was very sorry for him,
but they all sat still and no one ventured to make him
an angry answer, save only Antinous, who spoke thus:

" Telemachus, insolent braggart that you are, how
dare you try to throw the blame upon us suitors? It is
your mother's fault not ours, for she is a very artful
woman. This three years past, and close on four, she
has been driving us out of our minds, by encouraging
each one of us, and sending him messages without
meaning one word of what she says. And then there
was that other trick she played us. She set up a great
tambour frame in her room, and began to work on an
enormous piece of fine needlework. ' Sweet hearts,'
said she, ' Ulysses is indeed dead, still do not press me
to marry again immediately, wait—for I would not have
my skill in needlework perish unrecorded—till I have

---

[1] Il., xxii, 416. cχέcθε φίλοι, καί μ' οῖον ἐάcατε…. The authoress
has bungled by borrowing these words verbatim from the Iliad,
without prefixing the necessary " do not," which I have supplied.

[2] *I.e.*, you have money, and could pay when I got judgement,
whereas the suitors are men of straw.

completed a pall for the hero Laertes, to be in readiness
against the time when death shall take him. He is very
rich, and the women of the place will talk if he is laid
out without a pall.'

103   " This was what she said, and we assented; whereon
we could see her working on her great web all day long,
but at night she would unpick the stitches again by
torchlight. She fooled us in this way for three years
and we never found her out, but as time wore on and
she was now in her fourth year, one of her maids who
knew what she was doing told us, and we caught her
in the act of undoing her work, so she had to finish it
whether she would or no. The suitors, therefore, make
you this answer, that both you and the Achaeans may
understand—' Send your mother away, and bid her
marry the man of her own and of her father's choice ';
for I do not know what will happen if she goes on
plaguing us much longer with the airs she gives herself
on the score of the accomplishments Minerva has taught
her, and because she is so clever. We never yet heard
of such a woman; we know all about Tyro, Alcmena,
Mycene, and the famous women of old, but they were
nothing to your mother, any one of them. It was not
fair of her to treat us in that way, and as long as she
continues in the mind with which heaven has now
endowed her, so long shall we go on eating up your
estate; and I do not see why she should change, for
she gets all the honour and glory, and it is you who pay
for it, not she. Understand, then, that we will not go
back to our lands, neither here nor elsewhere, till she
has made her choice and married some one or other of
us."

129   Telemachus answered, " Antinous, how can I drive
the mother who bore me from my father's house? My
father is abroad and we do not know whether he is

18

alive or dead. It will be hard on me if I have to pay
Icarius the large sum which I muſt give him if I insiſt
on sending his daughter back to him. Not only will he
deal rigorously with me, but heaven will also punish
me; for my mother when she leaves the house will call
on the Erinyes to avenge her; besides, it would not be
a creditable thing to do, and I will have nothing to say
to it. If you choose to take offence at this, leave the
house and feaſt elsewhere at one another's houses at
your own coſt turn and turn about. If, on the other
hand, you eleft to persiſt in spunging upon one man,
heaven help me, but Jove shall reckon with you in full,
and when you fall in my father's house there shall be
no man to avenge you."

As he spoke Jove sent two eagles from the top of the 146
mountain, and they flew on and on with the wind,
sailing side by side in their own lordly flight. When
they were right over the middle of the assembly they
wheeled and circled about, beating the air with their
wings and glaring death into the eyes of them that were
below; then, fighting fiercely and tearing at one
another, they flew off towards the right over the town.
The people wondered as they saw them, and asked each
other what all this might be; whereon Halitherses, who
was the beſt prophet and reader of omens among them,
spoke to them plainly and in all honeſty, saying:

"Hear me, men of Ithaca, and I speak more par- 161
ticularly to the suitors, for I see mischief brewing for
them. Ulysses is not going to be away much longer;
indeed he is close at hand to deal out death and deſtruc-
tion, not on them alone, but on many another of us
who live in Ithaca. Let us then be wise in time, and
put a ſtop to this wickedness before he comes. Let the
suitors do so of their own accord; it will be better for
them, for I am not prophesying without due knowledge;

19

everything has happened to Ulysses as I foretold when the Argives set out for Troy, and he with them. I said that after going through much hardship and losing all his men he should come home again in the twentieth year and that no one would know him; and now all this is coming true."

177 Eurymachus son of Polybus then said, " Go home, old man, and prophesy to your own children, or it may be worse for them. I can read these omens myself much better than you can; birds are always flying about in the sunshine somewhere or other, but they seldom mean anything. Ulysses has died in a far country, and it is a pity you are not dead along with him, instead of prating here about omens and adding fuel to the anger of Telemachus which is fierce enough as it is. I suppose you think he will give you something for your family, but I tell you—and it shall surely be—when an old man like you, who should know better, talks a young one over till he becomes troublesome, in the first place his young friend will only fare so much the worse—he will take nothing by it, for the suitors will prevent this— and in the next, we will lay a heavier fine, sir, upon yourself than you will at all like paying, for it will bear hardly upon you. As for Telemachus, I warn him in the presence of you all to send his mother back to her father, who will find her a husband and provide her with all the marriage gifts so dear a daughter may expect. Till then we shall go on harassing him with our suit; for we fear no man, and care neither for him, with all his fine speeches, nor for any fortune-telling of yours. You may preach as much as you please, but we shall only hate you the more. We shall go back and continue to eat up Telemachus's estate without paying him, till such time as his mother leaves off tormenting us by keeping us day after day on the tip-toe of expecta-

tion, each vying with the other in his suit for a prize of such rare perfection. Besides we cannot go after the other women whom we should marry in due course, but for the way in which she treats us."

Then Telemachus said, " Eurymachus, and you other 208 suitors, I shall say no more, and entreat you no further, for the gods and the people of Ithaca now know my story. Give me, then, a ship and a crew of twenty men to take me hither and thither, and I will go to Sparta and to Pylos in quest of my father who has so long been missing. Some one may tell me something, or (and people often hear things in this way) some heaven-sent message may direct me. If I can hear of him as alive and on his way home I will put up with the waste you suitors will make for yet another twelve months. If on the other hand I hear of his death, I will return at once, celebrate his funeral rites with all due pomp, build a barrow to his memory, and make my mother marry again."

With these words he sat down, and Mentor[1] who had 224 been a friend of Ulysses, and had been left in charge of everything with full authority over the servants, rose to speak. He, then, plainly and in all honesty addressed them thus:

[1] *Cf.* Il., ii, 76:

ἦ τοι ὅ γ᾽ ὣς εἰπὼν κατ᾽ ἄρ᾽ ἕζετο τοῖϲι Δ᾽ ἀνέϲτη
Νέϲτωρ, ὅϲ ῥα...
ὅ ϲφιν ἐῢ φρονέων ἀγορήϲατο καὶ μετέειπεν.

The Odyssean passage runs :

"ἦ τοι ὅ γ᾽ ὣς εἰπὼν κατ᾽ ἄρ᾽ ἕζετο τοῖϲι Δ᾽ ἀνέϲτη
Μέντωρ ὅϲ ῥ᾽...
....
ὅ ϲφιν ἐῢ φρονέων ἀγορήϲατο καὶ μετέειπεν."

Is it possible not to suspect that the name Mentor was coined upon that of Nestor ?

229 " Hear me, men of Ithaca, I hope that you may never
have a kind and well-disposed ruler any more, nor one
who will govern you equitably; I hope that all your
chiefs henceforward may be cruel and unjust, for there
is not one of you but has forgotten Ulysses, who ruled
you as though he were your father. I am not half so
angry with the suitors, for if they choose to do violence
in the naughtiness of their hearts, and wager their heads
that Ulysses will not return, they can take the high hand
and eat up his estate, but as for you others I am shocked
at the way in which you all sit still without even trying
to stop such scandalous goings on—which you could
do if you chose, for you are many and they are few."

242 Leiocritus, son of Evenor, answered him saying,
" Mentor, what folly is all this, that you should set the
people to stay us? It is a hard thing for one man to
fight with many about his victuals. Even though
Ulysses himself were to set upon us while we are feasting in his house, and do his best to oust us, his wife,
who wants him back so very badly, would have small
cause for rejoicing, and his blood would be upon his
own head if he fought against such great odds. There
is no sense in what you have been saying. Now, therefore, do you people go about your business, and let his
father's old friends, Mentor and Halitherses, speed this
boy on his journey, if he goes at all—which I do not
think he will, for he is more likely to stay where he is
till some one comes and tells him something."

257 On this he broke up the assembly, and every man
went back to his own abode, while the suitors returned
to the house of Ulysses.

260 Then Telemachus went all alone by the sea side,
washed his hands in the grey waves, and prayed to
Minerva.

262 " Hear me," he cried, " you god who visited me

22

yesterday, and bade me sail the seas in search of my
father who has so long been missing. I would obey
you, but the Achaeans, and more particularly the wicked
suitors, are hindering me that I cannot do so."

As he thus prayed, Minerva came close up to him in 267
the likeness and with the voice of Mentor. "Telemachus," said she, "if you are made of the same stuff
as your father you will be neither fool nor coward
henceforward, for Ulysses never broke his word nor
left his work half done. If, then, you take after him,
your voyage will not be fruitless, but unless you have
the blood of Ulysses and of Penelope in your veins I see
no likelihood of your succeeding. Sons are seldom as
good men as their fathers; they are generally worse,
not better; still, as you are not going to be either fool
or coward henceforward, and are not entirely without
some share of your father's wise discernment, I look
with hope upon your undertaking. But mind you
never make common cause with any of those foolish
suitors, for they have neither sense nor virtue, and give
no thought to death and to the doom that will shortly
fall on one and all of them, so that they shall perish on
the same day. As for your voyage, it shall not be long
delayed; your father was such an old friend of mine
that I will find you a ship, and will come with you
myself. Now, however, return home, and go about
among the suitors; begin getting provisions ready for
your voyage; see everything well stowed, the wine in
jars, and the barley meal, which is the staff of life, in
leathern bags, while I go round the town and beat up
volunteers at once. There are many ships in Ithaca
both old and new; I will run my eye over them for you
and will choose the best; we will get her ready and
will put out to sea without delay."

Thus spoke Minerva daughter of Jove, and Tele- 296

23

machus lost no time in doing as the goddess told him. He went moodily home, and found the suitors flaying goats and singeing pigs in the outer court. Antinous came up to him at once and laughed as he took his hand in his own, saying, " Telemachus, my fine fire-eater, bear no more ill blood neither in word nor deed, but eat and drink with us as you used to do. The Achaeans will find you in everything—a ship and a picked crew to boot—so that you can set sail for Pylos at once and get news of your noble father."

309 " Antinous," answered Telemachus, " I cannot eat in peace, nor take pleasure of any kind with such men as you are. Was it not enough that you should waste so much good property of mine while I was yet a boy? Now that I am older and know more about it, I am also stronger, and whether here among this people, or by going to Pylos, I will do you all the harm I can. I shall go, and my going will not be in vain—though, thanks to you suitors, I have neither ship nor crew of my own, and must be passenger not captain."

321 As he spoke he snatched his hand from that of Antinous. Meanwhile the others went on getting dinner ready about the buildings,[1] jeering at him tauntingly as they did so.

325 " Telemachus," said one youngster, " means to be the death of us; I suppose he thinks he can bring friends to help him from Pylos, or again from Sparta, where he seems bent on going. Or will he go to Ephyra as well, for poison to put in our wine and kill us? "

331 Another said, " Perhaps if Telemachus goes on board ship, he will be like his father and perish far from his friends. In this case we should have plenty to do,

[1] *I.e.*, in the outer court, and in the uncovered part of the inner court.

for we could then divide up his property amongst us:
as for the house we can let his mother and the man who
marries her have that."

This was how they talked. But Telemachus went 337
down into the lofty and spacious store-room where his
father's treasure of gold and bronze lay heaped up upon
the floor, and where the linen and spare clothes were
kept in oaken chests. Here, too, there was a store of
fragrant olive oil, while casks of old well-ripened wine,
unblended and fit for a god to drink, were ranged
against the wall in case Ulysses should come home again
after all. The room was closed with well-made doors
opening in the middle; moreover the faithful old housekeeper Euryclea, daughter of Ops the son of Pisenor,
was in charge of everything both night and day. Telemachus called her to the store-room and said:

" Nurse, draw me off some of the best wine you have, 349
after what you are keeping for my father's own drinking, in case, poor man, he should escape death, and
find his way home again after all. Let me have twelve
jars, and see that they all have lids; also fill me some
well-sewn leathern bags with barley meal—about twenty
measures in all. Get these things put together at once,
and say nothing about it. I will take everything away
this evening as soon as my mother has gone upstairs
for the night. I am going to Sparta and to Pylos to see
if I can hear anything about the return of my dear
father."

When Euryclea heard this she began to cry, and spoke 361
fondly to him, saying, " My dear child, what ever can
have put such a notion as that into your head? Where
in the world do you want to go to—you, who are the
one hope of the house? Your poor father is dead and
gone in some foreign country nobody knows where,
and as soon as your back is turned these wicked ones

here will be scheming to get you put out of the way, and will share all your possessions among themselves; stay where you are among your own people, and do not go wandering and worrying your life out on the barren ocean."

371 "Fear not, nurse," answered Telemachus, "my scheme is not without heaven's sanction; but swear that you will say nothing about all this to my mother, till I have been away some ten or twelve days, unless she hears of my having gone, and asks you; for I do not want her to spoil her beauty by crying."

377 The old woman swore most solemnly that she would not, and when she had completed her oath, she began drawing off the wine into jars, and getting the barley meal into the bags, while Telemachus went back to the suitors.

382 Then Minerva bethought her of another matter. She took his shape, and went round the town to each one of the crew, telling them to meet at the ship by sundown. She went also to Noemon son of Phronius, and asked him to let her have a ship—which he was very ready to do. When the sun had set and darkness was over all the land, she got the ship into the water, put all the tackle on board her that ships generally carry, and stationed her at the end of the harbour. Presently the crew came up, and the goddess spoke encouragingly to each of them.

393 Furthermore she went to the house of Ulysses, and threw the suitors into a deep slumber. She caused their drink to fuddle them, and made them drop their cups from their hands, so that instead of sitting over their wine, they went back into the town to sleep, with their eyes heavy and full of drowsiness. Then she took the form and voice of Mentor, and called Telemachus to come outside.

402 "Telemachus," said she, "the men are on board and

26

at their oars, waiting for you to give your orders, so
make haste and let us be off."

On this she led the way, while Telemachus followed 405
in her steps. When they got to the ship they found the
crew waiting by the water side, and Telemachus said,
" Now my men, help me to get the stores on board;
they are all put together in the cloister, and my mother
does not know anything about it, nor any of the maid
servants except one."

With these words he led the way and the others 413
followed after. When they had brought the things as
he told them, Telemachus went on board, Minerva
going before him and taking her seat in the stern of the
vessel, while Telemachus sat beside her. Then the men
loosed the hawsers and took their places on the benches.
Minerva sent them a fair wind from the West,[1] that
whistled over the deep blue waves [2] whereon Telemachus
told them to catch hold of the ropes and hoist sail, and
they did as he told them. They set the mast in its
socket in the cross plank, raised it, and made it fast with
the forestays; then they hoisted their white sails aloft
with ropes of twisted ox hide. As the sail bellied out
with the wind, the ship flew through the deep blue
water, and the foam hissed against her bows as she sped
onward. Then they made all fast throughout the ship,
filled the mixing-bowls to the brim, and made drink
offerings to the immortal gods that are from everlasting,
but more particularly to the grey-eyed daughter of Jove.

Thus, then, the ship sped on her way through the 434
watches of the night from dark till dawn,

---

[1] This would be fair from Sicily, which was doing duty for
Ithaca in the mind of the writer, but a North wind would have
been preferable for a voyage from the real Ithaca to Pylos.

[2] κελάδοντ' ἐπὶ οἴνοπα πόντον. The wind does not whistle
over waves. It only whistles through rigging or some other ob-
stacle that cuts it.

but as the sun was rising from the fair sea[1] into the firmament of heaven to shed light on mortals and immortals, they reached Pylos the city of Neleus. Now the people of Pylos were gathered on the sea shore to offer sacrifice of black bulls to Neptune lord of the Earthquake. There were nine guilds with five hundred men in each, and there were nine bulls to each guild. As they were eating the inward meats[2] and burning the thigh bones [on the embers] in the name of Neptune, Telemachus and his crew arrived, furled their sails, brought their ship to anchor, and went ashore.

12   Minerva led the way and Telemachus followed her Presently she said, " Telemachus, you muſt not be in the leaſt shy or nervous; you have taken this voyage to try and find out where your father is buried and how he came by his end; so go ſtraight up to Neſtor that we may see what he has got to tell us. Beg of him to speak the truth, and he will tell no lies, for he is an excellent person."

21   " But how, Mentor," replied Telemachus, " dare I go up to Neſtor, and how am I to address him? I have never yet been used to holding long conversations with

[1] *Cf.* Il., v, 20, 'Ἰδαῖος δ' ἀπόρουσε λιπὼν περικαλλέα δίφρον, the Odyssean line is Ηέλιος δ' ἀνόρουσε λιπὼν περικαλλέα λίμνην. There can be no doubt that the Odyssean line was suggeſted by the Iliadic, but nothing can explain why Idaeus jumping from his chariot should suggeſt to the writer of the Odyssey the sun rising from the sea. The probability is that she never gave the matter a thought, but took the line in queſtion as an effeĉt of saturation with the Iliad, and of unconscious cerebration. The Odyssey contains many such examples.

[2] The heart, liver, lights, kidneys, etc., were taken out from the inside and eaten firſt as being more readily cooked; the κρέα ύπέρτερα, or bone meat, was cooking while the cπλάγχνα or inward meats were being eaten. I imagine that the thigh bones made a kind of gridiron, while at the same time the marrow inside them got cooked.

28

people, and am ashamed to begin questioning one who
is so much older than myself."

"Some things, Telemachus," answered Minerva, 25
"will be suggested to you by your own instinct, and
heaven will prompt you further; for I am assured that
the gods have been with you from the time of your
birth until now."

She then went quickly on, and Telemachus followed 29
in her steps till they reached the place where the guilds
of the Pylian people were assembled. There they found
Nestor sitting with his sons, while his company round
him were busy getting dinner ready, and putting pieces
of meat on to the spits [1] while other pieces were cooking.
When they saw the strangers they crowded round them,
took them by the hand and bade them take their places.
Nestor's son Pisistratus at once offered his hand to each
of them, and seated them on some soft sheepskins that
were lying on the sands near his father and his brother
Thrasymedes. Then he gave them their portions of the
inward meats and poured wine for them into a golden
cup, handing it to Minerva first, and saluting her at the
same time.

"Offer a prayer, sir," said he, "to King Neptune, for 43
it is his feast that you are joining; when you have duly
prayed and made your drink-offering, pass the cup to
your friend that he may do so also. I doubt not that
he too lifts his hands in prayer, for man cannot live

---

[1] *I.e.,* skewers, either single, double, or even five pronged.
The meat would be pierced with the skewer, and laid over the
ashes to grill–the two ends of the skewer being supported in
whatever way might be found convenient. Meat so cooking
may be seen in any eating house in Smyrna, or any Eastern town.
When I rode across the Troad from the Dardanelles to Hissarlik
and Mount Ida, I noticed that my dragoman and his men did
all our outdoor cooking exactly in the Odyssean and Iliadic
fashion.

without God in the world. Still he is younger than you are, and is much of an age with myself, so I will give you the precedence."

51 As he spoke he handed her the cup. Minerva thought it very right and proper of him to have given it to herself firſt;[1] she accordingly began praying heartily to Neptune. " O thou," she cried, " that encircleſt the earth, vouchsafe to grant the prayers of thy servants that call upon thee. More especially we pray thee send down thy grace on Neſtor and on his sons; thereafter also make the reſt of the Pylian people some handsome return for the goodly hecatomb they are offering you. Laſtly, grant Telemachus and myself a happy issue, in respeᵓt of the matter that has brought us in our ship to Pylos."

62 When she had thus made an end of praying, she handed the cup to Telemachus and he prayed likewise. By and by, when the outer meats were roaſted and had been taken off the spits, the carvers gave every man his portion and they all made an excellent dinner. As soon as they had had enough to eat and drink, Neſtor, knight of Gerene, began to speak.

69 " Now," said he, " that our gueſts have done their dinner, it will be beſt to ask them who they are. Who, then, sir ſtrangers, are you, and from what port have you sailed? Are you traders? or do you sail the seas as rovers with your hand againſt every man, and every man's hand againſt you? "

75 Telemachus answered boldly, for Minerva had given

---

[1] *Cf.* Il., xvii, 567:

ὣς φάτο γήθησεν δὲ θεά, γλαυκῶπις Ἀθήνη
ὅττι ῥά οἱ πάμπρωτα θεῶν ἡρήσατο πάντων.

The Odyssean lines are :

χαῖρε δ' Ἀθηναίη πεπνυμένῳ ἀνδρὶ δικαίῳ
οὕνεκα οἱ προτέρῃ δῶκε χρύσειον ἄλεισον.

him courage to ask about his father and get himself a
good name.

"Nestor," said he, "son of Neleus, honour to the 79.
Achaean name, you ask whence we come, and I will tell
you. We come from Ithaca under Neritum,[1] and the
matter about which I would speak is of private not
public import. I seek news of my unhappy father
Ulysses, who is said to have sacked the town of Troy
in company with yourself. We know what fate befell
each one of the other heroes who fought at Troy, but
as regards Ulysses heaven has hidden from us the
knowledge even that he is dead at all, for no one can
certify us in what place he perished, nor say whether he
fell in battle on the mainland, or was lost at sea amid the
waves of Amphitrite. Therefore I am suppliant at your
knees, if haply you may be pleased to tell me of his
melancholy end, whether you saw it with your own
eyes, or heard it from some other traveller, for he was a
man born to trouble. Do not soften things out of any
pity for me, but tell me in all plainness exactly what you
saw. If my brave father Ulysses ever did you loyal
service, either by word or deed, when you Achaeans
were harassed among the Trojans, bear it in mind now
as in my favour and tell me truly all."

"My friend," answered Nestor, "you recall a time 102
of much sorrow to my mind, for the brave Achaeans
suffered much both at sea, while privateering under
Achilles, and when fighting before the great city of
king Priam. Our best men all of them fell there—Ajax,
Achilles, Patroclus peer of gods in counsel, and my own
dear son Antilochus, a man singularly fleet of foot and
in fight valiant. But we suffered much more than this;
what mortal tongue indeed could tell the whole story?
Though you were to stay here and question me for

[1] Reading ὑπονηρίτου for ὑπονηίου , *cf.* Od., i, 186.

31

five years, or even six, I could not tell you all that the Achaeans suffered, and you would turn homeward weary of my tale before it ended. Nine long years did we try every kind of stratagem, but the hand of heaven was against us; during all this time there was no one who could compare with your father in subtlety–if indeed you are his son–I can hardly believe my eyes– and you talk just like him too–no one would say that people of such different ages could speak so much alike. He and I never had any kind of difference from first to last neither in camp nor council, but in singleness of heart and purpose we advised the Argives how all might be ordered for the best.

130   " When, however, we had sacked the city of Priam, and were setting sail in our ships as heaven had dispersed us, then Jove saw fit to vex the Argives on their homeward voyage; for they had not all been either wise or understanding, and hence many came to a bad end through the displeasure of Jove's daughter Minerva, who brought about a quarrel between the two sons of Atreus.

137   " The sons of Atreus called a meeting which was not as it should be, for it was sunset and the Achaeans were heavy with wine. When they explained why they had called the people together, it seemed that Menelaus was for sailing homeward at once, and this displeased Agamemnon, who thought that we should wait till we had offered hecatombs to appease the anger of Minerva. Fool that he was, he might have known that he would not prevail with her, for when the gods have made up their minds they do not change them lightly. So the two stood bandying hard words, whereon the Achaeans sprang to their feet with a cry that rent the air, and were of two minds as to what they should do.

151   " That night we rested and nursed our anger, for

32

Jove was hatching mischief against us. But in the morning some of us drew our ships into the water and put our goods with our women on board, while the rest, about half in number, stayed behind with Agamemnon. We–the other half–embarked and sailed; and the ships went well, for heaven had smoothed the sea. When we reached Tenedos we offered sacrifices to the gods, for we were longing to get home; cruel Jove, however, did not yet mean that we should do so, and raised a second quarrel in the course of which some among us turned their ships back again, and sailed away under Ulysses to make their peace with Agamemnon; but I, and all the ships that were with me pressed forward, for I saw that mischief was brewing. The son of Tydeus went on also with me, and his crews with him. Later on Menelaus joined us at Lesbos, and found us making up our minds about our course–for we did not know whether to go outside Chios by the island of Psyra, keeping this to our left, or inside Chios, over against the stormy headland of Mimas. So we asked heaven for a sign, and were shown one to the effect that we should be soonest out of danger if we headed our ships across the open sea to Euboea. This we therefore did, and a fair wind sprang up which gave us a quick passage during the night to Geraestus,[1] where we offered many sacrifices to Neptune for having helped us so far on our way. Four days later Diomed and his men stationed their ships in Argos, but I held on for Pylos, and the wind never fell light from the day when heaven first made it fair for me.

[1] The geography of the Aegean as above described is correct, but is probably taken from the lost poem, the Nosti, the existence of which is referred to Od., i, 326, 327, and 350, etc. A glance at the map will show that heaven advised its suppliants quite correctly.

D

184 " Therefore, my dear young friend, I returned without hearing anything about the others. I know neither who got home safely nor who were lost but, as in duty bound, I will give you without reserve the reports that have reached me since I have been here in my own house. They say the Myrmidons returned home safely under Achilles' son Neoptolemus; so also did the valiant son of Poias, Philoctetes. Idomeneus, again, lost no men at sea, and all his followers who escaped death in the field got safe home with him to Crete. No matter how far out of the world you live, you will have heard of Agamemnon and the bad end he came to at the hands of Aegisthus—and a fearful reckoning did Aegisthus presently pay. See what a good thing it is for a man to leave a son behind him to do as Orestes did, who killed false Aegisthus the murderer of his noble father. You too, then—for you are a tall, smart-looking fellow—show your mettle and make yourself a name in story."

201 " Nestor son of Neleus," answered Telemachus, " honour to the Achaean name, the Achaeans applaud Orestes and his name will live through all time for he has avenged his father nobly. Would that heaven might grant me to do like vengeance on the insolence of the wicked suitors, who are ill treating me and plotting my ruin; but the gods have no such happiness in store for me and for my father, so we must bear it as best we may."

210 " My friend," said Nestor, " now that you remind me, I remember to have heard that your mother has many suitors, who are ill disposed towards you and are making havoc of your estate. Do you submit to this tamely, or are public feeling and the voice of heaven against you? Who knows but what Ulysses may come back after all, and pay these scoundrels in full, either single-handed or with a force of Achaeans behind him?

If Minerva were to take as great a liking to you as she did to Ulysses when we were fighting before Troy (for I never yet saw the gods so openly fond of any one as Minerva then was of your father), if she would take as good care of you as she did of him, these wooers would soon some of them forget their wooing."

Telemachus answered, " I can expect nothing of the 225 kind; it would be far too much to hope for. I dare not let myself think of it. Even though the gods themselves willed it no such good fortune could befall me."

On this Minerva said, " Telemachus, what are you 229 talking about? Heaven has a long arm if it is minded to save a man; and if it were me, I should not care how much I suffered before getting home, provided I could be safe when I was once there. I would rather this, than get home quickly, and then be killed in my own house as Agamemnon was by the treachery of Aegisthus and his wife. Still, death is certain, and when a man's hour is come, not even the gods can save him, no matter how fond they are of him."

" Mentor," answered Telemachus, " do not let us 240 talk about it any more. There is no chance of my father's ever coming back; the gods have long since counselled his destruction. There is something else, however, about which I should like to ask Nestor, for he knows much more than any one else does. They say he has reigned for three generations so that it is like talking to an immortal. Tell me, therefore, Nestor, and tell me true; how did Agamemnon come to die in that way? What was Menelaus doing? And how came false Aegisthus to kill so far better a man than himself? Was Menelaus away from Achaean Argos, voyaging elsewhither among mankind, that Aegisthus took heart and killed Agamemnon? "

" I will tell you truly," answered Nestor, " and 254

35

indeed you have yourself divined how it all happened.
If Menelaus when he got back from Troy had found
Aegisthus still alive in his house, there would have been
no barrow heaped up for him, not even when he was
dead, but he would have been thrown outside the city
to dogs and vultures, and not a woman would have
mourned him, for he had done a deed of great wickedness; but we were over there, fighting hard at Troy,
and Aegisthus, who was taking his ease quietly in the
heart of Argos, cajoled Agamemnon's wife Clytemnestra with incessant flattery.

265 " At first she would have nothing to do with his
wicked scheme, for she was of a good natural disposition;[1] moreover there was a bard with her, to whom
Agamemnon had given strict orders on setting out for
Troy, that he was to keep guard over his wife; but
when heaven had counselled her destruction, Aegisthus
carried this bard off to a desert island, and left him there
for crows and seagulls to batten upon—after which she
went willingly enough to the house of Aegisthus. Then
he offered many burnt sacrifices to the gods, and
decorated many temples with tapestries and gilding, for
he had succeeded far beyond his expectations.

276 " Meanwhile Menelaus and I were on our way home
from Troy, on good terms with one another. When we
got to Sunium, which is the point of Athens, Apollo
with his painless shafts killed Phrontis the steersman of
Menelaus' ship (and never man knew better how to
handle a vessel in rough weather) so that he died then
and there with the helm in his hand, and Menelaus,
though very anxious to press forward, had to wait in

---

[1] The writer—ever jealous for the honour of women—
extenuates Clytemnestra's guilt as far as possible, and explains
it as due to her having been left unprotected, and fallen into the
hands of a wicked man.

36

order to bury his comrade and give him his due funeral
rites. Presently, when he too could put to sea again,
and had sailed on as far as the Malean heads, Jove
counselled evil against him and made it blow hard
till the waves ran mountains high. Here he divided his
fleet and took the one half towards Crete where the
Cydonians dwell round about the waters of the river
Iardanus. There is a high headland hereabouts stretching out into the sea from a place called Gortyn, and all
along this part of the coast as far as Phaestus the sea
runs high when there is a south wind blowing, but
after Phaestus the coast is more protected, for a small
headland can make a great shelter. Here this part of the
fleet was driven on to the rocks and wrecked; but the
crews just managed to save themselves. As for the
other five ships, they were taken by winds and seas to
Egypt, where Menelaus gathered much gold and
substance among people of an alien speech. Meanwhile
Aegisthus here at home plotted his evil deed. For seven
years after he had killed Agamemnon he ruled in
Mycene, and the people were obedient under him,
but in the eighth year Orestes came back from Athens
to be his bane, and killed the murderer of his father.
Then he celebrated the funeral rites of his mother and
of false Aegisthus by a banquet to the people of Argos,
and on that very day Menelaus came home,[1] with as
much treasure as his ships could carry.

[1] The Greek is

αὐτῆμαρ δέ οἱ ἦλθε βοὴν ὀγαθὸς Μενέλαος.

Cf. Iliad, ii, 408 :

αὐτόματος δέ οἱ ἦλθε βοὴν ἀγαθὸς Μενέλαος.

Surely the αὐτῆμαρ of the Odyssean passage was due to the
αὐτόματος of the Iliad. No other reason suggests itself for the
making Menelaus return on the very day of the feast given

313　"Take my advice then, and do not go travelling about for long so far from home, nor leave your property with such dangerous people in your house; they will eat up everything you have among them, and you will have been on a fool's errand. Still, I should advise you by all means to go and visit Menelaus, who has lately come off a voyage among such distant peoples as no man could ever hope to get back from, when the winds had once carried him so far out of his reckoning; even birds cannot fly the distance in a twelvemonth, so vast and terrible are the seas that they must cross. Go to him, therefore, by sea, and take your own men with you; or if you would rather travel by land you can have a chariot, you can have horses, and here are my sons who can escort you to Lacedaemon where Menelaus lives. Beg of him to speak the truth, and he will tell you no lies, for he is an excellent person."

329　As he spoke the sun set and it came on dark, whereon Minerva said, " Sir, all that you have said is well; now, however, order the tongues of the victims to be cut, and mix wine that we may make drink-offerings to Neptune, and the other immortals, and then go to bed, for it is bed time. People should go away early and not keep late hours at a religious festival."

337　Thus spoke the daughter of Jove, and they obeyed her saying. Men servants poured water over the hands of the guests, while pages filled the mixing-bowls with

by Orestes. The fact that in the Iliad Menelaus came to a banquet without waiting for an invitation, determines the writer of the Odyssey to make him come to a banquet, also uninvited, but as circumstances did not permit of his having been invited, his coming uninvited is shown to have been due to chance. I do not think the authoress thought all this out, but attribute the strangeness of the coincidence to unconscious cerebration and saturation.

THE
UNIVERSITY OF WINNIPEG
PORTAGE & BALMORAL
WINNIPEG 2. MAN.   CANADA

wine and water, and handed it round after giving every
man his drink-offering; then they threw the tongues of
the victims into the fire, and stood up to make their
drink-offerings. When they had made their offerings
and had drunk each as much as he was minded, Minerva
and Telemachus were for going on board their ship,
but Nestor caught them up at once and stayed them.

"Heaven and the immortal gods," he exclaimed, 346
"forbid that you should leave my house to go on board
of a ship. Do you think I am so poor and short of
clothes, or that I have so few cloaks and rugs as to be
unable to find comfortable beds both for myself and
for my guests? Let me tell you I have store both of
rugs and cloaks, and shall not permit the son of my old
friend Ulysses to camp down on the deck of a ship—not
while I live—nor yet will my sons after me, but they will
keep open house as I have done."

Then Minerva answered, "Sir, you have spoken well, 356
and it will be much better that Telemachus should do
as you have said; he, therefore, shall return with you
and sleep at your house, but I must go back to give
orders to my crew, and keep them in good heart. I am
the only older person among them; the rest are all
young men of Telemachus' own age, who have taken
this voyage out of friendship; so I must return to the
ship and sleep there. Moreover to-morrow I must go
to the Cauconians where I have a large sum of money
long owing to me. As for Telemachus, now that he is
your guest, send him to Lacedaemon in a chariot, and
let one of your sons go with him. Be pleased also to
provide him with your best and fleetest horses."

When she had thus spoken, she flew away in the 371
form of an eagle, and all marvelled as they beheld it.
Nestor was astonished, and took Telemachus by the
hand. "My friend," said he, "I see that you are going

39

to be a great hero some day, since the gods wait upon you thus while you are still so young. This can have been none other of those who dwell in heaven than Jove's redoubtable daughter, the Trito-born, who showed such favour towards your brave father among the Argives." " Holy queen," he continued, " vouchsafe to send down thy grace upon myself, my good wife, and my children. In return, I will offer you in sacrifice a broad-browed heifer of a year old, unbroken, and never yet brought by man under the yoke. I will gild her horns, and will offer her up to you in sacrifice."

385 Thus did he pray, and Minerva heard his prayer. He then led the way to his own house, followed by his sons and sons-in-law. When they had got there and had taken their places on the benches and seats, he mixed them a bowl of sweet wine that was eleven years old when the housekeeper took the lid off the jar that held it. As he mixed the wine, he prayed much and made drink-offerings to Minerva, daughter of Aegis-bearing Jove. Then, when they had made their drink-offerings and had drunk each as much as he was minded, the others went home to bed each in his own abode; but Nestor put Telemachus to sleep in the room that was over the gateway along with Pisistratus, who was the only unmarried son now left him. As for himself, he slept in an inner room of the house, with the queen his wife by his side.

404 Now when the child of morning, rosy-fingered Dawn, appeared, Nestor left his couch and took his seat on the benches of white and polished marble that stood in front of his house. Here aforetime sat Neleus, peer of gods in counsel, but he was now dead, and had gone to the house of Hades; so Nestor sat in his seat, sceptre in hand, as guardian of the public weal. His sons as they left their rooms gathered round him, Echephron,

Stratius, Perseus, Aretus, and Thrasymedes; the sixth
son was Pisistratus, and when Telemachus joined them
they made him sit with them. Nestor then addressed
them.

"My sons," said he, "make haste to do as I shall bid 418
you. I wish first and foremost to propitiate the great
goddess Minerva, who manifested herself visibly to me
during yesterday's festivities. Go, then, one or other
of you to the plain, tell the stockman to look me out a
heifer, and come on here with it at once. Another must
go to Telemachus's ship, and invite all the crew, leaving
two men only in charge of the vessel. Some one else
will run and fetch Laerceus the goldsmith to gild the
horns of the heifer. The rest, stay all of you where you
are; tell the maids in the house to prepare an excellent
dinner, and to fetch seats, and logs of wood for a burnt
offering. Tell them also to bring me some clear spring
water."

On this they hurried off on their several errands. The 430
heifer was brought in from the plain, and Telemachus's
crew came from the ship; the goldsmith brought the
anvil, hammer, and tongs, with which he worked his
gold, and Minerva herself came to accept the sacrifice.
Nestor gave out the gold, and the smith gilded the horns
of the heifer that the goddess might have pleasure in
their beauty. Then Stratius and Echephron brought
her in by the horns; Aretus fetched water from the
house in a ewer that had a flower pattern on it, and in
his other hand he held a basket of barley meal; sturdy
Thrasymedes stood by with a sharp axe, ready to strike
the heifer, while Perseus held a bucket. Then Nestor
began with washing his hands and sprinkling the barley
meal, and he offered many a prayer to Minerva as he
threw a lock from the heifer's head upon the fire.

When they had done praying and sprinkling the 447

41

barley meal[1] Thrasymedes dealt his blow, and brought
the heifer down with a stroke that cut through the
tendons at the base of her neck, whereon the daughters
and daughters-in-law of Nestor, and his venerable wife
Eurydice (she was eldest daughter to Clymenus)
screamed with delight. Then they lifted the heifer's
head from off the ground, and Pisistratus cut her throat.
When she had done bleeding and was quite dead, they
cut her up. They cut out the thigh bones all in due
course, wrapped them round in two layers of fat, and
set some pieces of raw meat on the top of them; then
Nestor laid them upon the wood fire and poured wine
over them, while the young men stood near him with
five-pronged spits in their hands. When the thighs
were burned and they had tasted the inward meats, they
cut the rest of the meat up small, put the pieces on the
spits and toasted them over the fire.

464   Meanwhile lovely Polycaste, Nestor's youngest daughter, washed Telemachus. When she had washed him
and anointed him with oil, she brought him a fair mantle
and shirt,[2] and he looked like a god as he came from the
bath and took his seat by the side of Nestor. When the
outer meats were done they drew them off the spits and
sat down to dinner where they were waited upon by
some worthy henchmen, who kept pouring them out
their wine in cups of gold. As soon as they had had
enough to eat and drink Nestor said, "Sons, put

---

[1] *Cf.* Il., i, 458; ii, 421. The writer here interrupts an Iliadic
passage (to which she returns immediately) for the double
purpose of dwelling upon the slaughter of the heifer, and of
letting Nestor's wife and daughters enjoy it also. A male
writer, if he was borrowing from the Iliad, would have stuck
to his borrowing.

[2] *Cf.* Il., xxiv, 587, 588, where the lines refer to the washing
the dead body of Hector.

COURTYARD AT SELINUNTE

COURTYARD AT SELINUNTE

Telemachus's horses to the chariot that he may start at once."

Thus did he speak, and they did even as he had said, 477 and yoked the fleet horses to the chariot. The house-keeper packed them up a provision of bread, wine, and sweetmeats fit for the sons of princes. Then Tele-machus got into the chariot, while Pisistratus gathered up the reins and took his seat beside him. He lashed the horses on and they flew forward nothing loth into the open country, leaving the high citadel of Pylos behind them. All that day did they travel, swaying the yoke upon their necks till the sun went down and darkness was over all the land. Then they reached Pherae where Diocles lived, who was son to Ortilochus and grandson to Alpheus. Here they passed the night and Diocles entertained them hospitably. When the child of morning, rosy-fingered Dawn, appeared, they again yoked their horses and drove out through the gateway under the echoing gatehouse.[1] Pisistratus lashed the horses on and they flew forward nothing loth; presently they came to the corn lands of the open country, and in the course of time completed their journey, so well did their steeds take them.[2]

---

[1] See illustration. This yard is typical of many that may be seen in Sicily. The existing ground-plan is probably unmodified from Odyssean, and indeed long pre-Odyssean times, but the earlier buildings would have no arches, and would, one would suppose, be mainly timber. The Odyssean αἴθουσαι were the sheds that ran round the yard as the arches do now. The αἴθουσα ἐρίδουπος was the one through which the main entrance passed, and which was hence " noisy," or reverberating. It had an upper story in which visitors were often lodged.

[2] This journey is an impossible one. Telemachus and Pisis-tratus would have been obliged to drive over the Taygetus range, over which there has never yet been a road for wheeled vehicles. It is plain therefore that the audience for whom the Odyssey

43

497 Now when the sun had set and darkness was over the land,

was written was one that would be unlikely to know anything about the topography of the Peloponnese, so that the writer might take what liberties she chose.

they reached the low lying city of Lacedaemon, where
they drove straight to the abode of Menelaus [1] [and
found him in his own house, feasting with his many
clansmen in honour of the wedding of his son, and also
of his daughter, whom he was marrying to the son of
that valiant warrior Achilles. He had given his consent
and promised her to him while he was still at Troy, and
now the gods were bringing the marriage about; so he
was sending her with chariots and horses to the city
of the Myrmidons over whom Achilles' son was reigning. For his only son he had found a bride from Sparta, [2]

[1] The lines which I have enclosed in brackets are evidently
an afterthought – added probably by the writer herself – for
they evince the same instinctively greater interest in anything
that may concern a woman, which is so noticeable throughout
the poem. There is no further sign of any special festivities
nor of any other guests than Telemachus and Pisistratus, until
lines 621-624 (ordinarily enclosed in brackets) are abruptly
introduced, probably with a view of trying to carry off the
introduction of the lines now in question.

The addition was, I imagine, suggested by a desire to excuse
and explain the non-appearance of Hermione in bk. xv, as also
of both Hermione and Megapenthes in the rest of bk. iv.
Megapenthes in bk. xv seems to be still a bachelor: the pre-
sumption therefore is that bk. xv was written before the story
of his marriage here given. I take it he is only married here
because his sister is being married. She having been properly
attended to, Megapenthes might as well be married at the same
time. Hermione could not now be less than thirty.

I have dealt with this passage somewhat more fully in my
Authoress of the Odyssey, pp. 142-144. See also p. 268 of the
same book.

[2] Sparta and Lacedaemon are here treated as two different
places, though in other parts of the poem it is clear that the
writer understands them as one. The catalogue in the Iliad,
which the writer is here presumably following, makes the
same mistake (Il., ii, 581, 582).

the daughter of Aleftor. This son, Megapenthes, was born to him of a bondwoman, for heaven vouchsafed Helen no more children after she had borne Hermione, who was fair as golden Venus herself.

15   So the neighbours and kinsmen of Menelaus were feafting and making merry in his house. There was a bard also to sing to them and play his lyre, while two tumblers went about performing in the midft of them when the man ftruck up with his tune.[1]]

20   Telemachus and the son of Neftor ftayed their horses at the gate, whereon Eteoneus servant to Menelaus came out, and as soon as he saw them ran hurrying back into the house to tell his Mafter.   He went close up to him and said, " Menelaus, there are some ftrangers come here, two men, who look like sons of Jove. What are we to do?   Shall we take their horses out, or tell them to find friends elsewhere as they beft can? "

30   Menelaus was very angry and said, " Eteoneus, son of Boethous, you never used to be a fool, but now you talk like a simpleton.   Take their horses out, of course, and show the ftrangers in that they may have supper; you and I have ftayed often enough at other people's houses before we got back here, where heaven grant that we may reft in peace henceforward."

37   So Eteoneus buftled back and bade the other servants come with him.   They took their sweating fteeds from under the yoke, made them faft to the mangers, and gave them a feed of oats and barley mixed.   Then they leaned the chariot againft the end wall of the court-yard, and led the way into the house.   Telemachus and Pisiftratus were aftonished when they saw it, for its splendour was as that of the sun and moon; then, when they had admired everything to their heart's content, they went into the bath room and washed themselves.

[1] These laft three lines are identical with Il., xviii, 604-606.

46

When the servants had washed them and anointed 49. them with oil, they brought them woollen cloaks and shirts, and the two took their seats by the side of Menelaus. A maid-servant brought them water in a beautiful golden ewer, and poured it into a silver basin for them to wash their hands; and she drew a clean table beside them. An upper servant brought them bread, and offered them many good things of what there was in the house, while the carver fetched them plates of all manner of meats and set cups of gold by their side.

Menelaus then greeted them saying, "Fall to, and 59. welcome; when you have done supper I shall ask who you are, for the lineage of such men as you cannot have been lost. You must be descended from a line of sceptre-bearing kings, for poor people do not have such sons as you are."

On this he handed them[1] a piece of fat roast loin, 65 which had been set near him as being a prime part, and they laid their hands on the good things that were before them; as soon as they had had enough to eat and drink, Telemachus said to the son of Nestor, with his head so close that no one might hear, "Look, Pisistratus, man after my own heart, see the gleam of bronze and gold–of amber,[2] ivory, and silver. Everything is so splendid that it is like seeing the palace of Olympian Jove. I am lost in admiration."

Menelaus overheard him and said, "No one, my 76

[1] From the Greek (ἐν χερσὶν ἑλών) it is plain that Menelaus took up the piece of meat with his fingers.
[2] Amber is never mentioned in the Iliad. Sicily, where I suppose the Odyssey to have been written, has always been, and still is, one of the principal amber producing countries. It was probably the only one known in the Odyssean age. See *The Authoress of the Odyssey*, p. 271.

47

sons, can hold his own with Jove, for his house and
everything about him is immortal; but among mortal
men—well, there may be another who has as much
wealth as I have, or there may not; but at all events I
have travelled much and have undergone much hardship, for it was nearly eight years before I could get
home with my fleet. I went to Cyprus, Phoenicia and
the Egyptians; I went also to the Ethiopians, the
Sidonians, and the Erembians, and to Libya where the
lambs have horns as soon as they are born, and the
sheep lamb down three times a year. Every one in
that country, whether master or man, has plenty of
cheese, meat, and good milk, for the ewes yield all the
year round. But while I was travelling and getting
great riches among these people, my brother was
secretly and shockingly murdered through the perfidy
of his wicked wife, so that I have no pleasure in being
lord of all this wealth. Whoever your parents may be
they must have told you about all this, and of my heavy
loss in the ruin [1] of a stately mansion fully and magnificently furnished. Would that I had only a third of
what I now have so that I had stayed at home, and all
those were living who perished on the plain of Troy,
far from Argos. I often grieve, as I sit here in my house,
for one and all of them. At times I cry aloud for sorrow,
but presently I leave off again, for crying is cold comfort
and one soon tires of it. Yet grieve for these as I may,
I do so for one man more than for them all. I cannot
even think of him without loathing both food and
sleep, so miserable does he make me, for no one of all
the Achaeans worked so hard or risked so much as he
did. He took nothing by it, and has left a legacy of

[1] This no doubt refers to the story told in the lost poem of the
Cypria about Paris and Helen robbing Menelaus of the greater
part of his treasures, when they sailed together for Troy.

sorrow to myself, for he has been gone a long time, and we know not whether he is alive or dead. His old father, his long-suffering wife Penelope, and his son Telemachus, whom he left behind him an infant in arms, are plunged in grief on his account."

Thus spoke Menelaus, and the heart of Telemachus 113 yearned as he bethought him of his father. Tears fell from his eyes as he heard him thus mentioned, so that he held his cloak before his face with both hands. When Menelaus saw this he doubted whether to let him choose his own time for speaking, or to ask him at once and find what it was all about.

While he was thus in two minds Helen came down 120 from her high vaulted and perfumed room, looking as lovely as Diana herself. Adraste brought her a seat, Alcippe a soft woollen rug, while Phylo fetched her the silver work-box which Alcandra wife of Polybus had given her. Polybus lived in Egyptian Thebes, which is the richest city in the whole world; he gave Menelaus two baths, both of pure silver, two tripods, and ten talents of gold; besides all this, his wife gave Helen some beautiful presents, to wit, a golden distaff, and a silver work-box that ran on wheels, with a gold band round the top of it. Phylo now placed this by her side, full of fine spun yarn, and a distaff charged with violet coloured wool was laid upon the top of it. Then Helen took her seat, put her feet upon the footstool, and began to question her husband.[1]

" Do we know, Menelaus," said she, " the names of 138 these strangers who have come to visit us? Shall I guess right or wrong?—but I cannot help saying what I

---

[1] It is inconceivable that Helen should enter thus, in the middle of supper, intending to work with her distaff, if great festivities were going on. Telemachus and Pisistratus are evidently dining *en famille*.

think. Never yet have I seen either man or woman so
like somebody else (indeed when I look at him I hardly
know what to think) as this young man is like Telemachus, whom Ulysses left as a baby behind him, when
you Achaeans went to Troy with battle in your hearts,
on account of my most shameless self."

147 "My dear wife," replied Menelaus, "I see the likeness just as you do. His hands and feet are just like
Ulysses'; so is his hair, with the shape of his head and
the expression of his eyes. Moreover, when I was talking about Ulysses, and saying how much he had suffered
on my account, tears fell from his eyes, and he hid his
face in his mantle."

155 Then Pisistratus said, "Menelaus, son of Atreus, you
are right in thinking that this young man is Telemachus,
but he is very modest, and is ashamed to come here and
begin opening up discourse with one whose conversation is so divinely interesting as your own. My father,
Nestor, sent me to escort him hither, for he wanted to
know whether you could give him any counsel or
suggestion. A son has always trouble at home when
his father has gone away leaving him without sup-
porters; and this is how Telemachus is now placed,
for his father is absent, and there is no one among his
own people to stand by him."

168 "Bless my heart," replied Menelaus, "then I am
receiving a visit from the son of a very dear friend, who
suffered much hardship for my sake. I had always
hoped to entertain him with most marked distinction
when heaven had granted us a safe return from beyond
the seas. I should have founded a city for him in Argos,
and built him a house. I should have made him leave
Ithaca with his goods, his son, and all his people, and
should have sacked for them some one of the neighbouring cities that are subject to me. We should thus
have seen one another continually, and nothing but

death could have interrupted so close and happy an
intercourse. I suppose, however, that heaven grudged
us such great good fortune, for it has prevented the
poor fellow from ever getting home at all."

Thus did he speak, and his words set them all a weep- 183
ing. Helen wept, Telemachus wept, and so did
Menelaus, nor could Pisistratus keep his eyes from
filling, when he remembered his dear brother Antilochus whom the son of bright Dawn had killed. Thereon he said to Menelaus,

" Sir, my father Nestor, when we used to talk about 190
you at home, told me you were a person of rare and
excellent understanding. If, then, it be possible, do as I
would urge you. I am not fond of crying while I am
getting my supper. Morning will come in due course,
and in the forenoon I care not how much I cry for those
that are dead and gone. This is all we can do for the
poor things. We can only shave our heads for them
and wring the tears from our cheeks. I had a brother
who died at Troy; he was by no means the worst man
there; you are sure to have known him—his name was
Antilochus; I never set eyes upon him myself, but they
say that he was singularly fleet of foot and in fight
valiant."

" Your discretion, my friend," answered Menelaus, 203
" is beyond your years. It is plain you take after your
father. One can soon see when a man is son to one
whom heaven has blessed both as regards wife and
offspring—and it has blessed Nestor from first to last all
his days, giving him a green old age in his own house,
with sons about him who are both well disposed and
valiant. We will put an end therefore to all this weeping, and attend to our supper again. Let water be
poured over our hands. Telemachus and I can talk
with one another fully in the morning."

On this Asphalion, one of the servants, poured water 216

over their hands and they laid their hands on the good
things that were before them.

219   Then Jove's daughter Helen bethought her of another
matter. She drugged the wine with an herb that
banishes all care, sorrow, and ill humour. Whoever
drinks wine thus drugged cannot shed a single tear all
the rest of the day, not even though his father and
mother both of them drop down dead, or he sees a
brother or a son hewn in pieces before his very eyes.
This drug, of such sovereign power and virtue, had
been given to Helen by Polydamna wife of Thon, a
woman of Egypt, where there grow all sorts of herbs,
some good to put into the mixing-bowl and others
poisonous. Moreover, every one in the whole country
is a skilled physician, for they are of the race of
Paeeon. When Helen had put this drug in the bowl,
and had told the servants to serve the wine round, she
said:

235   " Menelaus, son of Atreus, and you my good friends,
sons of honourable men (which is as Jove wills, for he
is the giver both of good and evil, and can do what he
chooses), feast here as you will, and listen while I tell
you a tale in season. I cannot indeed name every single
one of the exploits of Ulysses, but I can say what he did
when he was before Troy, and you Achaeans were in all
sorts of difficulties. He covered himself with wounds
and bruises, dressed himself all in rags, and entered
the enemy's city looking like a menial or a beggar, and
quite different from what he did when he was among
his own people. In this disguise he entered the city of
Troy, and no one said anything to him. I alone recognized him and began to question him, but he was too
cunning for me. When, however, I had washed and
anointed him and had given him clothes, and after I
had sworn a solemn oath not to betray him to the

52

Trojans till he had got safely back to his own camp and to the ships, he told me all that the Achaeans meant to do. He killed many Trojans and got much information before he reached the Argive camp, for all which things the Trojan women made lamentation, but for my own part I was glad, for my heart was beginning to yearn after my home, and I was unhappy about the wrong that Venus had done me in taking me over there, away from my country, my little girl, and my lawful wedded husband, who is indeed by no means deficient either in person or understanding."

Then Menelaus said, " All that you have been saying, 265 my dear wife, is true. I have travelled much, and have had much to do with heroes, but I have never seen such another man as Ulysses. What endurance too, and what courage he displayed within the wooden horse, wherein all the bravest of the Argives were lying in wait to bring death and destruction upon the Trojans.[1] At that moment you came up to us; some god who wished well to the Trojans must have set you on to it and you had Deiphobus with you. Three times did you go all round our hiding place and pat it; you called our chiefs each by his own name, and mimicked all our wives – Diomed, Ulysses, and I from our seats inside heard what a noise you made. Diomed and I could not make up our minds whether to spring out then and there, or to answer you from inside, but Ulysses held us all in check, so we sat quite still, all except Anticlus, who was beginning to answer you, when Ulysses clapped his two brawny hands over his

---

[1] In the Italian insurrection of 1848, eight young men who were being hotly pursued by the Austrian police hid themselves inside Donatello's colossal wooden horse in the Salone at Padua, and remained there for a week, being fed by their confederates. In 1898 the last survivor was carried round Padua in triumph.

mouth, and kept them there. It was this that saved us all, for he muzzled Anticlus till Minerva took you away again."

290 "How sad," exclaimed Telemachus, "that all this was of no avail to save him, nor yet his own iron courage. But now, sir, be pleased to send us all to bed, that we may lie down and enjoy the blessed boon of sleep."

296 On this Helen told the maid servants to set beds in the room that was in the gatehouse, and to make them with good red rugs, and spread coverlets on the top of them with woollen cloaks for the guests to wear. So the maids went out, carrying a torch, and made the beds, to which a man-servant presently conducted the strangers. Thus, then, did Telemachus and Pisistratus sleep there in the forecourt, while the son of Atreus lay in an inner room with lovely Helen by his side.

306 When the child of morning, rosy-fingered Dawn, appeared, Menelaus rose and dressed himself. He bound his sandals on to his comely feet, girded his sword about his shoulders, and left his room looking like an immortal god. Then, taking a seat near Telemachus he said:

312 "And what, Telemachus, has led you to take this long sea voyage to Lacedaemon? Are you on public or private business? Tell me all about it."

315 "I have come, sir," replied Telemachus, "to see if you can tell me anything about my father. I am being eaten out of house and home; my fair estate is being wasted, and my house is full of miscreants who keep killing great numbers of my sheep and oxen, on the pretence of paying their addresses to my mother. Therefore, I am suppliant at your knees if haply you may tell me about my father's melancholy end, whether you saw it with your own eyes, or heard it from some

other traveller; for he was a man born to trouble. Do
not soften things out of any pity for myself, but tell me
in all plainness exactly what you saw. If my brave
father Ulysses ever did you loyal service either by word
or deed, when you Achaeans were harassed by the
Trojans, bear it in mind now as in my favour and tell
me truly all."

Menelaus on hearing this was very much shocked. 332
" So," he exclaimed, " these cowards would usurp a
brave man's bed? A hind might as well lay her new
born young in the lair of a lion, and then go off to feed
in the forest or in some grassy dell: the lion when he
comes back to his lair will make short work with the
pair of them—and so will Ulysses with these suitors.
By father Jove, Minerva, and Apollo, if Ulysses is still
the man that he was when he wrestled with Philomeleides in Lesbos, and threw him so heavily that all
the Achaeans cheered him—if he is still such and were
to come near these suitors, they would have a short
shrift and a sorry wedding. As regards your questions,
however, I will not prevaricate nor deceive you, but
will tell you without concealment all that the old man
of the sea told me.

" I was trying to come on here, but the gods detained 351
me in Egypt, for my hecatombs had not given them full
satisfaction, and the gods are very strict about having
their dues. Now off Egypt, about as far as a ship can
sail in a day with a good stiff breeze behind her, there
is an island called Pharos—it has a good harbour from
which vessels can get out into open sea when they have
taken in water—and here the gods becalmed me twenty
days without so much as a breath of fair wind to help
me forward. We should have run clean out of provisions and my men would have starved, if a goddess
had not taken pity upon me and saved me in the person

55

of Idothea, daughter to Proteus, the old man of the sea, for she had taken a great fancy to me.

367 " She came to me one day when I was by myself, as I often was, for the men used to go with their barbed hooks, all over the island in the hope of catching a fish or two to save them from the pangs of hunger. ' Stranger,' said she, ' it seems to me that you like starving in this way—at any rate it does not greatly trouble you, for you stick here day after day, without even trying to get away though your men are dying by inches.'

375 " ' Let me tell you,' said I, ' whichever of the goddesses you may happen to be, that I am not staying here of my own accord, but must have offended the gods that live in heaven. Tell me, therefore, for the gods know everything, which of the immortals it is that is hindering me in this way, and tell me also how I may sail the sea so as to reach my home.'

382 " ' Stranger,' replied she, ' I will make it all quite clear to you. There is an old immortal who lives under the sea hereabouts and whose name is Proteus. He is an Egyptian, and people say he is my father; he is Neptune's head man and knows every inch of ground all over the bottom of the sea. If you can snare him and hold him tight, he will tell you about your voyage, what courses you are to take, and how you are to sail the sea so as to reach your home. He will also tell you, if you so will, all that has been going on at your house both good and bad, while you have been away on your long and dangerous journey.'

394 " ' Can you show me,' said I, ' some stratagem by means of which I may catch this old god without his suspecting it and finding me out? For a god is not easily caught—not by a mortal man.'

398 " ' Stranger,' said she, ' I will make it all quite clear to you. About the time when the sun shall have

56

reached mid heaven, the old man of the sea comes up
from under the waves, heralded by the West wind that
furs the water over his head. As soon as he has come
up he lies down, and goes to sleep in a great sea cave,
where the seals—Halosydne's chickens as they call them
—come up also from the grey sea, and go to sleep in
shoals all round him; and a very strong and fish-like
smell do they bring with them.[1] Early to-morrow
morning I will take you to this place and will lay you in
ambush. Pick out, therefore, the three best men you
have in your fleet, and I will tell you all the tricks that
the old man will play you.

"'First he will look over all his seals, and count 411
them; then, when he has seen them and tallied them
on his five fingers, he will go to sleep among them, as a
shepherd among his sheep. The moment you see that
he is asleep seize him; put forth all your strength and
hold him fast, for he will do his very utmost to get
away from you. He will turn himself into every kind
of creature that goes upon the earth, and will become
also both fire and water; but you must hold him fast
and grip him tighter and tighter, till he begins to talk
to you and comes back to what he was when you saw
him go to sleep; then you may slacken your hold and
let him go; and you can ask him which of the gods it is
that is angry with you, and what you must do to reach
your home over the seas.'

"Having so said she dived under the waves, whereon 425
I turned back to the place where my ships were ranged
upon the shore; and my heart was clouded with care
as I went along. When I reached my ship we got

---

[1] The Greek is πικρὸν ἀποπνείογcαι ἁλὸc πολγβενθέοc ὀδμήν.
Is it unfair to argue that the writer is a person of somewhat delicate
sensibility, to whom a strong smell of fish is distasteful?

supper ready, for night was falling, and camped down upon the beach.

431 " When the child of morning, rosy-fingered Dawn, appeared, I took the three men on whose prowess of all kinds I could moſt rely, and went along by the sea-side, praying heartily to heaven. Meanwhile the goddess fetched me up four seal skins from the bottom of the sea, all of them juſt skinned, for she meant playing a trick upon her father. Then she dug four pits for us to lie in, and sat down to wait till we should come up. When we were close to her, she made us lie down in the pits one after the other, and threw a seal skin over each of us. Our ambuscade would have been intoler-able, for the ſtench of the fishy seals was moſt diſtressing [1] —who would go to bed with a sea monſter if he could help it?—but here, too, the goddess helped us, and thought of something that gave us great relief, for she put some ambrosia under each man's noſtrils, which was so fragrant that it killed the smell of the seals.[2]

[1] The Greek is

......τεῖρε γὰρ αἰνῶς
φωκάων ἁλιοτρεφέων ὀλοώτατος ὀδμή.

I believe this to be a hit at the writer's own countrymen who were of Phocaean descent, and the next following line to be a rejoinder to complaints made againſt her in bk. vi, 273-288, to the effeſt that she gave herself airs and would marry none of her own people. For that the writer of the Odyssey was the person who has been introduced into the poem under the name of Nausicaa, I cannot bring myself to queſtion. I may remind English readers that φώκη (*i.e.*, phoca) means " seal." Seals almoſt always appear on Phocaean coins.

[2] Surely here again we are in the hands of a writer of delicate sensibility. It is not as though the seals were ſtale ; they had only juſt been killed. The writer, however, is obviously laughing at her own countrymen, and insulting them as openly as she dares.

"We waited the whole morning and made the best 447
of it, watching the seals come up in hundreds to bask
upon the sea shore, till at noon the old man of the sea
came up too, and when he had found his fat seals he
went over them and counted them. We were among
the first he counted, and he never suspected any guile,
but laid himself down to sleep as soon as he had done
counting. Then we rushed upon him with a shout
and seized him; on which he began at once with his
old tricks, and changed himself first into a lion with a
great mane; then all of a sudden he became a dragon,
a leopard, a wild boar; the next moment he was running
water, and then again directly he was a tree, but we
stuck to him and never lost hold, till at last the cunning
old creature became distressed, and said, 'Which of the
gods was it, Son of Atreus, that hatched this plot with
you for snaring me and seizing me against my will?
What do you want?'

"'You know that yourself, old man,' I answered, 464
'you will gain nothing by trying to put me off. It is
because I have been kept so long in this island, and
see no sign of my being able to get away. I am losing
all heart; tell me, then, for you gods know everything,
which of the immortals it is that is hindering me, and
tell me also how I may sail the sea so as to reach my
home?'

"'Then,' he said, 'if you would finish your voyage 471
and get home quickly, you must offer sacrifices to Jove
and to the rest of the gods before embarking; for it is
decreed that you shall not get back to your friends, and
to your own house, till you have returned to the heaven-
fed stream of Egypt, and offered holy hecatombs to the
immortal gods that reign in heaven. When you have
done this they will let you finish your voyage.'

"I was broken hearted when I heard that I must go 481

back all that long and terrible voyage to Egypt;[1] nevertheless, I answered, 'I will do all, old man, that you have laid upon me; but now tell me, and tell me true, whether all the Achaeans whom Nestor and I left behind us when we set sail from Troy have got home safely, or whether any one of them came to a bad end either on board his own ship or among his friends when the days of his fighting were done.'

491   " ' Son of Atreus,' he answered, ' why ask me? You had better not know what I can tell you, for your eyes will surely fill when you have heard my story. Many of those about whom you ask are dead and gone, but many still remain, and only two of the chief men among the Achaeans perished during their return home. As for what happened on the field of battle—you were there yourself. A third Achaean leader is still at sea, alive, but hindered from returning. Ajax was wrecked, for Neptune drove him on to the great rocks of Gyrae; nevertheless, he let him get safe out of the water, and in spite of all Minerva's hatred he would have escaped death, if he had not ruined himself by boasting. He said the gods could not drown him even though they had tried to do so, and when Neptune heard this large talk, he seized his trident in his two brawny hands, and split the rock of Gyrae in two pieces. The base remained where it was, but the part on which Ajax was sitting fell headlong into the sea and carried Ajax with it; so he drank salt water and was drowned.

512   " ' Your brother and his ships escaped, for Juno protected him, but when he was just about to reach the high promontory of Malea, he was caught by a heavy gale which carried him out to sea again sorely against his will, and drove him to the foreland where Thyestes

[1] We were told above (lines 356, 357) that it was only one day's sail.

60

used to dwell, but where Aegisthus was then living. By and by, however, it seemed as though he was to return safely after all, for the gods backed the wind into its old quarter and they reached home; whereon Agamemnon kissed his native soil, and shed tears of joy at finding himself again in his own country.

" ' Now there was a watchman whom Aegisthus kept 524 always on the watch, and to whom he had promised two talents of gold. This man had been looking out for a whole year to make sure that Agamemnon did not give him the slip and prepare war; when, therefore, this man saw Agamemnon go by, he went and told Aegisthus, who at once began to lay a plot for him. He picked twenty of his bravest warriors and placed them in ambuscade on one side the cloister, while on the opposite side he prepared a banquet. Then he sent his chariots and horsemen to Agamemnon, and invited him to the feast, but he meant foul play. He got him there, all unsuspicious of the doom that was awaiting him, and killed him when the banquet was over as though he were butchering an ox in the shambles; not one of Agamemnon's followers was left alive, nor yet one of Aegisthus', but they were all killed there in the cloisters.'

" Thus spoke Proteus, and I was broken hearted as I 538 heard him. I sat down upon the sands and wept; I felt as though I could no longer bear to live nor look upon the light of the sun. Presently, when I had had my fill of weeping and writhing upon the ground, the old man of the sea said, ' Son of Atreus, do not waste any more time in crying so bitterly; it can do no manner of good; find your way home as fast as ever you can, for Aegisthus may be still alive, and even though Orestes has been beforehand with you in killing him, you may yet come in for his funeral.'

" On this I took comfort in spite of all my sorrow, 548

61

and said, ' I know, then, about these two; tell me, therefore, about the third man of whom you spoke; is he
still alive, but at sea, and unable to get home? or is he
dead? Tell me, no matter how much it may grieve me.'

554   " ' The third man,' he answered, ' is Ulysses who
dwells in Ithaca. I can see him in an island sorrowing
bitterly in the house of the nymph Calypso, who is
keeping him prisoner, and he cannot reach his home
for he has no ships nor sailors to take him over the sea.
As for your own end, Menelaus, you shall not die in
Argos, but the gods will take you to the Elysian plain,
which is at the ends of the world. There fair-haired
Rhadamanthus reigns, and men lead an easier life than
any where else in the world, for in Elysium there falls
not rain, nor hail, nor snow, but Oceanus breathes ever
with a West wind that sings softly from the sea, and
gives fresh life to all men. This will happen to you
because you have married Helen, and are Jove's son-
in-law.'

570   " As he spoke he dived under the waves, whereon I
turned back to the ships with my companions, and my
heart was clouded with care as I went along. When we
reached the ships we got supper ready, for night was
falling, and camped down upon the beach. When the
child of morning, rosy-fingered Dawn appeared, we
drew our ships into the water, and put our masts and
sails within them; then we went on board ourselves,
took our seats on the benches, and smote the grey sea
with our oars. I again stationed my ships in the
heaven-fed stream of Egypt, and offered hecatombs that
were full and sufficient. When I had thus appeased
heaven's anger, I raised a barrow to the memory of
Agamemnon that his name might live for ever, after
which I had a quick passage home, for the gods sent me
a fair wind.

" And now for yourself–stay here some ten or $_{587}$ twelve days longer, and I will then speed you on your way. I will make you a noble present of a chariot and three horses. I will also give you a beautiful chalice that so long as you live may think of me whenever you make a drink-offering to the immortal gods."

" Son of Atreus," replied Telemachus, " do not $_{593}$ press me to stay longer; I should be contented to remain with you for another twelve months; I find your conversation so delightful that I should never once wish myself at home with my parents; but my crew whom I have left at Pylos are already impatient, and you are detaining me from them. As for any present you may be disposed to make me, I had rather that it should be a piece of plate. I will take no horses back with me to Ithaca, but will leave them to adorn your own stables, for you have much flat ground in your kingdom, where lotus thrives, as also meadow-sweet and wheat and barley, and oats with their white and spreading ears; whereas in Ithaca we have neither open fields nor racecourses, and the country is more fit for goats than horses, and I like it the better for that.[1]

---

[1] I give the usual translation, but I do not believe the Greek will warrant it. The Greek stands :

αἰγίβοτος καὶ μᾶλλον ἐπήρατος ἱπποβότοιο
οὐ γάρ τις νήσων ἱππήλατος οὐδ' εὐλείμων,

κ.τ.λ.

This is usually held to mean that Ithaca is an island fit for breeding goats, and on that account more delectable to the speaker than it would have been if it were fit for breeding horses. I find little authority for such a translation ; the most equitable translation of the text as it stands is, " Ithaca is an island fit for breeding goats, and delectable rather than fit for breeding horses ; for not one of the islands is good driving ground, nor well meadowed." Surely the writer does not mean that a pleasant or delectable island would not be fit for breeding horses ?

A Hazardous Emendation [ODYSSEY

None of our islands have much level ground, suitable for horses, and Ithaca least of all."

609 Menelaus smiled and took Telemachus's hand within his own. " What you say," said he, " shows that you

The most equitable translation, therefore, of the present text being thus halt and impotent, we may suspect corruption, and I hazard the following emendation, though I have not adopted it in my translation, as fearing that it would be deemed too fanciful. I would read :

αἰγίβοτος, μᾶλλον δ' ἱππήλατα γ' ἱπποβότοιο
οὐ γὰρ δὴ νήσων τις ἐπήρατος οὐδ' εὐλείμων,
κ.τ.λ.

As far as scanning goes the γ' is not necessary; δώματα ἠλήεντα iv, 72, κέλευσέ τε οἰνοχοῆσαι iv, 233, to go no further afield than earlier lines of this same book, give sufficient authority for ἱππή-λατα ἱπποβότοιο, but the γ' would not be redundant ; it would emphasize the surprise of the contrast, and I should prefer to have it, though it is not very important either way. This reading, of course, should be translated " Ithaca is an island fit for breeding goats, and (by your leave) itself a horseman rather than fit for breeding horses – for not one of the islands is good and well meadowed ground."

This would be sure to baffle the Alexandrian editors. " How," they would ask themselves, " could an island be a horse-man ? " and they would cast about for an emendation. A visit to the top of Mt. Eryx might perhaps make the meaning intelligible, and suggest my proposed restoration of the text to the reader as readily as it did to myself.

I have elsewhere stated my conviction that the writer of the Odyssey was familiar with the old Sican city at the top of Mt. Eryx, and that the Aegadean islands which are so striking when seen thence did duty with her for the Ionian islands – Marettimo, the highest and most westerly of the group, standing for Ithaca. When seen from the top of Mt. Eryx, Marettimo shows as it should do according to Od., ix, 25, 26, " on the horizon, all highest up in the sea towards the West," while the other islands lie " some way off it to the East." As we descend to Trapani, Marettimo appears to sink on to the top of the island of Levanzo, behind which it disappears. My friend, the late Signor E. Biaggini, pointed to it once as it was just standing on the top

64

come of good family. I both can, and will, make this exchange for you, by giving you the finest and most precious piece of plate in all my house. It is a mixing-bowl by Vulcan's own hand, of pure silver, except the rim, which is inlaid with gold. Phaedimus, king of the Sidonians, gave it me in the course of a visit which I paid him when I returned thither on my homeward journey. I will make you a present of it."

Thus did they converse [and guests kept coming to 620 the king's house. They brought sheep and wine, while their wives had put up bread for them to take with them; so they were busy cooking their dinners in the courts].[1]

Meanwhile the suitors were throwing discs or aiming 625 with spears at a mark on the levelled ground in front of Ulysses' house, and were behaving with all their old insolence. Antinous and Eurymachus, who were their ringleaders and much the foremost among them all, were sitting together when Noemon son of Phronius came up and said to Antinous,

" Have we any idea, Antinous, on what day Tele- 632 machus returns from Pylos? He has a ship of mine, and I want it, to cross over to Elis: I have twelve brood mares there with yearling mule foals by their side not yet broken in, and I want to bring one of them over here and break him."

of Levanzo, and said to me, " *Come cavalca bene* " ("How well it rides "), and this immediately suggested my emendation to me. Later on I found in the Hymn to the Pythian Apollo (which abounds with tags taken from the Odyssey) a line ending " ἐπήρατος οὔτ' εὐλείμων," which strengthened my suspicion that this was the original ending of the second of the two lines above under consideration.

[1] See note on line 3 of this book. The reader will observe that the writer has been unable to keep the women out even of an interpolation consisting only of four lines.

638   They were astounded when they heard this, for they had made sure that Telemachus had not gone to the city of Neleus. They thought he was only away somewhere on the farms, and was with the sheep, or with the swineherd; so Antinous said, " When did he go? Tell me truly, and what young men did he take with him? Were they freemen or his own bondsmen—for he might manage that too? Tell me also, did you let him have the ship of your own free will because he asked you, or did he take it without your leave? "

648   " I lent it him," answered Noemon, " what else could I do when a man of his position said he was in a difficulty, and asked me to oblige him? I could not possibly refuse. As for those who went with him they were the best young men we have, and I saw Mentor go on board as captain—or some god who was exactly like him. I cannot understand it, for I saw Mentor here myself yesterday morning, and yet he was then setting out for Pylos."

657   Noemon then went back to his father's house, but Antinous and Eurymachus were very angry. They told the others to leave off playing, and to come and sit down along with themselves. When they came, Antinous son of Eupeithes spoke in anger. His heart was black with rage, and his eyes flashed fire as he said:

663   " Good heavens, this voyage of Telemachus is a very serious matter; we had made sure that it would come to nothing, but the young fellow has got away in spite of us, and with a picked crew too. He will be giving us trouble presently; may Jove take him before he is full grown. Find me a ship, therefore, with a crew of twenty men, and I will lie in wait for him in the Straits between Ithaca and Samos; he will then rue the day that he set out to try and get news of his father."

673   Thus did he speak, and the others applauded his saying; they then all of them went inside the buildings.

66

It was not long ere Penelope came to know what the 675
suitors were plotting; for a man servant, Medon, overheard them from outside the outer court as they were
laying their schemes within, and went to tell his
mistress. As he crossed the threshold of her room
Penelope said: "Medon, what have the suitors sent
you here for? Is it to tell the maids to leave their
master's business and cook dinner for them? I wish
they may neither woo nor dine henceforward, neither
here nor anywhere else, but let this be the very last
time, for the waste you all make of my son's estate. Did
not your fathers tell you when you were children how
good Ulysses had been to them—never doing anything
high-handed, nor speaking harshly to anybody? Kings
may say things sometimes, and they may take a fancy
to one man and dislike another, but Ulysses never did
an unjust thing by anybody—which shows what bad
hearts you have, and that there is no such thing as
gratitude left in this world."

Then Medon said, "I wish, Madam, that this were 696
all; but they are plotting something much more dreadful now—may heaven frustrate their design. They are
going to try and murder Telemachus as he is coming
home from Pylos and Lacedaemon, where he has been
to get news of his father."

Then Penelope's heart sank within her, and for a long 703
time she was speechless; her eyes filled with tears, and
she could find no utterance. At last, however, she said,
"Why did my son leave me? What business had he to
go sailing off in ships that make long voyages over the
ocean like sea-horses? Does he want to die without
leaving any one behind him to keep up his name?"

"I do not know," answered Medon, "whether some 711
god set him on to it, or whether he went on his own
impulse to see if he could find out if his father was dead,
or alive and on his way home."

67

715 Then he went downstairs again, leaving Penelope in an agony of grief. There were plenty of seats in the house, but she had no heart for sitting on any one of them; she could only fling herself on the floor of her own room and cry; whereon all the maids in the house, both old and young, gathered round her and began to cry too, till at last in a transport of sorrow she exclaimed,

722 "My dears, heaven has been pleased to try me with more affliction than any other woman of my age and country. First I lost my brave and lion-hearted husband, who had every good quality under heaven, and whose name was great over all Hellas and middle Argos, and now my darling son is at the mercy of the winds and waves, without my having heard one word about his leaving home. You hussies, there was not one of you would so much as think of giving me a call out of my bed, though you all of you very well knew when he was starting. If I had known he meant taking this voyage, he would have had to give it up, no matter how much he was bent upon it, or leave me a corpse behind him— one or other. Now, however, go some of you and call old Dolius, who was given me by my father on my marriage, and who is my gardener. Bid him go at once and tell everything to Laertes, who may be able to hit on some plan for enlisting public sympathy on our side, as against those who are trying to exterminate his own race and that of Ulysses."

742 Then the dear old nurse Euryclea said, "You may kill me, Madam, or let me live on in your house, which-ever you please, but I will tell you the real truth. I knew all about it, and gave him everything he wanted in the way of bread and wine, but he made me take my solemn oath that I would not tell you anything for some ten or twelve days, unless you asked or happened to hear of his having gone, for he did not want you to spoil

68

your beauty by crying. And now, Madam, wash your face, change your dress, and go upstairs with your maids to offer prayers to Minerva, daughter of Aegis-bearing Jove, for she can save him even though he be in the jaws of death. Do not trouble Laertes: he has trouble enough already. Besides, I cannot think that the gods hate the race of the son of Arceisius so much, but there will be a son left to come up after him, and inherit both the house and the fair fields that lie far all round it."

With these words she made her mistress leave off 758 crying, and dried the tears from her eyes. Penelope washed her face, changed her dress, and went upstairs with her maids. She then put some bruised barley into a basket and began praying to Minerva.

" Hear me," she cried, " Daughter of Aegis-bearing 762 Jove, unweariable. If ever Ulysses while he was here burned you fat thigh bones of sheep or heifer, bear it in mind now as in my favour, and save my darling son from the villainy of the suitors."

She cried aloud as she spoke, and the goddess heard 767 her prayer; meanwhile the suitors were clamorous throughout the covered cloister, and one of them said:

" The queen is preparing for her marriage with one 770 or other of us. Little does she dream that her son has now been doomed to die."

This was what they said, but they did not know what 772 was going to happen. Then Antinous said, " Comrades, let there be no loud talking, lest some of it get carried inside. Let us be up and do that in silence, about which we are all of a mind."

He then chose twenty men, and they went down to 778 their ship and to the sea side; they drew the vessel into the water and got her mast and sails inside her; they bound the oars to the thole-pins with twisted thongs of leather, all in due course, and spread the white sails

69

aloft, while their fine servants brought them their armour. Then they made the ship fast a little way out, came on shore again, got their suppers, and waited till night should fall.

787   But Penelope lay in her own room upstairs unable to eat or drink, and wondering whether her brave son would escape, or be overpowered by the wicked suitors. Like a lioness caught in the toils with hunts-men hemming her in on every side, she thought and thought till she sank into a slumber, and lay on her bed bereft of thought and motion.

795   Then Minerva bethought her of another matter, and made a vision in the likeness of Penelope's sister Iphthime daughter of Icarius who had married Eumelus and lived in Pherae. She told the vision to go to the house of Ulysses, and to make Penelope leave off crying, so it came into her room by the hole through which the thong went for pulling the door to, and hovered over her head, saying,

804   " You are asleep, Penelope: the gods who live at ease will not suffer you to weep and be so sad. Your son has done them no wrong, so he will yet come back to you."

808   Penelope, who was sleeping sweetly at the gates of dreamland, answered, " Sister, why have you come here? You do not come very often, but I suppose that is because you live such a long way off. Am I, then, to leave off crying and refrain from all the sad thoughts that torture me? I, who have lost my brave and lion-hearted husband, who had every good quality under heaven, and whose name was great over all Hellas and middle Argos; and now my darling son has gone off on board of a ship–a foolish fellow who has never been used to roughing it, nor to going about among gatherings of men. I am even more anxious about him

70

than about my husband; I am all in a tremble when I
think of him, lest something should happen to him,
either from the people among whom he has gone, or by
sea, for he has many enemies who are plotting against
him, and are bent on killing him before he can return
home."

Then the vision said, " Take heart, and be not so 824
much dismayed. There is one gone with him whom
many a man would be glad enough to have stand by his
side, I mean Minerva; it is she who has compassion
upon you, and who has sent me to bear you this
message."

" Then," said Penelope, " if you are a god or have 830
been sent here by divine commission, tell me also about
that other unhappy one – is he still alive, or is he already
dead and in the house of Hades? "

And the vision said, " I shall not tell you for certain 835
whether he is alive or dead, and there is no use in idle
conversation."

Then it vanished through the thong-hole of the door 838
and was dissipated into thin air; but Penelope rose
from her sleep refreshed and comforted, so vivid had
been her dream.

Meantime the suitors went on board and sailed their 842
ways over the sea, intent on murdering Telemachus.
Now there is a rocky islet called Asteris, of no great size,
in mid channel between Ithaca and Samos, and there
is a harbour on either side of it where a ship can lie.
Here then the Achaeans placed themselves in ambush.

71

AND NOW, AS DAWN ROSE FROM HER
couch beside Tithonus–harbinger of light alike
to mortals and immortals–the gods met in
council and with them, Jove the lord of thunder,
who is their king. Thereon Minerva began to tell them
of the many sufferings of Ulysses, for she pitied him
away there in the house of the nymph Calypso.

7 "Father Jove," said she, "and all you other gods
that live in everlasting bliss, I hope there may never be
such a thing as a kind and well-disposed ruler any more,
nor one who will govern equitably. I hope they will
be all henceforth cruel and unjust, for there is not one
of his subjects but has forgotten Ulysses, who ruled
them as though he were their father. There he is,
lying in great pain in an island where dwells the nymph
Calypso, who will not let him go; and he cannot get
back to his own country, for he can find neither ships
nor sailors to take him over the sea. Furthermore,
wicked people are now trying to murder his only son
Telemachus, who is coming home from Pylos and
Lacedaemon, where he has been to see if he can get
news of his father."

21 "What, my dear, are you talking about?" replied her
father, "did you not send him there yourself, because
you thought it would help Ulysses to get home and
punish the suitors? Besides, you are perfectly able to
protect Telemachus, and to see him safely home again,
while the suitors have to come hurry-skurrying back
without having killed him."

28 When he had thus spoken, he said to his son Mercury,
"Mercury, you are our messenger, go therefore and tell
Calypso we have decreed that poor Ulysses is to return
home. He is to be convoyed neither by gods nor men,
but after a perilous voyage of twenty days upon a raft

72

he is to reach fertile Scheria,[1] the land of the Phaeacians, who are near of kin to the gods, and will honour him as though he were one of ourselves. They will send him in a ship to his own country, and will give him more bronze and gold and raiment than he would have brought back from Troy, if he had had all his prize money and had got home without disaster. This is how we have settled that he shall return to his country and his friends."

Thus he spoke, and Mercury, guide and guardian, 43 slayer of Argus, did as he was told. Forthwith he bound on his glittering golden sandals with which he could fly like the wind over land and sea. He took the wand with which he seals men's eyes in sleep or wakes them just as he pleases, and flew holding it in his hand over Pieria; then he swooped down through the firmament till he reached the level of the sea, whose waves he skimmed like a cormorant that flies fishing every hole and corner of the ocean, and drenching its thick plumage in the spray. He flew and flew over many a weary wave, but when at last he got to the island which was his journey's end, he left the sea and went on by land till he came to the cave where the nymph Calypso lived.

He found her at home. There was a large fire burn- 58 ing on the hearth, and one could smell from far the fragrant reek of burning cedar and sandal wood. As for herself, she was busy at her loom, shooting her golden shuttle through the warp and singing beautifully. Round her cave there was a thick wood of alder, poplar, and sweet smelling cypress trees, wherein all

---

[1] Scheria means a piece of land jutting out into the sea. In my *Authoress of the Odyssey*, I thought " Jutland " would be a suitable translation, but it has been pointed out to me that " Jutland " only means the land of the Jutes.

73

kinds of great birds had built their nests—owls, hawks, and chattering sea-crows that occupy their business in the waters. A vine loaded with grapes was trained and grew luxuriantly about the mouth of the cave; there were also four running rills of water in channels cut pretty close together, and turned hither and thither so as to irrigate the beds of violets and luscious herbage over which they flowed.[1] Even a god could not help being charmed with such a lovely spot, so Mercury stood still and looked at it; but when he had admired it sufficiently he went inside the cave.

77   Calypso knew him at once—for the gods all know each other, no matter how far they live from one another—but Ulysses was not within; he was on the sea-shore as usual, looking out upon the barren ocean with tears in his eyes, groaning and breaking his heart for sorrow. Calypso gave Mercury a seat and said: "Why have you come to see me, Mercury—honoured, and ever welcome —for you do not visit me often? Say what you want; I will do it for you at once if I can, and if it can be done at all; but come inside, and let me set refreshment before you.

92   As she spoke she drew a table loaded with ambrosia beside him and mixed him some red nectar, so Mercury ate and drank till he had had enough, and then said:

97   "We are speaking god and goddess to one another, and you ask me why I have come here, and I will tell you truly as you would have me do. Jove sent me; it was no doing of mine; who could possibly want to come all this way over the sea where there are no cities full of people to offer me sacrifices or choice hecatombs? Nevertheless I had to come, for none of us other gods

[1] Irrigation as here described is common in gardens near Trapani. The water that supplies the ducts is drawn from wells by a mule who turns a wheel with buckets on it.

can cross Jove, nor transgress his orders. He says that
you have here the most ill-starred of all those who
fought nine years before the city of King Priam and
sailed home in the tenth year after having sacked it.
On their way home they sinned against Minerva,[1] who
raised both wind and waves against them, so that all
his brave companions perished, and he alone was
carried hither by wind and tide. Jove says that you are
to let this man go at once, for it is decreed that he shall
not perish here, far from his own people, but shall
return to his house and country and see his friends
again."

Calypso trembled with rage when she heard this, 116
" You gods," she exclaimed, " ought to be ashamed of
yourselves. You are always jealous, and hate seeing a
goddess take a fancy to a mortal man, and live with him
in open matrimony. So when rosy-fingered Dawn made
love to Orion, you precious gods were all of you furious
till Diana went and killed him in Ortygia. So again
when Ceres fell in love with Iasion, and yielded to him
in a thrice-ploughed fallow field, Jove came to hear of
it before so very long and killed Iasion with his thunderbolts. And now you are angry with me too because I
have a man here. I found the poor creature sitting all
alone astride of a keel, for Jove had struck his ship with
lightning and sunk it in mid ocean, so that all his crew
were drowned, while he himself was driven by wind and
waves on to my island. I got fond of him and cherished
him, and had set my heart on making him immortal, so
that he should never grow old all his days; still I cannot
cross Jove, nor bring his counsels to nothing; therefore, if he insists upon it, let the man go beyond the seas
again; but I cannot send him anywhere myself for I
have neither ships nor men who can take him. Never-

[1] There is not a word here about the cattle of the sun-god.

theless I will readily give him such advice, in all good faith, as will be likely to bring him safely to his own country."

145 "Then send him away," said Mercury, " or Jove will be angry with you and punish you."

148 On this he took his leave, and Calypso went out to look for Ulysses, for she had heard Jove's message. She found him sitting upon the beach with his eyes ever filled with tears, and dying of sheer home-sickness; for he had got tired of Calypso, and though he was forced to sleep with her in the cave by night, it was she, not he, that would have it so. As for the day time, he spent it on the rocks and on the sea-shore, weeping, crying aloud for his despair, and always looking out upon the sea. Calypso then went close up to him and said:

160 " My poor fellow, you shall not stay here grieving and fretting your life out any longer. I am going to send you away of my own free will; so go, cut some beams of wood, and make yourself a large raft with an upper deck that it may carry you safely over the sea. I will put bread, wine, and water on board to save you from starving. I will also give you clothes, and will send you a fair wind to take you home, if the gods in heaven so will it—for they know more about these things, and can settle them better than I can."

171 Ulysses shuddered as he heard her. " Now goddess," he answered, " there is something behind all this; you cannot be really meaning to help me home when you bid me do such a dreadful thing as put to sea on a raft. Not even a well-found ship with a fair wind could venture on such a distant voyage: nothing that you can say or do shall make me go on board a raft unless you first solemnly swear that you mean me no mischief."

180 Calypso smiled at this and caressed him with her hand: " You know a great deal," said she, " but you

76

are quite wrong here. May heaven above and earth below be my witnesses, with the waters of the river Styx—and this is the moSt solemn oath which a blessed god can take—that I mean you no sort of harm, and am only advising you to do exaƈtly what I should do myself in your place. I am dealing with you quite Straightforwardly; my heart is not made of iron, and I am very sorry for you."

When she had thus spoken she led the way rapidly 192 before him, and Ulysses followed in her Steps; so the pair, goddess and man, went on and on till they came to Calypso's cave, where Ulysses took the seat that Mercury had juSt left. Calypso set meat and drink before him of the food that mortals eat; but her maids brought ambrosia and neƈtar for herself, and they laid their hands on the good things that were before them. When they had satisfied themselves with meat and drink, Calypso spoke, saying:

" Ulysses, noble son of Laertes, so you would Start 203 home to your own land at once? Good luck go with you, but if you could only know how much suffering is in Store for you before you get back to your own country, you would Stay where you are, keep house along with me, and let me make you immortal, no matter how anxious you may be to see this wife of yours, of whom you are thinking all the time day after day; yet I flatter myself that I am no whit less tall or well-looking than she is, for it is not to be expeƈted that a mortal woman should compare in beauty with an immortal."

" Goddess," replied Ulysses, " do not be angry with 214 me about this. I am quite aware that my wife Penelope is nothing like so tall or so beautiful as yourself. She is only a woman, whereas you are an immortal. Nevertheless, I want to get home, and can think of nothing else. If some god wrecks me when I am on the sea,

I will bear it and make the best of it. I have had infinite trouble both by land and sea already, so let this go with the rest."

225 Presently the sun set and it became dark, whereon the pair retired into the inner part of the cave and went to bed.

228 When the child of morning, rosy-fingered Dawn, appeared, Ulysses put on his shirt and cloak, while the goddess wore a dress of a light gossamer fabric, very fine and graceful, with a beautiful golden girdle about her waist and a veil to cover her head. She at once set herself to think how she could speed Ulysses on his way. So she gave him a great bronze axe that suited his hands; it was sharpened on both sides, and had a beautiful olive-wood handle fitted firmly on to it. She also gave him a sharp adze, and then led the way to the far end of the island where the largest trees grew—alder, poplar and pine, that reached the sky—very dry and well seasoned, so as to sail light for him in the water.[1] Then, when she had shown him where the best trees grew, Calypso went home, leaving him to cut them, which he soon finished doing. He cut down twenty trees in all and adzed them smooth, squaring them by rule in good workmanlike fashion. Meanwhile Calypso came back with some augers, so he bored holes with them and fitted the timbers together with bolts and rivets. He made the raft as broad as a skilled ship-wright makes the beam of a large vessel, and he fixed a deck on top of the ribs, and ran a gunwale all round it. He also made a mast with a yard arm, and a rudder to steer with. He fenced the raft all round with wicker hurdles as a protection against the waves, and then he

---

[1] The writer evidently thought that green, growing wood might also be well seasoned. The Greek is ᾱγᾱ πάλαι περίκηλα τά οἱ πλώοιεν ἐλαφρῶς.

threw on a quantity of wood. By and by Calypso brought him some linen to make the sails, and he made these too, excellently, making them faſt with braces and sheets. Laſt of all, with the help of levers, he drew the raft down into the water.

In four days he had completed the whole work, and 262 on the fifth Calypso sent him from the island after washing him and giving him some clean clothes. She gave him a goat skin full of black wine,[1] and another larger one of water; she also gave him a wallet full of provisions, and found him in much good meat. Moreover, she made the wind fair and warm for him, and gladly did Ulysses spread his sail before it, while he sat and guided the raft skilfully by means of the rudder. He never closed his eyes, but kept them fixed on the Pleiads, on late-setting Bootes, and on the Bear— which men also call the wain, and which turns round and round where it is, facing Orion, and alone never dipping into the ſtream of Oceanus—for Calypso had told him to keep this to his left. Days seven and ten did he sail over the sea, and on the eighteenth the dim outlines of the mountains on the neareſt part of the Phaeacian coaſt appeared, rising like a shield[2] on the horizon.

But King Neptune, who was returning from the 282 Ethiopians, caught sight of Ulysses a long way off, from the mountains of the Solymi. He could see him sailing upon the sea, and it made him very angry, so he wagged his head and muttered to himself, saying, "Good heavens, so the gods have been changing their minds about Ulysses while I was away in Ethiopia, and now he is close to the land of the Phaeacians, where it is

---

[1] *I.e.*, very deep red like some of the present Sicilian wines that look more black than anything else.

[2] Reading, ὡс ὅτε ῥινόν, etc.

79

decreed that he shall escape from the calamities that
have befallen him. Still, he shall have plenty of hardship yet before he has done with it."

291   Thereon he gathered his clouds together, grasped his
trident, stirred it round in the sea, and roused the rage
of every wind that blows till earth, sea, and sky were
hidden in cloud, and night sprang forth out of the
heavens. Winds from East, South, North, and West
fell upon him all at the same time, and a tremendous sea
got up, so that Ulysses' heart began to fail him. "Alas,"
he said to himself in his dismay, "what ever will become
of me? I am afraid Calypso was right when she said
I should have trouble by sea before I got back home.
It is all coming true. How black is Jove making
heaven with his clouds, and what a sea the winds are
raising from every quarter at once. I am now safe to
perish. Blest and thrice blest were those Danaans who
fell before Troy in the cause of the sons of Atreus.
Would that I had been killed on the day when the
Trojans were pressing me so sorely about the dead body
of Achilles, for then I should have had due burial and
the Achaeans would have honoured my name; but now
it seems that I shall come to a most pitiable end."

313   As he spoke a sea broke over him with such terrific
fury that the raft reeled again, and he was carried overboard a long way off. He let go the helm, and the force
of the hurricane was so great that it broke the mast half
way up, and both sail and yard went over into the sea.
For a long time Ulysses was under water, and it was
all he could do to rise to the surface again, for the
clothes Calypso had given him weighed him down; but
at last he got his head above water and spat out the
bitter brine that was running down his face in streams.
In spite of all this, however, he did not lose sight of his
raft, but swam as fast as he could towards it, got hold

of it, and climbed on board again so as to escape drown-
ing. The sea took the raft and tossed it about as Autumn
winds whirl thistledown round and round upon a road.
It was as though the South, North, East, and West
winds were all playing battledore and shuttlecock with
it at once.

When he was in this plight, Ino daughter of Cadmus, 333
also called Leucothea, saw him. She had formerly
been a mere mortal, but had been since raised to the
rank of a marine goddess. Seeing in what great distress
Ulysses now was, she had compassion upon him, and,
rising like a sea-gull from the waves, took her seat
upon the raft.

" My poor good man," said she, " why is Neptune 339
so furiously angry with you? He is giving you a great
deal of trouble, but for all his bluster he will not kill
you. You seem to be a sensible person, do then as I
bid you; strip, leave your raft to drive before the wind,
and swim to the Phaeacian coast where better luck
awaits you. And here, take my veil and put it round
your chest; it is enchanted, and you can come to no
harm so long as you wear it. As soon as you touch land
take it off, throw it back as far as you can into the sea,
and then go away again." With these words she took
off her veil and gave it him. Then she dived down
again like a sea-gull and vanished beneath the dark blue
waters.

But Ulysses did not know what to think. " Alas," 354
he said to himself in his dismay, " this is only some one
or other of the gods who is luring me to ruin by advising me to quit my raft. At any rate I will not do so at
present, for the land where she said I should be quit of
all my troubles seemed to be still a good way off. I know
what I will do—I am sure it will be best—no matter what
happens I will stick to the raft as long as her timbers

81   G

hold together, but when the sea breaks her up I will swim for it; I do not see how I can do any better than this."

365 While he was thus in two minds, Neptune sent a terrible great wave that seemed to rear itself above his head till it broke right over the raft, which then went to pieces as though it were a heap of dry chaff tossed about by a whirlwind. Ulysses got astride of one plank and rode upon it as if he were on horseback; he then took off the clothes Calypso had given him, bound Ino's veil under his arms, and plunged into the sea—meaning to swim on shore. King Neptune watched him as he did so, and wagged his head, muttering to himself and saying, " There now, swim up and down as you best can till you fall in with well-to-do people. I do not think you will be able to say that I have let you off too lightly." On this he lashed his horses and drove to Aegae where his palace is.

382 But Minerva resolved to help Ulysses, so she bound the ways of all the winds except one, and made them lie quite still; but she roused a good stiff breeze from the North that should lay the waters till Ulysses reached the land of the Phaeacians where he would be safe.

388 Thereon he floated about for two nights and two days in the water, with a heavy swell on the sea and death staring him in the face; but when the third day broke, the wind fell and there was a dead calm without so much as a breath of air stirring. As he rose on the swell he looked eagerly ahead, and could see land quite near. Then, as children rejoice when their dear father begins to get better after having for a long time borne sore affliction sent him by some angry spirit, but the gods deliver him from evil, so was Ulysses thankful when he again saw land and trees, and swam on with all his strength that he might once more set foot upon dry

82

ground. When, however, he got within earshot, he began to hear the surf thundering up against the rocks, for the swell still broke against them with a terrific roar. Everything was enveloped in spray; there were no harbours where a ship might ride, nor shelter of any kind, but only headlands, low-lying rocks, and mountain tops.

Ulysses' heart now began to fail him, and he said 406 despairingly to himself, " Alas, Jove has let me see land after swimming so far that I had given up all hope, but I can find no landing place, for the coast is rocky and surf-beaten, the rocks are smooth and rise sheer from the sea, with deep water close under them so that I cannot climb out for want of foothold. I am afraid some great wave will lift me off my legs and dash me against the rocks as I leave the water—which would give me a sorry landing. If, on the other hand, I swim further in search of some shelving beach or harbour, a hurricane may carry me out to sea again sorely against my will, or heaven may send some great monster of the deep to attack me; for Amphitrite breeds many such, and I know that Neptune is very angry with me."

While he was thus in two minds a wave caught him 424 and took him with such force against the rocks that he would have been smashed and torn to pieces if Minerva had not shown him what to do. He caught hold of the rock with both hands and clung to it groaning with pain till the wave retired, so he was saved that time; but presently the wave came on again and carried him back with it far into the sea—tearing his hands as the suckers of a polypus are torn when some one plucks it from its bed, and the stones come up along with it— even so did the rocks tear the skin from his strong hands, and then the wave drew him deep down under the water.

436 Here poor Ulysses would have certainly perished even in spite of his own destiny, if Minerva had not helped him to keep his wits about him. He swam seaward again, beyond reach of the surf that was beating against the land, and at the same time he kept looking towards the shore to see if he could find some haven, or a spit that should take the waves aslant. By and by, as he swam on, he came to the mouth of a river, and here he thought would be the best place, for there were no rocks, and it afforded shelter from the wind. He felt that there was a current, so he prayed inwardly and said:

445 "Hear me, O king, whoever you may be, and save me from the anger of the sea-god Neptune, for I approach you prayerfully. Any one who has lost his way has at all times a claim even upon the gods, wherefore in my distress I draw near to your stream, and cling to the knees of your riverhood. Have mercy upon me, O king, for I declare myself your suppliant."

451 Then the god stayed his stream and stilled the waves, making all calm before him, and bringing him safely into the mouth of the river. Here at last Ulysses' knees and strong hands failed him, for the sea had completely broken him. His body was all swollen, and his mouth and nostrils ran down like a river with sea-water, so that he could neither breathe nor speak, and lay swooning from sheer exhaustion; presently, when he had got his breath and came to himself again, he took off the scarf that Ino had given him and threw it back into the salt [1] stream of the river, whereon Ino received it into her hands from the wave that bore it towards her. Then he left the river, laid himself down among the rushes, and kissed the bounteous earth.

464 "Alas," he cried to himself in his dismay; "what

[1] The reader will note that the river was flowing with salt water, *i.e.*, that it was tidal.

SALT WORKS OF S. CUSUMANO, FORMERLY A TIDAL INLET—
the tide here ranging sometimes as much as three feet. These salt works
were an open mere till 1840. The former exit, though now silted up, is
still often filled with sea water in winter

MOUTH OF THE TIDAL INLET UP WHICH ULYSSES SWAM,
NOW SALT WORKS OF S. CUSUMANO

This same spot (at this point of the story supposed to be in Scheria) was
also used by the Authoress for (1) the Harbour Rheithron, *i.e.* "with a
current," in Ithaca, (2) the place where Ulysses landed on his return to Ithaca,
(3) the place where Telemachus landed on his return from Pylos to Ithaca

ever will become of me, and how is it all to end? If I
stay here upon the river bed through the long watches
of the night, I am so exhausted that the bitter cold and
damp may make an end of me—for towards sunrise there
will be a keen wind blowing from off the river. If, on
the other hand, I climb the hill side, find shelter in the
woods, and sleep in some thicket, I may escape the cold
and have a good night's rest, but some savage beast
may take advantage of me and devour me."

In the end he deemed it best to take to the woods, and 474
he found one upon some high ground not far from the
water. There he crept beneath two shoots of olive
that grew from a single stock—the one an ungrafted
sucker, while the other had been grafted. No wind,
however squally, could break through the cover they
afforded, nor could the sun's rays pierce them, nor the
rain get through them, so closely did they grow into
one another. Ulysses crept under these and began to
make himself a bed to lie on, for there was a great litter
of dead leaves lying about—enough to make a covering
for two or three men even in hard winter weather. He
was glad enough to see this, so he laid himself down
and heaped the leaves all round him. Then, as one who
lives alone in the country, far from any neighbour,
hides a brand as fire-seed in the ashes to save himself
from having to get a light elsewhere, even so did Ulysses
cover himself up with leaves; and Minerva shed a
sweet sleep upon his eyes, closed his eyelids, and made
him lose all memory of his sorrows.   493

S O HERE ULYSSES SLEPT, OVERCOME BY
sleep and toil; but Minerva went off to the country
and city of the Phaeacians—a people who used to
live in the fair town of Hypereia, near the lawless
Cyclopes. Now the Cyclopes were Stronger than they
and plundered them, so their king Nausithous moved
them thence and settled them in Scheria, far from all
other people. He surrounded the city with a wall,
built houses and temples, and divided the lands among
his people; but he was dead and gone to the house of
Hades, and King Alcinous, whose counsels were
inspired of heaven, was now reigning. To his house,
then, did Minerva hie in furtherance of the return of
Ulysses.

15 She went Straight to the beautifully decorated bedroom in which there slept a girl who was as lovely as a
goddess, Nausicaa, daughter to King Alcinous. Two
maid servants were sleeping near her, both very pretty,
one on either side of the doorway, which was closed
with well-made folding doors. Minerva took the form
of the famous sea captain Dymas's daughter, who was
a bosom friend of Nausicaa and juSt her own age; then,
coming up to the girl's bedside like a breath of wind,
she hovered over her head and said:

25 "Nausicaa, what can your mother have been about,
to have such a lazy daughter? Here are your clothes all
lying in disorder, yet you are going to be married
almoSt immediately, and should not only be well
dressed yourself, but should find good clothes for
those who attend you. This is the way to get yourself
a good name, and to make your father and mother
proud of you. Suppose, then, that we make to-morrow
a washing day, and Start at daybreak. I will come and
help you so that you may have everything ready as soon

86

as possible, for all the best young men among your own people are courting you, and you are not going to remain a maid much longer. Ask your father, therefore, to have a waggon and mules ready for us at daybreak, to take the rugs, robes, and girdles; and you can ride, too, which will be much pleasanter for you than walking, for the washing-cisterns are some way from the town."

When she had said this Minerva went away to 41 Olympus, which they say is the everlasting home of the gods. Here no wind beats roughly, and neither rain nor snow can fall; but it abides in everlasting sunshine and in a great peacefulness of light, wherein the blessed gods are illumined for ever and ever. This was the place to which the goddess went when she had given instructions to the girl.

By and by morning came and woke Nausicaa, who 48 began wondering about her dream; she therefore went to the other end of the house to tell her father and mother all about it, and found them in their own room. Her mother was sitting by the fireside spinning her purple yarn with her maids around her, and she happened to catch her father just as he was going out to attend a meeting of the town council, which the Phaeacian aldermen had convened. She stopped him and said:

" Papa dear, could you manage to let me have a good 57 big waggon? I want to take all our dirty clothes to the river and wash them. You are the chief man here, so it is only right that you should have a clean shirt when you attend meetings of the council. Moreover, you have five sons at home, two of them married, while the other three are good-looking bachelors; you know they always like to have clean linen when they go to a dance, and I have been thinking about all this."

87

66　She did not say a word about her own wedding, for she did not like to, but her father knew and said, "You shall have the mules, my love, and whatever else you have a mind for. Be off with you, and the men shall get you a good strong waggon with a body to it that will hold all your clothes."

71　On this he gave his orders to the servants, who got the waggon out, harnessed the mules, and put them to, while the girl brought the clothes down from the linen room and placed them on the waggon. Her mother prepared her a basket of provisions with all sorts of good things, and a goat skin full of wine; the girl now got into the waggon, and her mother gave her also a golden cruse of oil, that she and her women might anoint themselves. Then she took the whip and reins and lashed the mules on, whereon they set off, and their hoofs clattered on the road. They pulled without flagging, and carried not only Nausicaa and her wash of clothes, but the maids also who were with her.

85　When they reached the water side they went to the washing-cisterns, through which there ran at all times enough pure water to wash any quantity of linen, no matter how dirty. Here they unharnessed the mules and turned them out to feed on the sweet juicy herbage that grew by the water side. They took the clothes out of the waggon, put them in the water, and vied with one another in treading them in the pits to get the dirt out. After they had washed them and got them quite clean, they laid them out by the sea side, where the waves had raised a high beach of shingle, and set about washing themselves and anointing themselves with olive oil. Then they got their dinner by the side of the stream, and waited for the sun to finish drying the clothes. When they had done dinner they threw off the veils that covered their heads and began to play at ball,

88

while Nausicaa sang for them. As the huntress Diana goes forth upon the mountains of Taygetus or Erymanthus to hunt wild boars or deer, and the wood-nymphs, daughters of Aegis-bearing Jove, take their sport along with her (then is Leto proud at seeing her daughter stand a full head taller than the others, and eclipse the loveliest amid a whole bevy of beauties), even so did the girl outshine her handmaids.

When it was time for them to start home, and they were folding the clothes and putting them into the waggon, Minerva began to consider how Ulysses should wake up and see the handsome girl who was to conduct him to the city of the Phaeacians. The girl, therefore, threw a ball at one of the maids, which missed her and fell into deep water. On this they all shouted, and the noise they made woke Ulysses, who sat up in his bed of leaves and began to wonder what it might all be.

" Alas," said he to himself, " what kind of people have I come amongst? Are they cruel, savage, and uncivilized, or hospitable and humane? I seem to hear the voices of young women, and they sound like those of the nymphs that haunt mountain tops, or springs of rivers and meadows of green grass. At any rate I am among a race of men and women. Let me try if I cannot manage to get a look at them."

As he said this he crept from under his bush, and broke off a bough covered with thick leaves to hide his nakedness. He looked like some lion of the wilderness that stalks about exulting in his strength and defying both wind and rain; his eyes glare as he prowls in quest of oxen, sheep, or deer, for he is famished, and will dare break even into a well-fenced homestead, trying to get at the sheep—even such did Ulysses seem to the young women, as he drew near to them all naked as he

89

was, for he was in great want. On seeing one so un-
kempt and so begrimed with salt water, the others
scampered off along the spits that jutted out into the
sea, but the daughter of Alcinous stood firm, for
Minerva put courage into her heart and took away all
fear from her. She stood right in front of Ulysses, and
he doubted whether he should go up to her, throw
himself at her feet, and embrace her knees as a suppliant,
or stay where he was and entreat her to give him some
clothes and show him the way to the town. In the end
he deemed it best to entreat her from a distance in case
the girl should take offence at his coming near enough
to clasp her knees, so he addressed her in honeyed and
persuasive language.

149 " O queen," he said, " I implore your aid—but tell
me, are you a goddess or are you a mortal woman? If
you are a goddess and dwell in heaven, I can only con-
jecture that you are Jove's daughter Diana, for your
face and figure resemble none but hers; if on the other
hand you are a mortal and live on earth, thrice happy
are your father and mother—thrice happy, too, are your
brothers and sisters; how proud and delighted they
must feel when they see so fair a scion as yourself going
out to a dance; most happy, however, of all will he be
whose wedding gifts have been the richest, and who
takes you to his own home. I never yet saw any one so
beautiful, neither man nor woman, and am lost in
admiration as I behold you. I can only compare you
to a young palm tree which I saw when I was at Delos
growing near the altar of Apollo—for I was there, too,
with much people after me, when I was on that journey
which has been the source of all my troubles. Never
yet did such a young plant shoot out of the ground as
that was, and I admired and wondered at it exactly as I
now admire and wonder at yourself. I dare not clasp

90

your knees, but I am in great distress; yesterday made the twentieth day that I had been tossing about upon the sea. The winds and waves have taken me all the way from the Ogygian island,[1] and now fate has flung me upon this coast that I may endure still further suffering; for I do not think that I have yet come to the end of it, but rather that heaven has still much evil in store for me.

" And now, O queen, have pity upon me, for you 175 are the first person I have met, and I know no one else in this country. Show me the way to your town, and let me have anything that you may have brought hither to wrap your clothes in. May heaven grant you in all things your heart's desire—husband, house, and a happy, peaceful home; for there is nothing better in this world than that man and wife should be of one mind in a house. It discomfits their enemies, makes the hearts of their friends glad, and they themselves know more about it than any one."

To this Nausicaa answered, " Stranger, you appear 186 to be a sensible, well-disposed person. There is no accounting for luck; Jove gives prosperity to rich and poor just as he chooses, so you must take what he has seen fit to send you, and make the best of it. Now, however, that you have come to this our country, you shall not want for clothes nor for anything else that a foreigner in distress may reasonably look for. I will show you the way to the town, and will tell you the name of our people; we are called Phaeacians, and I am daughter to Alcinous, in whom the whole power of the state is vested."

Then she called her maids and said, " Stay where you 198 are, you girls. Can you not see a man without running

[1] Then the Ogygian island was not so far off, but that Nausicaa might be assumed to know where it was.

away from him? Do you take him for a robber or a
murderer? Neither he nor any one else can come here
to do us Phaeacians any harm, for we are dear to the
gods, and live apart on a land's end that juts into the
sounding sea, and have nothing to do with any other
people. This is only some poor man who has loſt his
way, and we muſt be kind to him, for ſtrangers and
foreigners in diſtress are under Jove's proteƈion, and
will take what they can get and be thankful; so, girls,
give the poor fellow something to eat and drink, and
wash him in the ſtream at some place that is sheltered
from the wind."

211   On this the maids left off running away and began
calling one another back. They made Ulysses sit down
in the shelter as Nausicaa had told them, and brought
him a shirt and cloak. They also brought him the little
golden cruse of oil, and told him to go and wash in the
ſtream. But Ulysses said, " Young women, please to
ſtand a little on one side that I may wash the brine from
my shoulders and anoint myself with oil, for it is long
enough since my skin has had a drop of oil upon it.
I cannot wash as long as you all keep ſtanding there.
I am ashamed to ſtrip [1] before a number of good-looking
young women."

223   Then they ſtood on one side and went to tell the
girl, while Ulysses washed himself in the ſtream and
scrubbed the brine from his back and from his broad
shoulders. When he had thoroughly washed himself,
and had got the brine out of his hair, he anointed himself with oil, and put on the clothes which the girl had
given him; Minerva then made him look taller and
ſtronger than before, she also made the hair grow thick
on the top of his head, and flow down in curls like
hyacinth blossoms; she glorified him about the head

---

[1] Gr. ΓΥΜΝΟῖϹΘΑΙ.

and shoulders as a skilful workman who has studied art
of all kinds under Vulcan and Minerva enriches a piece
of silver plate by gilding it—and his work is full of
beauty. Then he went and sat down a little way off
upon the beach, looking quite young and handsome,
and the girl gazed on him with admiration; then she
said to her maids:

" Hush, my dears, for I want to say something. I 239
believe the gods who live in heaven have sent this man
to the Phaeacians. When I first saw him I thought him
plain, but now his appearance is like that of the gods
who dwell in heaven. I should like my future husband
to be just such another as he is, if he would only stay
here and not want to go away. However, give him
something to eat and drink."

They did as they were told, and set food before 247
Ulysses, who ate and drank ravenously, for it was long
since he had had food of any kind. Meanwhile,
Nausicaa bethought her of another matter. She got the
linen folded and placed in the waggon, she then yoked
the mules, and, as she took her seat, she called Ulysses:

" Stranger," said she, " rise and let us be going back 255
to the town; I will introduce you at the house of my
excellent father, where I can tell you that you will meet
all the best people among the Phaeacians. But be sure
and do as I bid you, for you seem to be a sensible person.
As long as we are going past the fields and farm lands,
follow briskly behind the waggon along with the maids
and I will lead the way myself. Presently, however, we
shall come to the town, where you will find a high wall
running all round it, and a good harbour on either side
with a narrow entrance into the city, and the ships will
be drawn up by the road side, for every one has a place
where his own ship can lie. You will see the market
place with a temple of Neptune in the middle of it, and

93

paved with large stones bedded in the earth. Here people deal in ship's gear of all kinds, such as cables and sails, and here, too, are the places where oars are made, for the Phaeacians are not a nation of archers; they know nothing about bows and arrows, but are a seafaring folk, and pride themselves on their masts, oars, and ships, with which they travel far over the sea.

273   " I am afraid of the gossip and scandal that may be set on foot against me later on; for the people here are very ill-natured, and some low fellow, if he met us, might say, ' Who is this fine-looking stranger that is going about with Nausicaa? Where did she find him? I suppose she is going to marry him. Perhaps he is a vagabond sailor whom she has taken from some foreign vessel, for we have no neighbours; or some god has at last come down from heaven in answer to her prayers, and she is going to live with him all the rest of her life. It would be a good thing if she would take herself off and find a husband somewhere else, for she will not look at one of the many excellent young Phaeacians who are in love with her.' This is the kind of disparaging remark that would be made about me, and I could not complain, for I should myself be scandalized at seeing any other girl do the like, and go about with men in spite of everybody, while her father and mother were still alive, and without having been married in the face of all the world.

289   " If, therefore, you want my father to give you an escort and to help you home, do as I bid you; you will see a beautiful grove of poplars by the road side dedicated to Minerva; it has a well in it and a meadow all round it. Here my father has a field of rich garden ground, about as far from the town as a man's voice will carry. Sit down there and wait for a while till the rest of us can get into the town and reach my father's

94

house. Then, when you think we muſt have done this, come into the town and ask the way to the house of my father Alcinous. You will have no difficulty in finding it; any child will point it out to you, for no one else in the whole town has anything like such a fine house as

MAP OF TRAPANI AND ITS IMMEDIATE NEIGHBOURHOOD

he has. When you have got paſt the gates and through the outer court, go right across the inner court till you come to my mother. You will find her sitting by the fire and spinning her purple wool by firelight. It is a fine sight to see her as she leans back againſt one of the bearing-poſts with her maids all ranged behind her.

95

Close to her seat stands that of my father, on which he
sits and topes like an immortal god. Never mind him,
but go up to my mother, and lay your hands upon her
knees if you would get home quickly. If you can gain
her over, you may hope to see your own country again,
no matter how distant it may be."

316 So saying she lashed the mules with her whip and
they left the river. The mules drew well, and their
hoofs went up and down upon the road. She was
careful not to go too fast for Ulysses and the maids who
were following on foot along with the waggon, so she
plied her whip with judgement. As the sun was going
down they came to the sacred grove of Minerva, and
there Ulysses sat down and prayed to the mighty
daughter of Jove.

324 "Hear me," he cried, "daughter of Aegis-bearing
Jove, unweariable, hear me now, for you gave no heed
to my prayers when Neptune was wrecking me. Now,
therefore, have pity upon me and grant that I may find
friends and be hospitably received by the Phaeacians."

328 Thus did he pray, and Minerva heard his prayer, but
she would not show herself to him openly, for she was
afraid of her uncle Neptune, who was still furious in his
331 endeavours to prevent Ulysses from getting home.

TRAPANI AND THE ISLANDS FROM MOUNT ERYX.

From a drawing by H. F. Jones

THUS, THEN, DID ULYSSES WAIT AND
pray; but the girl drove on to the town. When
she reached her father's house she drew up at the
gateway, and her brothers—comely as the gods—
gathered round her, took the mules out of the waggon,
and carried the clothes into the house, while she went
to her own room, where an old servant, Eurymedusa of
Apeira, lit the fire for her. This old woman had been
brought by sea from Apeira, and had been chosen as a
prize for Alcinous because he was king over the
Phaeacians, and the people obeyed him as though he
were a god.[1] She had been nurse to Nausicaa, and had
now lit the fire for her, and brought her supper for her
into her own room.

Presently Ulysses got up to go towards the town; 14
and Minerva shed a thick mist all round him to hide him
in case any of the proud Phaeacians who met him should
be rude to him, or ask him who he was. Then, as he
was just entering the town, she came towards him in
the likeness of a little girl carrying a pitcher. She stood
right in front of him, and Ulysses said:

" My dear, will you be so kind as to show me the 22
house of king Alcinous? I am an unfortunate foreigner
in distress, and do not know any one in your town and
country."

Then Minerva said, " Yes, father stranger, I will 27
show you the house you want, for Alcinous lives quite
close to my own father. I will go before you and show
the way, but say not a word as you go, and do not look

---

[1] I suspect a family joke, or sly allusion to something of which
we know nothing, in this story of Eurymedusa's having been
brought from Apeira. The Greek word " apeiros " means " in-
experienced," " ignorant." Is it possible that Eurymedusa was
notoriously incompetent ?

at any man, nor ask him questions; for the people here cannot abide strangers, and do not like men who come from some other place. They are a sea-faring folk, and sail the seas by the grace of Neptune in ships that glide along like thought, or as a bird in the air."

37   On this she led the way, and Ulysses followed in her steps; but not one of the Phaeacians could see him as he passed through the city in the midst of them; for the great goddess Minerva in her good will towards him had hidden him in a thick cloud of darkness. He admired their harbours, ships, places of assembly, and the lofty walls of the city, which, with the palisade on top of them, were very striking, and when they reached the king's house Minerva said:

48   " This is the house, father stranger, which you would have me show you. You will find a number of great people sitting at table, but do not be afraid; go straight in, for the bolder a man is the more likely he is to carry his point, even though he is a stranger. First find the queen. Her name is Arete, and she comes of the same family as her husband Alcinous. They both descend originally from Neptune, who was father to Nausithous by Periboea, a woman of great beauty. Periboea was the youngest daughter of Eurymedon, who at one time reigned over the giants, but he ruined his ill-fated people and lost his own life to boot.

61   " Neptune, however, lay with his daughter, and she had a son by him, the great Nausithous, who reigned over the Phaeacians. Nausithous had two sons Rhexenor and Alcinous;[1] Apollo killed the first of them while he was still a bridegroom and without male issue; but he left a daughter Arete, whom Alcinous

---

[1] Polyphemus was also son to Neptune, see Od., ix, 412, 529. He was therefore half-brother to Nausithous, half-uncle to King Alcinous, and half-great-uncle to Nausicaa.

98

married, and honours as no other woman is honoured
of all those that keep house along with their husbands.

"Thus she both was, and still is, respected beyond 69
measure by her children, by Alcinous himself, and by
the whole people, who look upon her as a goddess, and
greet her whenever she goes about the city, for she is a
thoroughly good woman both in head and heart, and
when any women are friends of hers, she will help their
husbands also to settle their disputes. If you can gain
her good will, you may have every hope of seeing your
friends again, and getting safely back to your home and
country."

Then Minerva left Scheria and went away over the 78.
sea. She went to Marathon[1] and to the spacious streets
of Athens, where she entered the abode of Erechtheus;
but Ulysses went on to the house of Alcinous, and he
pondered much as he paused a while before reaching
the threshold of bronze, for the splendour of the palace
was like that of the sun or moon. The walls on either
side were of bronze from end to end, and the cornice
was of blue enamel. The doors were gold, and hung
on pillars of silver that rose from a floor of bronze,
while the lintel was silver and the hook of the door was
of gold.

On either side there stood gold and silver mastiffs 91
which Vulcan, with his consummate skill, had fashioned
expressly to keep watch over the palace of king Alcinous;
so they were immortal and could never grow old.
Seats were ranged all along the wall, here and there
from one end to the other, with coverings of fine woven
work which the women of the house had made. Here
the chief persons of the Phaeacians used to sit and eat
and drink, for there was abundance at all seasons; and

[1] It would seem as though the writer thought that Marathon
was close to Athens.

99

there were golden figures of young men with lighted
torches in their hands, raised on pedestals, to give light
by night to those who were at table. There are[1] fifty
maid servants in the house, some of whom are always
grinding rich yellow grain at the mill, while others work
at the loom, or sit and spin, and their shuttles go backwards and forwards like the fluttering of aspen leaves,
while the linen is so closely woven that it will turn oil.
As the Phaeacians are the best sailors in the world, so
their women excel all others in weaving, for Minerva
has taught them all manner of useful arts, and they are
very intelligent.

112   Outside the gate of the outer court there is a large
garden of about four acres with a wall all round it. It
is full of beautiful trees—pears, pomegranates, and the
most delicious apples. There are luscious figs also, and
olives in full growth. The fruits never rot nor fail
all the year round, neither winter nor summer, for the
air is so soft that a new crop ripens before the old has
dropped. Pear grows on pear, apple on apple, and fig
on fig, and so also with the grapes, for there is an
excellent vineyard: on the level ground of a part of
this, the grapes are being made into raisins; in another
part they are being gathered; some are being trodden
in the wine tubs, others further on have shed their
blossom and are beginning to show fruit, others again
are just changing colour. In the furthest part of the
ground there are beautifully arranged beds of flowers
that are in bloom all the year round. Two streams go
through it, the one turned in ducts throughout the
whole garden, while the other is carried under the
ground of the outer court to the house itself, and the

[1] Here the writer, knowing that she is drawing (with embellishments) from things actually existing, becomes impatient
of past tenses and slides into the present.

town's people draw water from it. Such, then, were
the splendours with which the gods had endowed the
house of king Alcinous.

So here Ulysses ſtood for a while and looked about 133
him, but when he had looked long enough he crossed
the threshold and went within the precinᵈts of the
house. There he found all the chief people among the
Phaeacians making their drink-offerings to Mercury,
which they always did the laſt thing before going away
for the night.[1] He went ſtraight through the court,
ſtill hidden by the cloak of darkness in which Minerva
had enveloped him, till he reached Arete and King
Alcinous; then he laid his hands upon the knees of the
queen, and at that moment the miraculous darkness fell
away from him and he became visible. Every one was
speechless with surprise at seeing a man there, but
Ulysses began at once with his petition.

"Queen Arete," he exclaimed, "daughter of great 146
Rhexenor, in my diſtress I humbly pray you, as also
your husband and these your gueſts (whom may heaven
prosper with long life and happiness, and may they
leave their possessions to their children, and all the
honours conferred upon them by the ſtate) to help me
home to my own country as soon as possible; for I
have been long in trouble and away from my friends."

Then he sat down on the hearth among the ashes and 153
they all held their peace, till presently the old hero
Echeneus, who was an excellent speaker and an elder

---

[1] This is hidden malice, implying that the Phaeacian magnates
were no better than they should be. The final drink-offering
should have been made to Jove or Neptune, not to the god of
thievishness and rascality of all kinds. In line 164 we do indeed
find Echeneus proposing that a drink-offering should be made
to Jove, but Mercury is evidently, according to our authoress,
the god who was moſt likely to be of use to them.

among the Phaeacians, plainly and in all honesty addressed them thus:

159 " Alcinous," said he, " it is not creditable to you that a stranger should be seen sitting among the ashes of your hearth; every one is waiting to hear what you are about to say; tell him, then, to rise and take a seat on a stool inlaid with silver, and bid your servants mix some wine and water that we may make a drink-offering to Jove the lord of thunder, who takes all well-disposed suppliants under his protection; and let the housekeeper give him some supper, of whatever there may be in the house."

167 When Alcinous heard this he took Ulysses by the hand, raised him from the hearth, and bade him take the seat of Laodamas, who had been sitting beside him, and was his favourite son. A maid servant then brought him water in a beautiful golden ewer and poured it into a silver basin for him to wash his hands, and she drew a clean table beside him; an upper servant brought him bread and offered him many good things of what there was in the house, and Ulysses ate and drank. Then Alcinous said to one of the servants, " Pontonous, mix a cup of wine and hand it round that we may make drink-offerings to Jove the lord of thunder, who is the protector of all well-disposed suppliants."

182 Pontonous then mixed wine and water, and handed it round after giving every man his drink-offering. When they had made their offerings, and had drunk each as much as he was minded, Alcinous said:

186 " Aldermen and town councillors of the Phaeacians, hear my words. You have had your supper, so now go home to bed. To-morrow morning I shall invite a still larger number of aldermen, and will give a sacrificial banquet in honour of our guest; we can then discuss the question of his escort, and consider how we may at

once send him back rejoicing to his own country without trouble or inconvenience to himself, no matter how distant it may be. We must see that he comes to no harm while on his homeward journey, but when he is once at home he will have to take the luck he was born with for better or worse like other people. It is possible, however, that the stranger is one of the immortals who has come down from heaven to visit us; but in this case the gods are departing from their usual practice, for hitherto they have made themselves perfectly clear to us when we have been offering them hecatombs. They come and sit at our feasts just like one of our selves, and if any solitary wayfarer happens to stumble upon some one or other of them, they affect no concealment, for we are as near of kin to the gods as the Cyclopes and the savage giants are." [1]

Then Ulysses said: " Pray, Alcinous, do not take any 207 such notion into your head. I have nothing of the immortal about me, neither in body nor mind, and most resemble those among you who are the most afflicted. Indeed, were I to tell you all that heaven has seen fit to lay upon me, you would say that I was still worse off than they are. Nevertheless, let me sup in spite of sorrow, for an empty stomach is a very importunate thing, and thrusts itself on a man's notice no matter how dire is his distress. I am in great trouble, yet it insists that I shall eat and drink, bids me lay aside all memory of my sorrows and dwell only on the due replenishing of itself. As for yourselves, do as you propose, and at break of day set about helping me to get home. I shall be content to die if I may first once more behold

---

[1] The fact of Alcinous knowing anything about the Cyclopes suggests that in the writer's mind Scheria and the country of the Cyclopes were not very far from one another. I take the Cyclopes and the giants to be one and the same people.

my property, my bondsmen, and all the greatness of my house." [1]

226 Thus did he speak. Every one approved his saying, and agreed that he should have his escort inasmuch as he had spoken reasonably. Then when they had made their drink-offerings, and had drunk each as much as he was minded they went home to bed every man in his own abode, leaving Ulysses in the cloister with Arete and Alcinous while the servants were taking the things away after supper. Arete was the first to speak, for she recognized the shirt, cloak, and good clothes that Ulysses was wearing, as the work of herself and of her maids; so she said, " Stranger, before we go any further, there is a question I should like to ask you. Who, and whence are you, and who gave you those clothes? Did you not say you had come here from beyond the sea? "

240 And Ulysses answered, " It would be a long story Madam, were I to relate in full the tale of my misfortunes, for the hand of heaven has been laid heavy upon me; but as regards your question, there is an island far away in the sea which is called ' the Ogygian.' Here dwells the cunning and powerful goddess Calypso, daughter of Atlas. She lives by herself far from all neighbours human or divine. Fortune, however, brought me to her hearth all desolate and alone, for Jove struck my ship with his thunderbolts, and broke it up in mid-ocean. My brave comrades were drowned every man of them, but I stuck to the keel and was carried hither and thither for the space of nine days, till

---

[1] " My property, etc." The authoress is here adopting an Iliadic line (xix, 333), and this must account for the absence of all reference to Penelope. If she had happened to remember Il., v, 213, she would doubtless have appropriated it by preference, for that line reads " my country, *my wife*, and all the greatness of my house."

at last during the darkness of the tenth night the gods brought me to the Ogygian island where the great goddess Calypso lives. She took me in and treated me with the utmost kindness; indeed she wanted to make me immortal that I might never grow old, but she could not persuade me to let her do so.

" I stayed with Calypso seven years straight on end, 259 and watered the good clothes she gave me with my tears during the whole time; but at last when the eighth year came round she bade me depart of her own free will, either because Jove had told her she must, or because she had changed her mind. She sent me from her island on a raft, which she provisioned with abundance of bread and wine. Moreover she gave me good stout clothing, and sent me a wind that blew both warm and fair. Days seven and ten did I sail over the sea, and on the eighteenth I caught sight of the first outlines of the mountains upon your coast—and glad indeed was I to set eyes upon them. Nevertheless there was still much trouble in store for me, for at this point Neptune would let me go no further, and raised a great storm against me; the sea was so terribly high that I could no longer keep to my raft, which went to pieces under the fury of the gale, and I had to swim for it, till wind and current brought me to your shores.

" There I tried to land, but could not, for it was a bad 278 place and the waves dashed me against the rocks, so I again took to the sea and swam on till I came to a river that seemed the most likely landing place, for there were no rocks and it was sheltered from the wind. Here, then, I got out of the water and gathered my senses together again. Night was coming on, so I left the river, and went into a thicket, where I covered myself all over with leaves, and presently heaven sent me off into a very deep sleep. Sick and sorry as I was I slept

among the leaves all night, and through the next day
till afternoon, when I woke as the sun was westering,
and saw your daughter's maid servants playing upon
the beach, and your daughter among them looking like
a goddess. I besought her aid, and she proved to be
of an excellent disposition, much more so than could be
expected from so young a person—for young people
are apt to be thoughtless. She gave me plenty of bread
and wine, and when she had had me washed in the
river she also gave me the clothes in which you see me.
Now, therefore, though it has pained me to do so, I
have told you the whole truth."

298 Then Alcinous said, " Stranger, it was very wrong of
my daughter not to bring you on at once to my house
along with the maids, seeing that she was the first
person whose aid you asked."

302 " Pray do not scold her," replied Ulysses; " she is
not to blame. She did tell me to follow along with the
maids, but I was ashamed and afraid, for I thought you
might perhaps be displeased if you saw me. Every
human being is sometimes a little suspicious and
irritable."

308 " Stranger," replied Alcinous, " I am not the kind of
man to get angry about nothing; it is always better to
be reasonable; but by Father Jove, Minerva, and
Apollo, now that I see what kind of person you are, and
how much you think as I do, I wish you would stay
here, marry my daughter, and become my son-in-law.
If you will stay I will give you a house and an estate, but
no one (heaven forbid) shall keep you here against your
own wish, and that you may be sure of this I will attend
to-morrow to the matter of your escort. You can sleep [1]

[1] The at first inexplicable sleep of Ulysses (bk. xiii, 79, etc.) is
here, as also in viii, 445, being obviously prepared. The writer
evidently attached the utmost importance to it. Those who know

during the whole voyage if you like, and the men shall
sail you over smooth waters either to your own home,
or wherever you please, even though it be a long way
further off than Euboea, which those of my people who
saw it when they took yellow-haired Rhadamanthus to
see Tityus the son of Gaia, tell me is the furthest of any
place—and yet they did the whole voyage in a single day
without distressing themselves, and came back again
afterwards. You will thus see how much my ships
excel all others, and what magnificent oarsmen my
sailors are."

Then was Ulysses glad and prayed aloud, saying, 329
" Father Jove, grant that Alcinous may do all as he has
said, for so he will win an imperishable name among
mankind, and at the same time I shall return to my own
country."

Thus did they converse. Then Arete told her maids 334
to set a bed in the room that was in the gatehouse, and
make it with good red rugs, and to spread coverlets
on the top of them with woollen cloaks for Ulysses to
wear. The maids thereon went out with torches in
their hands, and when they had made the bed they came
up to Ulysses and said, " Rise, sir stranger, and come
with us for your bed is ready," and glad indeed was he
to go to his rest.

So Ulysses slept in a bed placed in a room over the 344
echoing gateway; but Alcinous lay in the inner part
of the house, with the queen his wife by his side.   347

that the harbour which did duty with the writer of the Odyssey
for the one in which Ulysses landed in Ithaca, was only about
two miles from the place in which Ulysses is now talking with
Alcinous, will understand why the sleep was so necessary.

NOW WHEN THE CHILD OF MORNING, rosy-fingered Dawn, appeared, Alcinous and Ulysses both rose, and Alcinous led the way to the Phaeacian place of assembly, which was near the ships. When they got there they sat down side by side on a seat of polished stone, while Minerva took the form of one of Alcinous' servants, and went round the town in order to help Ulysses to get home. She went up to the citizens, man by man, and said, " Aldermen and town councillors of the Phaeacians, come to the assembly all of you and listen to the stranger who has just come off a long voyage to the house of King Alcinous; he looks like an immortal god."

15   With these words she made them all want to come, and they flocked to the assembly till seats and standing room were alike crowded. Every one was struck with the appearance of Ulysses, for Minerva had beautified him about the head and shoulders, making him look taller and stouter than he really was, that he might impress the Phaeacians favourably as being a very remarkable man, and might come off well in the many trials of skill to which they would challenge him. Then, when they were got together, Alcinous spoke:

26   " Hear me," said he, " aldermen and town councillors of the Phaeacians, that I may speak even as I am minded. This stranger, whoever he may be, has found his way to my house from somewhere or other either East or West. He wants an escort and wishes to have the matter settled. Let us then get one ready for him, as we have done for others before him; indeed, no one who ever yet came to my house has been able to complain of me for not speeding him on his way soon enough. Let us draw a ship into the sea—one that has never yet made a voyage—and man her with two and

fifty of our smartest young sailors. Then when you have made fast your oars each by his own seat, leave the ship and come to my house to prepare a feast.[1] I will find you in everything. I am giving these instructions to the young men who will form the crew, for as regards you aldermen and town councillors, you will join me in entertaining our guest in the cloisters. I can take no excuses, and we will have Demodocus to sing to us; for there is no bard like him whatever he may choose to sing about."

Alcinous then led the way, and the others followed 46 after, while a servant went to fetch Demodocus. The fifty-two picked oarsmen went to the sea shore as they had been told, and when they got there they drew the ship into the water, got her mast and sails inside her, bound the oars to the thole-pins with twisted thongs of leather, all in due course, and spread the white sails aloft. They moored the vessel a little way out from land, and then came on shore and went to the house of King Alcinous. The outhouses,[2] yards, and all the precincts were filled with crowds of men in great multitudes both old and young; and Alcinous killed them a dozen sheep, eight full grown pigs, and two oxen. These they skinned and dressed so as to provide a magnificent banquet.

A servant presently led in the famous bard Demo- 62 docus, whom the muse had dearly loved, but to whom she had given both good and evil, for though she had

[1] There were two classes—the lower who were found in provisions which they had to cook for themselves in the yards and outer precincts, where they would also eat—and the upper who would eat in the cloisters of the inner court, and have their cooking done for them.

[2] Translation very dubious. I suppose the αἴθουσαι here to be the covered sheds that ran round the outer courtyard. See illustrations at the end of bk. iii.

endowed him with a divine gift of song, she had robbed
him of his eyesight. Pontonous set a seat for him
among the guests, leaning it up against a bearing-post.
He hung the lyre for him on a peg over his head, and
showed him where he was to feel for it with his hands.
He also set a fair table with a basket of victuals by his
side, and a cup of wine from which he might drink
whenever he was so disposed.

71 The company then laid their hands upon the good
things that were before them, but as soon as they had
had enough to eat and drink, the muse inspired Demodocus to sing the feats of heroes, and more especially
a matter that was then in the mouths of all men, to wit,
the quarrel between Ulysses and Achilles, and the fierce
words that they heaped on one another as they sat
together at a banquet. But Agamemnon was glad when
he heard his chieftains quarrelling with one another, for
Apollo had foretold him this at Pytho when he crossed
the stone floor to consult the oracle. Here was the
beginning of the evil that by the will of Jove fell both
upon Danaans and Trojans.

83 Thus sang the bard, but Ulysses drew his purple
mantle over his head and covered his face, for he was
ashamed to let the Phaeacians see that he was weeping.
When the bard left off singing he wiped the tears from
his eyes, uncovered his face, and, taking his cup, made
a drink-offering to the gods; but when the Phaeacians
pressed Demodocus to sing further, for they delighted
in his lays, then Ulysses again drew his mantle over his
head and wept bitterly. No one noticed his distress
except Alcinous, who was sitting near him, and heard
the heavy sighs that he was heaving. So he at once
said, "Aldermen and town councillors of the Phaeacians,
we have had enough now, both of the feast, and of the
minstrelsy that is its due accompaniment; let us proceed

therefore to the athletic sports, so that our guest on his
return home may be able to tell his friends how much
we surpass all other nations as boxers, wrestlers,
jumpers, and runners."

With these words he led the way, and the others 104
followed after. A servant hung Demodocus's lyre on
its peg for him, led him out of the cloister, and set him
on the same way as that along which all the chief men
of the Phaeacians were going to see the sports; a crowd
of several thousands of people followed them, and there
were many excellent competitors for all the prizes.
Acroneos, Ocyalus, Elatreus, Nauteus, Prymneus,
Anchialus, Eretmeus, Ponteus, Proreus, Thoon, Ana-
besineus, and Amphialus son of Polyneus son of Tecton.
There was also Euryalus son of Naubolus, who was
like Mars himself, and was the best looking man among
the Phaeacians except Laodamas. Three sons of
Alcinous, Laodamas, Halios, and Clytoneus, competed
also.

The foot races came first. The course was set out for 120
them from the starting post, and they raised a dust upon
the plain as they all flew forward at the same moment.
Clytoneus came in first by a long way; he left every one
else behind him by the length of the furrow that a
couple of mules can plough in a fallow field.[1] They
then turned to the painful art of wrestling, and here
Euryalus proved to be the best man. Amphialus
excelled all the others in jumping, while at throwing the
disc there was no one who could approach Elatreus.
Alcinous's son Laodamas was the best boxer, and he it

---

[1] The writer apparently deems that the words " as compared
with what oxen can plough in the same time " go without
saying. Not so the writer of the Iliad from which the Odyssean
passage is probably taken. He explains that mules can plough
quicker than oxen (Il., x, 351-353).

was who presently said, when they had all been diverted
with the games, " Let us ask the stranger whether he
excels in any of these sports; he seems very powerfully
built; his thighs, calves, hands, and neck are of prodigious strength, nor is he at all old, but he has suffered
much lately, and there is nothing like the sea for making
havoc with a man, no matter how strong he is."

140 " You are quite right, Laodamas," replied Euryalus,
" go up to your guest and speak to him about it yourself."

143 When Laodamas heard this he made his way into the
middle of the crowd and said to Ulysses, " I hope, Sir,
that you will enter yourself for some one or other of our
competitions if you are skilled in any of them—and you
must have gone in for many a one before now. There
is nothing that does any one so much credit all his life
long as the showing himself a proper man with his
hands and feet. Have a try therefore at something, and
banish all sorrow from your mind. Your return home
will not be long delayed, for the ship is already drawn
into the water, and the crew is found."

152 Ulysses answered, " Laodamas, why do you taunt me
in this way? my mind is set rather on cares than contests;
I have been through infinite trouble, and am come
among you now as a suppliant, praying your king and
people to further me on my return home."

158 Then Euryalus reviled him outright and said, " I
gather, then, that you are unskilled in any of the many
sports that men generally delight in. I suppose you
are one of those grasping traders that go about in ships
as captains or merchants, and who think of nothing but
of their outward freights and homeward cargoes. There
does not seem to be much of the athlete about you."

165 " For shame, Sir," answered Ulysses, fiercely, " you
are an insolent fellow—so true is it that the gods do not

grace all men alike in speech, person, and understanding. One man may be of weak presence, but heaven has adorned this with such a good conversation that he charms every one who sees him; his honeyed moderation carries his hearers with him so that he is leader in all assemblies of his fellows, and wherever he goes he is looked up to. Another may be as handsome as a god, but his good looks are not crowned with discretion. This is your case. No god could make a finer looking fellow than you are, but you are a fool. Your ill-judged remarks have made me exceedingly angry, and you are quite mistaken, for I excel in a great many athletic exercises; indeed, so long as I had youth and strength, I was among the first athletes of the age. Now, however, I am worn out by labour and sorrow, for I have gone through much both on the field of battle and by the waves of the weary sea; still, in spite of all this I will compete, for your taunts have stung me to the quick."

So he hurried up without even taking his cloak off, 186 and seized a disc, larger, more massive and much heavier than those used by the Phaeacians when disc-throwing among themselves.[1] Then, swinging it back, he threw it from his brawny hand, and it made a humming sound in the air as he did so. The Phaeacians quailed beneath the rushing of its flight as it sped gracefully from his hand, and flew beyond any mark that had been made yet. Minerva, in the form of a man, came and marked the place where it had fallen. " A blind man, Sir," said she, " could easily tell your mark by groping for it—it is so far ahead of any other. You may make your mind easy about this contest, for no Phaeacian can come near to such a throw as yours."

[1] It was very fortunate that such a disc happened to be there, seeing that none like it were in common use.

199 Ulysses was glad when he found he had a friend among the lookers-on, so he began to speak more pleasantly. " Young men," said he, " come up to that throw if you can, and I will throw another disc as heavy or even heavier. If anyone wants to have a bout with me let him come on, for I am exceedingly angry; I will box, wrestle, or run, I do not care what it is, with any man of you all except Laodamas, but not with him because I am his guest, and one cannot compete with one's own personal friend. At least I do not think it a prudent or a sensible thing for a guest to challenge his host's family at any game, especially when he is in a foreign country. He will cut the ground from under his own feet if he does; but I make no exception as regards any one else, for I want to have the matter out and know which is the best man. I am a good hand at every kind of athletic sport known among mankind. I am an excellent archer. In battle I am always the first to bring a man down with my arrow, no matter how many more are taking aim at him alongside of me. Philoctetes was the only man who could shoot better than I could when we Achaeans were before Troy and in practice. I far excel every one else in the whole world, of those who still eat bread upon the face of the earth, but I should not like to shoot against the mighty dead, such as Hercules, or Eurytus the Oechalian—men who could shoot against the gods themselves. This in fact was how Eurytus came prematurely by his end, for Apollo was angry with him and killed him because he challenged him as an archer. I can throw a dart farther than any one else can shoot an arrow. Running is the only point in respect of which I am afraid some of the Phaeacians might beat me, for I have been brought down very low at sea; my provisions ran short, and therefore I am still weak."

They all held their peace except King Alcinous, who ₂₃₄ began, " Sir, we have had much pleasure in hearing all that you have told us, from which I understand that you are willing to show your prowess, as having been displeased with some insolent remarks that have been made to you by one of our athletes, and which could never have been uttered by any one who knows how to talk with propriety. I hope you will apprehend my meaning, and will explain to any one of your chief men who may be dining with yourself and your family when you get home, that we have an hereditary aptitude for accomplishments of all kinds. We are not particularly remarkable for our boxing, nor yet as wrestlers, but we are singularly fleet of foot and are excellent sailors. We are extremely fond of good dinners, music, and dancing; we also like frequent changes of linen, warm baths, and good beds, so now, please, some of you who are the best dancers set about dancing, that our guest on his return home may be able to tell his friends how much we surpass all other nations as sailors, runners, dancers, and minstrels. Demodocus has left his lyre at my house, so run some one or other of you and fetch it for him."

On this a servant hurried off to bring the lyre from ₂₅₆ the king's house, and the nine men who had been chosen as stewards stood forward. It was their business to manage everything connected with the sports, so they made the ground smooth and marked a wide space for the dancers. Presently the servant came back with Demodocus's lyre, and he took his place in the midst of them, whereon the best young dancers in the town began to foot and trip it so nimbly that Ulysses was delighted with the merry twinkling of their feet.

Meanwhile the bard began to sing the loves of Mars ₂₆₆ and Venus, and how they first began their intrigue in

115

the house of Vulcan. Mars made Venus many presents, and defiled King Vulcan's marriage bed, so the sun, who saw what they were about, told Vulcan. Vulcan was very angry when he heard such dreadful news, so he went to his smithy brooding mischief, got his great anvil into its place, and began to forge some chains which none could either unloose or break, so that they might stay there in that place.[1] When he had finished his snare he went into his bedroom and festooned the bed-posts all over with chains like cobwebs; he also let many hang down from the great beam of the ceiling. Not even a god could see them, so fine and subtle were they. As soon as he had spread the chains all over the bed, he made as though he were setting out for the fair state of Lemnos, which of all places in the world was the one he was most fond of. But Mars kept no blind look out, and as soon as he saw him start, hurried off to his house, burning with love for Venus.

289   Now Venus was just come in from a visit to her father Jove, and was about sitting down when Mars came inside the house, and said as he took her hand in his own, "Let us go to the couch of Vulcan: he is not at home, but is gone off to Lemnos among the Sintians, whose speech is barbarous."

295   She was nothing loth, so they went to the couch to take their rest, whereon they were caught in the toils which cunning Vulcan had spread for them, and could

---

[1] Il., xiii, 37. Here, as so often elsewhere in the Odyssey, the appropriation of an Iliadic line which is not quite appropriate puzzles the reader. The "they" is not the chains, nor yet Mars and Venus. It is an overflow from the Iliadic passage in which Neptune hobbles his horses in bonds "which none could either unloose or break so that they might stay there in that place." If the line would have scanned without the addition of the words "so that they might stay there in that place," they would have been omitted in the Odyssey.

116

neither get up nor stir hand or foot, but found too late
that they were in a trap. Then Vulcan came up to them,
for he had turned back before reaching Lemnos, when
his scout the sun told him what was going on. He was
in a furious passion, and stood in the vestibule making
a dreadful noise as he shouted to all the gods.

"Father Jove," he cried, "and all you other blessed 306
gods who live for ever, come here and see the ridiculous
and disgraceful sight that I will show you. Jove's
daughter Venus is always dishonouring me because I
am lame. She is in love with Mars, who is handsome
and clean built, whereas I am a cripple—but my parents
are to blame for that, not I; they ought never to have
begotten me. Come and see the pair together asleep
on my bed. It makes me furious to look at them. They
are very fond of one another, but I do not think they
will lie there longer than they can help, nor do I think
that they will sleep much; there, however, they shall
stay till her father has repaid me the sum I gave him
for his baggage of a daughter, who is fair but not
honest."

On this the gods gathered to the house of Vulcan. 321
Earth-encircling Neptune came, and Mercury the
bringer of luck, and King Apollo, but the goddesses
stayed at home all of them for shame. Then the givers
of all good things stood in the doorway, and the blessed
gods roared with inextinguishable laughter, as they saw
how cunning Vulcan had been, whereon one would
turn towards his neighbour saying:

"Ill deeds do not prosper, and the weak confound 329
the strong. See how limping Vulcan, lame as he is, has
caught Mars who is the fleetest god in heaven; and now
Mars will be cast in heavy damages."

Thus did they converse, but King Apollo said to 333
Mercury, "Messenger Mercury, giver of good things,

you would not care how strong the chains were, would you, if you could sleep with Venus?"

338 "King Apollo," answered Mercury, "I only wish I might get the chance, though there were three times as many chains—and you might look on, all of you, gods and goddesses, but I would sleep with her if I could."

343 The immortal gods burst out laughing as they heard him, but Neptune took it all seriously, and kept on imploring Vulcan to set Mars free again. "Let him go," he cried, "and I will undertake, as you require, that he shall pay you all the damages that are held reasonable among the immortal gods."

349 "Do not," replied Vulcan, "ask me to do this; a bad man's bond is bad security; what remedy could I enforce against you if Mars should go away and leave his debts behind him along with his chains?"

354 "Vulcan," said Neptune, "if Mars goes away without paying his damages, I will pay you myself." So Vulcan answered, "In this case I cannot and must not refuse you."

359 Thereon he loosed the bonds that bound them, and as soon as they were free they scampered off, Mars to Thrace and laughter-loving Venus to Cyprus and to Paphos, where is her grove and her altar fragrant with burnt offerings. Here the Graces bathed her, and anointed her with oil of ambrosia such as the immortal gods make use of, and they clothed her in raiment of the most enchanting beauty.

367 Thus sang the bard, and both Ulysses and the seafaring Phaeacians were charmed as they heard him.

370 Then Alcinous told Laodamas and Halius to dance alone, for there was no one to compete with them. So they took a red ball which Polybus had made for them, and one of them bent himself backwards and threw it up towards the clouds, while the other jumped from off

118

the ground and caught it with ease before it came down
again. When they had done throwing the ball straight
up into the air they began to dance, and at the same
time kept on throwing it backwards and forwards to
one another, while all the young men in the ring
applauded and made a great stamping with their feet.
Then Ulysses said:

" King Alcinous, you said your people were the 382
nimblest dancers in the world, and indeed they have
proved themselves to be so. I was astonished as I saw
them."

The king was delighted at this, and exclaimed to the 385
Phaeacians, " Aldermen and town councillors, our
guest seems to be a person of singular judgement; let
us give him such proof of our hospitality as he may
reasonably expect. There are twelve chief men among
you, and counting myself there are thirteen; contribute,
each of you, a clean cloak, a shirt, and a talent of fine
gold; let us give him all this in a lump down at once,
so that when he gets his supper he may do so with a
light heart. As for Euryalus he will have to make a
formal apology and a present too, for he has been
rude."

Thus did he speak. The others all of them applauded 398
his saying, and sent their servants to fetch the presents.
Then Euryalus said, " King Alcinous, I will give the
stranger all the satisfaction you require. He shall have
my sword, which is of bronze, all but the hilt, which is
of silver. I will also give him the scabbard of newly
sawn ivory into which it fits. It will be worth a great
deal to him."

As he spoke he placed the sword in the hands of 406
Ulysses and said, " Good luck to you, father stranger;
if anything has been said amiss may the winds blow it
away with them, and may heaven grant you a safe

return, for I understand you have been long away from home, and have gone through much hardship."

412   To which Ulysses answered, " Good luck to you too my friend, and may the gods grant you every happiness. I hope you will not miss the sword you have given me along with your apology."

416   With these words he girded the sword about his shoulders and towards sundown the presents began to make their appearance, as the servants of the donors kept bringing them to the house of King Alcinous; here his sons received them, and placed them under their mother's charge.   Then Alcinous led the way to the house and bade his guests take their seats.

424   " Wife," said he, turning to Queen Arete, " Go, fetch the best chest we have, and put a clean cloak and shirt in it.   Also, set a copper on the fire and heat some water; our guest will take a warm bath; see also to the careful packing of the presents that the noble Phaeacians have made him; he will thus better enjoy both his supper and the singing that will follow.   I shall myself give him this golden goblet[1]–which is of exquisite workmanship–that he may be reminded of me for the rest of his life whenever he makes a drink-offering to Jove, or to any of the gods."

413   Then Arete told her maids to set a large tripod upon the fire as fast as they could, whereon they set a tripod full of bath water on to a clear fire; they threw on sticks

----

[1] The reader will note that Alcinous never gets beyond saying that he is going to give the goblet; he never gives it.   Elsewhere in both Iliad and Odyssey the offer of a present is immediately followed by the statement that it was given and was received gladly–Alcinous actually does give a chest and a cloak and shirt –probably also some of the corn and wine for the long two-mile voyage was provided by him–but it is quite plain that he gave no talent and no cup.

to make it blaze, and the water became hot as the flame played about the belly of the tripod.[1] Meanwhile Arete brought a magnificent chest from her own room, and inside it she packed all the beautiful presents of gold and raiment which the Phaeacians had brought. Lastly she added a cloak and a good shirt from Alcinous, and said to Ulysses:

"See to the lid yourself, and have the whole bound 443 round at once, for fear any one should rob you by the way when you are asleep in your ship."[2]

When Ulysses heard this he put the lid on the chest 446 and made it fast with a bond that Circe had taught him. He had hardly done so before an upper servant told him to come to the bath and wash himself. He was very glad of a warm bath, for he had had no one to wait upon him ever since he left the house of Calypso, who as long as he remained with her had taken as good care of him as though he had been a god. When the servants had done washing and anointing him with oil, and had given him a clean cloak and shirt, he left the bath room and joined the guests who were sitting over their wine. Lovely Nausicaa stood by one of the bearing-posts supporting the roof of the cloister, and admired him as she saw him pass. "Farewell stranger," said she, "do not forget me when you are safe at home again, for it is to me first that you owe a ransom for having saved your life."

And Ulysses said, "Nausicaa, daughter of great 463 Alcinous, may Jove the mighty husband of Juno, grant that I may reach my home; so shall I bless you as my

---

[1] Il., xviii, 344-349. These lines in the Iliad tell of the preparation for washing the body of Patroclus, and I am not pleased that the writer of the Odyssey should have adopted them here.

[2] See note on vii, 318.

guardian angel all my days, for it was you who saved me."

469 When he had said this, he seated himself beside Alcinous. Supper was then served, and the wine was mixed for drinking. A servant led in the favourite bard Demodocus, and set him in the midst of the company, near one of the bearing-posts supporting the cloister, that he might lean against it. Then Ulysses cut off a piece of roast pork with plenty of fat (for there was abundance left on the joint) and said to a servant, " Take this piece of pork over to Demodocus and tell him to eat it; for all the pain his lays may cause me I will salute him none the less; bards are honoured and respected throughout the world, for the muse teaches them their songs and loves them."

482 The servant carried the pork in his fingers over to Demodocus, who took it and was very much pleased. They then laid their hands on the good things that were before them, and as soon as they had had enough to eat and drink, Ulysses said to Demodocus, " Demodocus, there is no one in the world whom I admire more than I do you. You must have studied under the Muse, Jove's daughter, and under Apollo, so accurately do you sing the return of the Achaeans with all their sufferings and adventures. If you were not there yourself, you must have heard it all from some one who was. Now, however, change your song and tell us of the wooden horse which Epeus made with the assistance of Minerva, and which Ulysses got by stratagem into the fort of Troy after freighting it with the men who afterwards sacked the city. If you will sing this tale aright I will tell all the world how magnificently heaven has endowed you."

499 The bard inspired of heaven took up the story at the point where some of the Argives set fire to their tents

122

and sailed away while others, hidden within the horse,[1] were waiting with Ulysses in the Trojan place of assembly. For the Trojans themselves had drawn the horse into their fortress, and it ftood there while they sat in council round it, and were in three minds as to what they should do. Some were for breaking it up then and there; others would have it dragged to the top of the rock on which the fortress ftood, and then thrown down the precipice; while yet others were for letting it remain as an offering and propitiation for the gods. And this was how they settled it in the end, for the city was doomed when it took in that horse, within which were all the bravest of the Argives waiting to bring death and deftruction on the Trojans. Anon he sang how the sons of the Achaeans issued from the horse, and sacked the town, breaking out from their ambuscade. He sang how they overran the city hither and thither and ravaged it, and how Ulysses went raging like Mars along with Menelaus to the house of Deiphobus. It was there that the fight raged moft furiously, nevertheless by Minerva's help he was victorious.

All this he told, but Ulysses was overcome as he heard 521 him, and his cheeks were wet with tears. He wept as a woman weeps when she throws herself on the body of her husband who has fallen before his own city and people, fighting bravely in defence of his home and children. She screams aloud and flings her arms about him as he lies gasping for breath and dying, but her enemies beat her from behind about the back and shoulders, and carry her off into slavery, to a life of labour and sorrow, and the beauty fades from her cheeks—even so piteously did Ulysses weep, but none of those present perceived his tears except Alcinous,

[1] See note on p. 53.

who was sitting near him, and could hear the sobs and
sighs that he was heaving. The king, therefore, at once
rose and said:

536   " Aldermen and town councillors of the Phaeacians,
let Demodocus cease his song, for there are those
present who do not seem to like it. From the moment
that we had done supper and Demodocus began to sing,
our guest has been all the time groaning and lamenting.
He is evidently in great trouble, so let the bard leave off,
that we may all enjoy ourselves, hosts and guest alike.
This will be much more as it should be, for all these
festivities, with the escort and the presents that we are
making with so much good will, are wholly in his
honour, and any one with even a moderate amount of
right feeling knows that he ought to treat a guest and a
suppliant as though he were his own brother.

548   " Therefore, Sir, do you on your part affect no more
concealment nor reserve in the matter about which I
shall ask you; it will be more polite in you to give me
a plain answer; tell me the name by which your father
and mother over yonder used to call you, and by which
you were known among your neighbours and fellow-
citizens. There is no one, neither rich nor poor, who
is absolutely without any name whatever, for people's
fathers and mothers give them names as soon as they
are born. Tell me also your country, nation, and city,
that our ships may shape their purpose accordingly and
take you there. For the Phaeacians have no pilots;
their vessels have no rudders as those of other nations
have, but the ships themselves understand what it is
that we are thinking about and want; they know all the
cities and countries in the whole world, and can traverse
the sea just as well even when it is covered with mist
and cloud, so that there is no danger of being wrecked
or coming to any harm. Still I do remember hearing

my father say that Neptune was angry with us for being
too easy-going in the matter of giving people escorts.
He said that one of these days he should wreck a ship
of ours as it was returning from having escorted some
one,[1] and bury our city under a high mountain. This
is what my father used to say, but whether the god will
carry out his threat or no is a matter which he will
decide for himself.

" And now, tell me and tell me true. Where have 572
you been wandering, and in what countries have you
travelled? Tell us of the peoples themselves, and of
their cities—who were hostile, savage and uncivilized,
and who, on the other hand, hospitable and humane.
Tell us also why you are made so unhappy on hearing
about the return of the Argive Danaans from Troy.
The gods arranged all this, and sent them their misfortunes in order that future generations might have
something to sing about. Did you lose some brave
kinsman of your wife's when you were before Troy?
a son-in-law or father-in-law—which are the nearest
relations a man has outside his own flesh and blood?
or was it some brave and kindly-natured comrade—for
a good friend is as dear to a man as his own brother? " 586

[1] The reader will find this threat fulfilled in bk. xiii.

A ND ULYSSES ANSWERED, "KING
Alcinous, it is a good thing to hear a bard with
such a divine voice as this man has. There is
nothing better or more delightful than when a
whole people make merry together, with the guests
sitting orderly to listen, while the table is loaded with
bread and meats, and the cup-bearer draws wine and
fills his cup for every man. This is indeed as fair a
sight as a man can see. Now, however, since you are
inclined to ask the story of my sorrows, and rekindle
my own sad memories in respect of them, I do not
know how to begin, nor yet how to continue and con-
clude my tale, for the hand of heaven has been laid
heavily upon me.

16 " Firstly, then, I will tell you my name that you too
may know it, and one day, if I outlive this time of
sorrow, may become my guests though I live so far
away from all of you. I am Ulysses son of Laertes,
renowned among mankind for all manner of subtlety,
so that my fame ascends to heaven. I live in Ithaca,
where there is a high mountain called Neritum, covered
with forests; and not far from it there is a group of
islands very near to one another—Dulichium, Same, and
the wooded island of Zacynthus. It lies squat on the
horizon, all highest up in the sea towards the sunset,
while the others lie away from it towards dawn.[1] It is

---

[1] If the other islands lay some distance away from Ithaca
(which the word ἄνευθε suggests), what becomes of the πόρθμος
or gut between Ithaca and Samos, which we hear of in bks. iv and
xv? I suspect that the authoress in her mind makes Telemachus
come back from Pylos to the Lilybaean promontory and thence
to Trapani through the strait between the Isola Grande and the
mainland—the island of Asteris being the one on which Motya
afterwards stood.

126

MAP OF THE AEGADEAN, OR "GOAT" ISLANDS—FROM WHICH THE
AUTHORESS IS REALLY DRAWING, AND IN RESPECT OF WHICH SHE
IS ACCURATE. MARETTIMO WAS, FOR HER, ITHACA, AND THE ISOLA
GRANDE, DULICHIUM—WHICH MEANS LONG AND NARROW

MAP OF THE IONIAN ISLANDS, WHICH THE AUTHORESS PROFESSES
TO BE DESCRIBING BUT DOES NOT DESCRIBE

a rugged island, but it breeds brave men, and my eyes know none that they better love to look upon. The goddess Calypso kept me with her in her cave, and wanted me to marry her, as did also the cunning Aeaean goddess Circe; but they could neither of them persuade me, for there is nothing dearer to a man than his own country and his parents, and however splendid a home he may have in a foreign country, if it be far from father or mother, he does not care about it. Now, however, I will tell you of the many hazardous adventures which by Jove's will I met with on my return from Troy.

39   " When I had set sail thence the wind took me first to Ismarus, which is the city of the Cicons. There I sac.:ed the town and put the people to the sword. We took their wives and also much booty, which we divided equitably amongst us, so that none might have reason to complain. I then said that we had better make off at once, but my men very foolishly would not obey me, so they stayed there drinking much wine and killing great numbers of sheep and oxen on the sea shore. Meanwhile the Cicons cried out for help to other Cicons who lived inland. These were more in number, and stronger, and they were more skilled in the art of war, for they could fight, either from chariots or on foot as the occasion served; in the morning, therefore, they came as thick as leaves and bloom in summer, and the hand of heaven was against us, so that we were hard pressed. They set the battle in array near the ships, and the hosts aimed their bronze-shod spears at one another.[1] So long as the day waxed and it was still morning, we held our own against them, though they were more in number than we; but as the sun went down, towards

[1] Il., xviii, 533, 534. The sudden lapse into the third person here for a couple of lines is due to the fact that the two Iliadic lines taken are in the third person.

the time when men loose their oxen, the Cicons got the better of us, and we lost half a dozen men from every ship we had; so we got away with those that were left.

" Thence we sailed onward with sorrow in our 62 hearts, but glad to have escaped death though we had lost our comrades, nor did we leave till we had thrice invoked each one of the poor fellows who had perished by the hands of the Cicons. Then Jove raised the North wind against us till it blew a hurricane, so that land and sky were hidden in thick clouds, and night sprang forth out of the heavens. We let the ships run before the gale, but the force of the wind tore our sails to tatters, so we took them down for fear of shipwreck, and rowed our hardest towards the land. There we lay two days and two nights suffering much alike from toil and distress of mind, but on the morning of the third day we again raised our masts, set sail, and took our places, letting the wind and steersmen direct our ship. I should have got home at that time unharmed had not the North wind and the currents been against me as I was doubling Cape Malea, and set me off my course hard by the island of Cythera.

" I was driven thence by foul winds for a space of 82 nine days upon the sea, but on the tenth day we reached the land of the Lotus-eaters, who live on a food that comes from a kind of flower. Here we landed to take in fresh water, and our crews got their mid-day meal on the shore near the ships. When they had eaten and drunk I sent two of my company to see what manner of men the people of the place might be, and they had a third man under them. They started at once, and went about among the Lotus-eaters, who did them no hurt, but gave them to eat of the lotus, which was so delicious that those who ate of it left off caring about home, and

did not even want to go back and say what had happened to them, but were for staying and munching lotus[1]
with the Lotus-eaters without thinking further of their
return; nevertheless, though they wept bitterly I forced
them back to the ships and made them fast under the
benches. Then I told the rest to go on board at once,
lest any of them should taste of the lotus and leave off
wanting to get home, so they took their places and
smote the grey sea with their oars.

105 " We sailed hence, always in much distress, till we
came to the land of the lawless and inhuman Cyclopes.
Now the Cyclopes neither plant nor plough, but trust
in providence, and live on such wheat, barley, and
grapes as grow wild without any kind of tillage, and
their wild grapes yield them wine as the sun and the
rain may grow them. They have no laws nor assemblies
of the people, but live in caves on the tops of high
mountains; each is lord and master in his family, and
they take no account of their neighbours.

116 " Now off their harbour there lies a wooded and
fertile island not quite close to the land of the Cyclopes,
but still not far. It is overrun with wild goats, that
breed there in great numbers and are never disturbed
by foot of man; for sportsmen—who as a rule will
suffer so much hardship in forest or among mountain
precipices—do not go there, nor yet again is it ever
ploughed or fed down, but it lies a wilderness untilled
and unsown from year to year, and has no living thing
upon it but only goats. For the Cyclopes have no
ships, nor yet shipwrights who could make ships for
them; they cannot therefore go from city to city, or
sail over the sea to one another's country as people who

[1] *Cf.* Il., ii, 776. The words in both Iliad and Odyssey
are λωτὸν ἐρεπτόμενοι. In the Iliad they are used of the horses
of Achilles' followers as they stood idle, " champing lotus."

have ships can do; if they had had these they would
have colonized the island,[1] for it is a very good one,
and would yield everything in due season. There are
meadows that in some places come right down to the
sea shore, well watered and full of luscious grass;
grapes would do there excellently; there is level land
for ploughing, and it would always yield heavily at
harvest time, for the soil is deep. There is a good
harbour where no cables are wanted, nor yet anchors,
nor need a ship be moored, but all one has to do is to
beach one's vessel and stay there till the wind becomes
fair for putting out to sea again. At the head of the
harbour there is a spring of clear water coming out of a
cave, and there are poplars growing all round it.

" Here we entered, but so dark was the night that 142
some god must have brought us in, for there was
nothing whatever to be seen. A thick mist hung all
round our ships;[2] the moon was hidden behind a mass
of clouds so that no one could have seen the island if
he had looked for it, nor were there any breakers to tell
us we were close in shore before we found ourselves
upon the land itself; when, however, we had beached
the ships, we took down the sails, went ashore and
camped upon the beach till daybreak.

" When the child of morning, rosy-fingered Dawn, 152
appeared, we admired the island and wandered all over

[1] I take all this passage about the Cyclopes having no ships to
be sarcastic – meaning, " You people of Drepanum have no
excuse for not colonizing the island of Favognana, which you
could easily do, for you have plenty of ships, and the island is
a very good one." For that the island so fully described here
is the Aegadean or " goat " island of Favognana, and that the
Cyclopes are the old Sican inhabitants of Mt. Eryx should not
be doubted.

[2] For the reasons why it was necessary that the night should be
so exceptionally dark see *The Authoress of the Odyssey*, pp. 198, 199.

it, while the nymphs Jove's daughters roused the wild
goats that we might get some meat for our dinner. On
this we fetched our spears and bows and arrows from
the ships, and dividing ourselves into three bands began
to shoot the goats. Heaven sent us excellent sport; I
had twelve ships with me, and each ship got nine goats,
while my own ship had ten; thus through the livelong
day to the going down of the sun we ate and drank our
fill, and we had plenty of wine left, for each one of us
had taken many jars full when we sacked the city of the
Cicons, and this had not yet run out. While we were
feasting we kept turning our eyes towards the land of
the Cyclopes, which was hard by, and saw the smoke
of their stubble fires. We could almost fancy we heard
their voices and the bleating of their sheep and goats,
but when the sun went down and it came on dark, we
camped down upon the beach, and next morning I
called a council.

172   " ' Stay here, my brave fellows,' said I, ' all the rest of
you, while I go with my ship and exploit these people
myself: I want to see if they are uncivilized savages, or
a hospitable and humane race.'

177   " I went on board, bidding my men to do so also
and loose the hawsers; so they took their places and
smote the grey sea with their oars. When we got to
the land, which was not far, there, on the face of a cliff
near the sea, we saw a great cave overhung with laurels.
It was a station for a great many sheep and goats, and
outside there was a large yard, with a high wall round
it made of stones built into the ground and of trees both
pine and oak. This was the abode of a huge monster
who was then away from home shepherding his flocks.
He would have nothing to do with other people, but
led the life of an outlaw. He was a horrid creature, not
like a human being at all, but resembling rather some

SHEEPFOLD INSIDE THE GROTTA DI POLIFEMO

OUTSIDE VIEW OF THE GROTTA EMILIANA, ALSO CURRENTLY
CALLED " LA GROTTA DI POLIFEMO "

crag that stands out boldly against the sky on the top
of a high mountain.

" I told my men to draw the ship ashore, and stay 193
where they were, all but the twelve best among them,
who were to go along with myself. I also took a goat-
skin of sweet black wine which had been given me by
Maron, son of Euanthes, who was priest of Apollo the
patron god of Ismarus, and lived within the wooded
precincts of the temple. When we were sacking the
city we respected him, and spared his life, as also his
wife and child; so he made me some presents of great
value—seven talents of fine gold, and a bowl of silver,
with twelve jars of sweet wine, unblended, and of the
most exquisite flavour. Not a man nor maid in the
house knew about it, but only himself, his wife, and one
housekeeper: when he drank it he mixed twenty parts
of water to one of wine, and yet the fragrance from the
mixing-bowl was so exquisite that it was impossible to
refrain from drinking. I filled a large skin with this
wine, and took a wallet full of provisions with me, for
my mind misgave me that I might have to deal with
some savage who would be of great strength, and would
respect neither right nor law.

" We soon reached his cave, but he was out shepherd- 216
ing, so we went inside and took stock of all that we
could see. His cheese-racks were loaded with cheeses,
and he had more lambs and kids than his pens could
hold. They were kept in separate flocks; first there
were the hoggets, then the oldest of the younger lambs
and lastly the very young ones [1] all kept apart from one
another; as for his dairy, all the vessels, bowls, an'd

---

[1] None but such lambs as would suck if they were with their
mothers would be left in the yard. The older lambs should have
been out feeding. The authoress has got it all wrong, but it
does not matter. See *The Authoress of the Odyssey*, pp. 155, 156.

milk pails into which he milked, were swimming with whey. When they saw all this, my men begged me to let them first steal some cheeses, and make off with them to the ship; they would then return, drive down the lambs and kids, put them on board and sail away with them. It would have been indeed better if we had done so but I would not listen to them, for I wanted to see the owner himself, in the hope that he might give me a present. When, however, we saw him my poor men found him ill to deal with.

231   "We lit a fire, offered some of the cheeses in sacrifice, ate others of them, and then sat waiting till the Cyclops should come in with his sheep. When he came, he brought in with him a huge load of dry firewood to light the fire for his supper, and this he flung with such a noise on to the floor of his cave that we hid ourselves for fear at the far end of the cavern. Meanwhile he drove all the ewes inside, as well as the she-goats that he was going to milk, leaving the males, both rams and he-goats, outside in the yards. Then he rolled a huge stone to the mouth of the cave—so huge that two and twenty strong four-wheeled waggons would not be enough to draw it from its place against the doorway. When he had so done he sat down and milked his ewes and goats, all in due course, and then let each of them have her own young. He curdled half the milk and set it aside in wicker strainers, but the other half he poured into bowls that he might drink it for his supper. When he had got through with all his work, he lit the fire, and then caught sight of us, whereon he said:

252   "'Strangers, who are you? Where do you sail from? Are you traders, or do you sail the sea as rovers, with your hands against every man, and every man's hand against you?'

256   "We were frightened out of our senses by his loud

voice and monstrous form, but I managed to say, ' We are Achaeans on our way home from Troy, but by the will of Jove, and stress of weather, we have been driven far out of our course. We are the people of Agamemnon, son of Atreus, who has won infinite renown throughout the whole world, by sacking so great a city and killing so many people. We therefore humbly pray you to show us some hospitality, and otherwise make us such presents as visitors may reasonably expect. May your excellency fear the wrath of heaven, for we are your suppliants, and Jove takes all respectable travellers under his protection, for he is the avenger of all suppliants and foreigners in distress.'

" To this he gave me but a pitiless answer, ' Stranger,' 272 said he, ' you are a fool, or else you know nothing of this country. Talk to me, indeed, about fearing the gods or shunning their anger? We Cyclopes do not care about Jove or any of your blessed gods, for we are ever so much stronger than they. I shall not spare either yourself or your companions out of any regard for Jove, unless I am in the humour for doing so. And now tell me where you made your ship fast when you came on shore. Was it round the point, or is she lying straight off the land? '

" He said this to draw me out, but I was too cunning 281 to be caught in that way, so I answered with a lie; ' Neptune,' said I, ' sent my ship on to the rocks at the far end of your country, and wrecked it. We were driven on to them from the open sea, but I and those who are with me escaped the jaws of death.'

" The cruel wretch vouchsafed me not one word of 287 answer, but with a sudden clutch he gripped up two of my men at once and dashed them down upon the ground as though they had been puppies. Their brains were shed upon the ground, and the earth was wet with their blood. Then he tore them limb from limb and supped upon them. He gobbled them up like a lion in the wilderness, flesh, bones, marrow, and entrails, without leaving anything uneaten. As for us, we wept and lifted up our hands to heaven on seeing such a horrid sight, for we did not know what else to do; but when the Cyclops had filled his huge paunch, and had washed down his meal of human flesh with a drink of neat milk, he stretched himself full length upon the ground among his sheep, and went to sleep. I was at first inclined to seize my sword, draw it, and drive it into his vitals, but I reflected that if I did we should all certainly be lost, for we should never be able to shift the stone which the monster had put in front of the door. So we stayed sobbing and sighing where we were till morning came.

307 " When the child of morning, rosy-fingered Dawn, appeared, he again lit his fire, milked his goats and ewes, all quite rightly, and then let each have her own young one; as soon as he had got through with all his work, he clutched up two more of my men, and began eating them for his morning's meal. Presently, with the utmost ease, he rolled the stone away from the door and drove out his sheep, but he at once put it back again —as easily as though he were merely clapping the lid on to a quiver full of arrows. As soon as he had done so he shouted, and cried ' Shoo, shoo,' after his sheep to drive them on to the mountain; so I was left to scheme some way of taking my revenge and covering myself with glory.

318 " In the end I deemed it would be the best plan to do as follows. The Cyclops had a great club which was lying near one of the sheep pens; it was of green olive wood, and he had cut it intending to use it for a staff as soon as it should be dry. It was so huge that we

could only compare it to the mast of a twenty-oared merchant vessel of large burden, and able to venture out into open sea. I went up to this club and cut off about six feet of it; I then gave this piece to the men and told them to fine it evenly off at one end, which they proceeded to do, and lastly I brought it to a point myself, charring the end in the fire to make it harder. When I had done this I hid it under the dung, which was lying about all over the cave, and told the men to cast lots which of them should venture along with myself to lift it and bore it into the monster's eye while he was asleep. The lot fell upon the very four whom I should have chosen, and I myself made five. In the evening the wretch came back from shepherding, and drove his flocks into the cave—this time driving them all inside, and not leaving any in the yards; I suppose some fancy must have taken him, or a god must have prompted him to do so. As soon as he had put the stone back to its place against the door, he sat down, milked his ewes and his goats all quite rightly, and then let each have her own young one; when he had got through with all this work, he gripped up two more of my men, and made his supper off them. So I went up to him with an ivy-wood bowl of black wine in my hands:

" ' Look here, Cyclops,' said I, ' you have been eating ₃₄₇ a great deal of man's flesh, so take this and drink some wine, that you may see what kind of liquor we had on board my ship. I was bringing it to you as a drink-offering, in the hope that you would take compassion upon me and further me on my way home, whereas all you do is to go on ramping and raving most intolerably. You ought to be ashamed of yourself; how can you expect people to come and see you any more if you treat them in this way? '

" He then took the cup and drank. He was so ₃₅₃

137

delighted with the taste of the wine that he begged me
for another bowl full. ' Be so kind,' he said, ' as to give
me some more, and tell me your name at once. I want
to make you a present that you will be glad to have.
We have wine even in this country, for our soil grows
grapes and the sun ripens them, but this drinks like
nectar and ambrosia all in one.'

360   " I then gave him some more; three times did I fill
the bowl for him, and three times did he drain it without
thought or heed; then, when I saw that the wine had
got into his head, I said to him as plausibly as I could:
' Cyclops, you ask my name and I will tell it you; give
me, therefore, the present you promised me; my name
is Noman; this is what my father and mother and my
friends have always called me.'

368   " But the cruel wretch said, ' Then I will eat all
Noman's comrades before Noman himself, and will
keep Noman for the last. This is the present that I will
make him.'

371   " As he spoke he reeled, and fell sprawling face
upwards on the ground. His great neck hung heavily
backwards and a deep sleep took hold upon him.
Presently he turned sick, and threw up both wine and
the gobbets of human flesh on which he had been
gorging, for he was very drunk. Then I thrust the
beam of wood far into the embers to heat it, and
encouraged my men lest any of them should turn faint-
hearted. When the wood, green though it was, was
about to blaze, I drew it out of the fire glowing with
heat, and my men gathered round me, for heaven had
filled their hearts with courage. We drove the sharp
end of the beam into the monster's eye, and bearing
upon it with all my weight I kept turning it round and
round as though I were boring a hole in a ship's plank
with an auger, which two men with a wheel and strap

can keep on turning as long as they choose. Even thus did we bore the red hot beam into his eye, till the boiling blood bubbled all over it as we worked it round and round, so that the steam from the burning eyeball scalded his eyelids and eyebrows, and the roots of the eye sputtered in the fire. As a blacksmith plunges an axe or hatchet into cold water to temper it—for it is this that gives strength to the iron—and it makes a great hiss as he does so, even thus did the Cyclops' eye hiss round the beam of olive wood, and his hideous yells made the cave ring again. We ran away in a fright, but he plucked the beam all besmirched with gore from his eye, and hurled it from him in a frenzy of rage and pain, shouting as he did so to the other Cyclopes who lived on the bleak headlands near him; so they gathered from all quarters round his cave when they heard him crying, and asked what was the matter with him.

" 'What ails you, Polyphemus,' said they, ' that you 403 make such a noise, breaking the stillness of the night, and preventing us from being able to sleep? Surely no man is carrying off your sheep? Surely no man is trying to kill you either by fraud or by force? '

" But Polyphemus shouted to them from inside the 407 cave, 'Noman is killing me by fraud! Noman is killing me by force!'

" 'Then,' said they, ' if no man is attacking you, you 409 must be ill; when Jove makes people ill, there is no help for it, and you had better pray to your father Neptune.'

" Then they went away, and I laughed inwardly at the 413 success of my clever stratagem, but the Cyclops, groaning and in an agony of pain, felt about with his hands till he found the stone and took it from the door; then he sat in the doorway and stretched his hands in front of it to catch anyone going out with the sheep, for he thought I might be foolish enough to attempt this.

420 " As for myself I kept on puzzling to think how I could best save my own life and those of my companions; I schemed and schemed, as one who knows that his life depends upon it, for the danger was very great. In the end I deemed that this plan would be the best. The male sheep were well grown, and carried a heavy black fleece, so I bound them noiselessly in threes together, with some of the withies on which the wicked monster used to sleep. There was to be a man under the middle sheep, and the two on either side were to cover him, so that there were three sheep to each man. As for myself there was a ram finer than any of the others, so I caught hold of him by the back, esconced myself in the thick wool under his belly, and hung on patiently to his fleece, face upwards, keeping a firm hold on it all the time.

436 " Thus, then, did we wait in great fear of mind till morning came, but when the child of morning, rosy-fingered Dawn, appeared, the male sheep hurried out to feed, while the ewes remained bleating about the pens waiting to be milked, for their udders were full to bursting; but their master in spite of all his pain felt the backs of all the sheep as they stood upright, without being sharp enough to find out that the men were underneath their bellies. As the ram was going out, last of all, heavy with its fleece and with the weight of my crafty self, Polyphemus laid hold of it and said:

447 " ' My good ram, what is it that makes you the last to leave my cave this morning? You are not wont to let the ewes go before you, but lead the mob with a run whether to flowery mead or bubbling fountain, and are the first to come home again at night; but now you lag last of all. Is it because you know your master has lost his eye, and are sorry because that wicked Noman and his horrid crew have got him down in his drink and blinded him? But I will have his life yet. If

you could understand and talk, you would tell me where
the wretch is hiding, and I would dash his brains upon
the ground till they flew all over the cave. I should
thus have some satisfaction for the harm this no-good
Noman has done me.'

"As he spoke he drove the ram outside, but when 461
we were a little way out from the cave and yards, I first
got from under the ram's belly, and then freed my
comrades; as for the sheep, which were very fat, by
constantly heading them in the right direction we
managed to drive them down to the ship. The crew
rejoiced greatly at seeing those of us who had escaped
death, but wept for the others whom the Cyclops had
killed. However, I made signs to them by nodding and
frowning that they were to hush their crying, and told
them to get all the sheep on board at once and put out
to sea; so they went aboard, took their places, and
smote the grey sea with their oars. Then, when I had
got as far out as my voice would reach, I began to jeer
at the Cyclops.

"'Cyclops,' said I, 'you should have taken better 475
measure of your man before eating up his comrades in
your cave. You wretch, eat up your visitors in your
own house? You might have known that your sin
would find you out, and now Jove and the other gods
have punished you.'

"He got more and more furious as he heard me, so 480
he tore the top from off a high mountain, and flung it
just in front of my ship so that it was within a little of
hitting the end of the rudder.[1] The sea quaked as the
rock fell into it, and the wash of the wave it raised
carried us back towards the mainland, and forced us

---

[1] This line is enclosed in brackets in the received text, and is
omitted (with note) by Messrs. Butcher and Lang. But lines
enclosed in brackets are almost always genuine; all that brackets
mean is that the bracketed passage puzzled some early editor,

towards the shore. But I snatched up a long pole and kept the ship off, making signs to my men by nodding my head, that they must row for their lives, whereon they laid out with a will. When we had got twice as far as we were before, I was for jeering at the Cyclops again, but the men begged and prayed of me to hold my tongue.

494   " ' Do not,' they exclaimed, ' be mad enough to provoke this savage creature further; he has thrown one rock at us already which drove us back again to the mainland, and we made sure it had been the death of us; if he had then heard any further sound of voices he would have pounded our heads and our ship's timbers into a jelly with the rugged rocks he would have heaved at us, for he can throw them a long way.'

500   " But I would not listen to them, and shouted out to him in my rage, ' Cyclops, if any one asks you who it was that put your eye out and spoiled your beauty, say it was the valiant warrior Ulysses, son of Laertes, who lives in Ithaca.'

who nevertheless found it too well established in the text for him to venture on omitting it. In the present case the line bracketed is the very last which a full-grown male editor would be likely to interpolate. It is safer to infer that the writer, a young woman, not knowing or caring at which end of the ship the rudder should be, determined to make sure by placing it at both ends, which we shall find she presently does by repeating it (line 540) at the stern of the ship.

As for the two rocks thrown, the first I take to be the Asinelli, see map on p. 95. The second I see as the two contiguous islands of the Formiche, which are treated as one, see map on p. 127. The Asinelli is an island shaped like a boat, and pointing to the island of Favognana. I think the authoress's compatriots who probably did not like her much better than she did them, jeered at the absurdity of Ulysses' conduct, and saw the Asinelli or " donkeys," not as the rock thrown by Polyphemus, but as the boat itself containing Ulysses and his men.

" On this he groaned, and cried out, ' Alas, alas, then 506 the old prophecy about me is coming true. There was a prophet here, at one time, a man both brave and of great stature, Telemus son of Eurymus, who was an excellent seer, and did all the prophesying for the Cyclopes till he grew old; he told me that all this would happen to me some day, and said I should lose my sight by the hand of Ulysses. I have been all along expecting some one of imposing presence and superhuman strength, whereas he turns out to be a little insignificant weakling, who has managed to blind my eye by taking advantage of me in my drink; come here, then, Ulysses, that I may make you presents to show my hospitality, and urge Neptune to help you forward on your journey —for Neptune and I are father and son. He, if he so will, shall heal me, which no one else neither god nor man can do.'

" Then I said, ' I wish I could be as sure of killing you 522 outright and sending you down to the house of Hades, as I am that it will take more than Neptune to cure that eye of yours.'

" On this he lifted up his hands to the firmament of 526 heaven and prayed, saying, ' Hear me, great Neptune; if I am indeed your own true-begotten son, grant that Ulysses may never reach his home alive; or if he must get back to his friends at last, let him do so late and in sore plight after losing all his men [let him reach his home in another man's ship and find trouble in his house.' ¹]

---

¹ This line exists in the text here, but not in the corresponding passage xii, 141. I am inclined to think it is interpolated (probably by the poetess herself) from the first of lines xi, 115-137, which I can hardly doubt were added by the writer when the scheme of the work was enlarged and altered. See *The Authoress of the Odyssey*, pp. 265, 266.

536   " Thus did he pray, and Neptune heard his prayer.
Then he picked up a rock much larger than the firSt,
swung it aloft and hurled it with prodigious force. It
fell juSt short of the ship, but was within a little of
hitting the end of the rudder. The sea quaked as the
rock fell into it, and the wash of the wave it raised
drove us onwards on our way towards the shore of the
island.

543   " When at laSt we got to the island where we had left
the reSt of our ships, we found our comrades lamenting
us, and anxiously awaiting our return. We ran our
vessel upon the sands and got out of her on to the sea
shore; we also landed the Cyclops' sheep, and divided
them equitably amongSt us so that none might have
reason to complain. As for the ram, my companions
agreed that I should have it as an extra share; so I
sacrificed it on the sea shore, and burned its thigh bones
to Jove, who is the lord of all. But he heeded not my
sacrifice, and only thought how he might deStroy both
my ships and my comrades.

556   " Thus through the livelong day to the going down
of the sun we feaSted our fill on meat and drink, but
when the sun went down and it came on dark, we
camped upon the beach. When the child of morning,
rosy-fingered Dawn, appeared, I bade my men go on
board and loose the hawsers. Then they took their
places and smote the grey sea with their oars; so we
sailed on with sorrow in our hearts, but glad to have
566 escaped death though we had loSt our comrades.

"THENCE WE WENT ON TO THE AEOLIAN island where lives Aeolus son of Hippotas, dear to the immortal gods. It is an island that floats (as it were) upon the sea,[1] iron bound with a wall that girds it. Now Aeolus has six daughters and six lusty sons, so he made the sons marry the daughters, and they all live with their dear father and mother, feasting and enjoying every conceivable kind of luxury. All day long the atmosphere of the house is loaded with the savour of roasting meats till it groans again, yard and all; but by night they sleep on their well-made bedsteads, each with his own wife between the blankets. These were the people among whom we had now come.

"Aeolus entertained me for a whole month asking [14] me questions all the time about Troy, the Argive fleet, and the return of the Achaeans. I told him exactly how everything had happened, and when I said I must go, and asked him to further me on my way, he made no sort of difficulty, but set about doing so at once. Moreover, he flayed me a prime ox-hide to hold the ways of the roaring winds, which he shut up in the hide as in a sack—for Jove had made him captain over the winds, and he could stir or still each one of them according to his own pleasure. He put the sack in the ship, and bound the mouth so tightly with a silver thread that not even a breath of a side-wind could blow from any quarter. The West wind which was fair for us did he

---

[1] " Floating " (πλωτῇ) is not to be taken literally. The island itself, as apart from its inhabitants, was quite normal. There is no indication of its moving during the month that Ulysses stayed with Aeolus, and on his return from his unfortunate voyage, he seems to have found it in the same place. The πλωτῆ in fact should no more be pressed than θοῆ̄ισι as applied to islands, Odyssey, xv, 299—where they are called " flying " because the ship would fly past them. So also the " Wanderers," as explained by Buttmann ; see note on Odyssey, xii, 57.

alone let blow as it chose; but it all came to nothing,
for we were lost through our own folly.

28   " Nine days and nine nights did we sail, and on the
tenth day our native land showed on the horizon. We
got so close in that we could see the stubble fires burning, and I, being then dead beat, fell into a light sleep,
for I had never let the rudder out of my own hands, that
we might get home the faster. On this the men fell to
talking among themselves, and said I was bringing back
gold and silver in the sack that Aeolus had given me.
' Bless my heart,' would one turn to his neighbour,
saying, ' how this man gets honoured and makes friends
to whatever city or country he may go. See what fine
prizes he is taking home from Troy, while we, who have
travelled just as far as he has, come back with hands as
empty as we set out with—and now Aeolus has given
him ever so much more. Quick—let us see what it all
is, and how much gold and silver there is in the sack he
gave him.'

46   " Thus they talked and evil counsels prevailed. They
loosed the sack, whereupon the wind flew howling forth
and raised a storm that carried us weeping out to sea
and away from our own country. Then I awoke, and
knew not whether to throw myself into the sea or to
live on and make the best of it; but I bore it, covered
myself up, and lay down in the ship, while the men
lamented bitterly as the fierce winds bore our fleet
back to the Aeolian island.

56   " When we reached it we went ashore to take in
water, and dined hard by the ships. Immediately after
dinner I took a herald and one of my men and went
straight to the house of Aeolus, where I found him
feasting with his wife and family; so we sat down as
suppliants on the threshold. They were astounded
when they saw us and said, ' Ulysses, what brings you
here? What god has been ill-treating you? We took

great pains to further you on your way home to Ithaca,
or wherever it was that you wanted to go to.'

"Thus did they speak, but I answered sorrowfully, 67
'My men have undone me; they, and cruel sleep, have
ruined me. My friends, mend me this mischief, for you
can if you will.'

"I spoke as movingly as I could, but they said 70
nothing, till their father answered, ' Vilest of mankind,
get you gone at once out of the island; him whom
heaven hates will I in no wise help. Be off, for you
come here as one abhorred of heaven.' And with these
words he sent me sorrowing from his door.

"Thence we sailed sadly on till the men were worn 77
out with long and fruitless rowing, for there was no
longer any wind to help them. Six days, night and day
did we toil, and on the seventh day we reached the
rocky stronghold of Lamus—Telepylus, the city of the
Laestrygonians, where the shepherd who is driving in
his sheep and goats [to be milked] salutes him who is
driving out his flock [to feed] and this last answers the
salute. In that country a man who could do without
sleep might earn double wages, one as a herdsman of
cattle, and another as a shepherd, for they work much
the same by night as they do by day.[1]

[1] Literally " for the ways of the night and of the day are near."
I have seen what Mr. Andrew Lang says (*Homer and the Epic*,
p. 236, and *Longman's Magazine* for January, 1898, p. 277) about
the " amber route " and the " Sacred Way " in this connection ;
but until he gives his grounds for holding that the Mediterranean
peoples in the Odyssean age used to go far North for their
amber instead of getting it in Sicily, where it is still found in
considerable quantities, I do not know what weight I ought
to attach to his opinion. I have been unable to find grounds
for asserting that 1000 B.C. there was any commerce between
the Mediterranean and the " Far North," but I shall be very
ready to learn if Mr. Lang will enlighten me. See *The Authoress
of the Odyssey*, pp. 195, 196.

87   " When we reached the harbour we found it land-locked under ſteep cliffs, with a narrow entrance between two headlands. My captains took all their ships inside, and made them faſt close to one another, for there was never so much as a breath of wind inside, but it was always dead calm. I kept my own ship outside, and moored it to a rock at the very end of the point; then I climbed a high rock to reconnoitre, but could see no sign neither of man nor cattle, only some smoke rising from the ground. So I sent two of my company with an attendant to find out what sort of people the in-habitants were.

103   " The men when they got on shore followed a level road by which the people draw their firewood from the mountains into the town, till presently they met a young woman who had come outside to fetch water, and who was daughter to a Laeſtrygonian named Antiphates. She was going to the fountain Artacia from which the people bring in their water, and when my men had come close up to her, they asked her who the king of that country might be, and over what kind of people he ruled; so she directed them to her father's house, but when they got there they found his wife to be a giantess as huge as a mountain, and they were horrified at the sight of her.

114   " She at once called her husband Antiphates from the place of assembly, and forthwith he set about killing my men. He snatched up one of them, and began to make his dinner off him then and there, whereon the other two ran back to the ships as faſt as ever they could. But Antiphates raised a hue and cry after them, and thousands of ſturdy Laeſtrygonians sprang up from every quarter—ogres, not men. They threw vaſt rocks at us from the cliffs as though they had been mere ſtones, and I heard the horrid sound of the ships crunching up

against one another, and the death cries of my men, as
the Laestrygonians speared them like fishes and took
them home to eat them. While they were thus killing
my men within the harbour I drew my sword, cut the
cable of my own ship, and told my men to row with all
their might if they too would not fare like the rest; so
they laid out for their lives, and we were thankful
enough when we got into open water out of reach of
the rocks they hurled at us. As for the others there
was not one of them left.

"Thence we sailed sadly on, glad to have escaped 133
death, though we had lost our comrades, and came to
the Aeaean island, where Circe lives—a great and cunning goddess who is own sister to the magician Aeetes—
for they are both children of the sun by Perse, who is
daughter to Oceanus. We brought our ship into a safe
harbour without a word, for some god guided us
thither, and having landed we lay there for two days
and two nights, worn out in body and mind. When the
morning of the third day came I took my spear and my
sword, and went away from the ship to reconnoitre, and
see if I could discover signs of human handiwork, or
hear the sound of voices. Climbing to the top of a high
look-out I espied the smoke of Circe's house rising
upwards amid a dense forest of trees, and when I saw
this I doubted whether, having seen the smoke, I
would not go on at once and find out more, but in the
end I deemed it best to go back to the ship, give the
men their dinners, and send some of them instead of
going myself.

"When I had nearly got back to the ship some god 156
took pity upon my solitude, and sent a fine antlered stag
right into the very middle of my path. He was coming
down from his pasture in the forest to drink of the
river, for the heat of the sun drove him, and as he

149

passed I struck him in the middle of the back; the bronze point of the spear went clean through him, and he lay groaning in the dust until the life went out of him. Then I set my foot upon him, drew my spear from the wound, and laid it down; I also gathered rough grass and rushes and twisted them into a fathom or so of good stout rope, with which I bound the four feet of the noble creature together; having so done I hung him round my neck and walked back to the ship leaning upon my spear, for the stag was much too big for me to be able to carry him on my shoulder, steadying him with one hand. As I threw him down in front of the ship, I called the men and spoke cheeringly man by man to each of them. 'Look here my friends,' said I, 'we are not going to die so much before our time after all, and at any rate we will not starve so long as we have got something to eat and drink on board.' On this they uncovered their heads upon the sea shore and admired the stag, for he was indeed a splendid fellow. Then, when they had feasted their eyes upon him sufficiently, they washed their hands and began to cook him for dinner.

183   " Thus through the livelong day to the going down of the sun we stayed there eating and drinking our fill, but when the sun went down and it came on dark, we camped upon the sea shore. When the child of morning, rosy-fingered Dawn, appeared, I called a council and said, ' My friends, we are in very great difficulties; listen therefore to me. We have no idea where the sun either sets or rises,[1] so that we do not even know East from West. I see no way out of it; nevertheless, we must try and find one. We are certainly on an

[1] One would have thought that when the sun was driving the stag down to the water, Ulysses might have observed its whereabouts.

island, for I went as high as I could this morning, and
saw the sea reaching all round it to the horizon; it lies
low, but towards the middle I saw smoke rising from
out of a thick forest of trees.'

" Their hearts sank as they heard me, for they 198
remembered how they had been treated by the Laestrygonian Antiphates, and by the savage ogre Polyphemus.
They wept bitterly in their dismay, but there was
nothing to be got by crying, so I divided them into two
companies and set a captain over each; I gave one
company to Eurylochus, while I took command of the
other myself. Then we cast lots in a helmet, and the lot
fell upon Eurylochus; so he set out with his twenty-
two men, and they wept, as also did we who were left
behind.

" When they reached Circe's house they found it 210
built of cut stones, on a site that could be seen from far,
in the middle of the forest. There were wild mountain
wolves and lions prowling all round it—poor bewitched
creatures whom she had tamed by her enchantments and
drugged into subjection. They did not attack my men,
but wagged their great tails, fawned upon them, and
rubbed their noses lovingly against them.[1] As hounds
crowd round their master when they see him coming
from dinner—for they know he will bring them something—even so did these wolves and lions with their
great claws fawn upon my men, but the men were
terribly frightened at seeing such strange creatures.
Presently they reached the gates of the goddess's house,
and as they stood there they could hear Circe within,
singing most beautifully as she worked at her loom,
making a web so fine, so soft, and of such dazzling
colours as no one but a goddess could weave. On this
Polites, whom I valued and trusted more than any other

[1] See Hobbes of Malmesbury's translation.

151

of my men, said, ' There is some one inside working at
a loom and singing moSt beautifully; the whole place
resounds with it, let us call her and see whether she is
woman or goddess.'

229   " They called her and she came down, unfaStened the
door, and bade them enter. They, thinking no evil,
followed her, all except Eurylochus, who suspected
mischief and Stayed outside. When she had got them
into her house, she set them upon benches and seats
and mixed them a mess with cheese, honey, meal, and
Pramnian wine, but she drugged it with wicked poisons
to make them forget their homes, and when they had
drunk she turned them into pigs by a Stroke of her
wand, and shut them up in her pigSties. They were like
pigs—head, hair, and all, and they grunted juSt as pigs
do; but their senses were the same as before, and they
remembered everything.

241   " Thus then were they shut up squealing, and Circe
threw them some acorns and beech maSts such as pigs
eat, but Eurylochus hurried back to tell me about the
sad fate of our comrades. He was so overcome with
dismay that though he tried to speak he could find no
words to do so; his eyes filled with tears and he could
only sob and sigh, till at laSt we forced his Story out of
him, and he told us what had happened to the others.

251   " ' We went,' said he, ' as you told us, through the
foreSt, and in the middle of it there was a fine house
built with cut Stones in a place that could be seen from
far. There we found a woman, or else she was a
goddess, working at her loom and singing sweetly; so
the men shouted to her and called her, whereon she at
once came down, opened the door, and invited us in.
The others did not suspect any mischief so they followed
her into the house, but I Stayed where I was, for I thought
there might be some treachery. From that moment I

saw them no more, for not one of them ever came out,
though I sat a long time watching for them.'

" Then I took my sword of bronze and slung it over 261
my shoulders; I also took my bow, and told Eurylochus to come back with me and show me the way.
But he laid hold of me with both his hands and spoke
piteously, saying, ' Sir, do not force me to go with you,
but let me stay here, for I know you will not bring one
of them back with you, nor even return alive yourself;
let us rather see if we cannot escape at any rate with the
few that are left us, for we may still save our lives.'

" ' Stay where you are, then,' answered I, ' eating and 270
drinking at the ship, but I must go, for I am most
urgently bound to do so.'

" With this I left the ship and went up inland. When 274
I got through the charmed grove, and was near the
great house of the enchantress Circe, I met Mercury
with his golden wand, disguised as a young man in the
hey-day of his youth and beauty with the down just
coming upon his face. He came up to me and took my
hand within his own, saying, ' My poor unhappy man,
whither are you going over this mountain top, alone
and without knowing the way? Your men are shut up
in Circe's pigsties, like so many wild boars in their lairs.
You surely do not fancy that you can set them free? I
can tell you that you will never get back and will have
to stay there with the rest of them. But never mind, I
will protect you and get you out of your difficulty.
Take this herb, which is one of great virtue, and keep it
about you when you go to Circe's house, it will be a
talisman to you against every kind of mischief.

" ' And I will tell you of all the wicked witchcraft 289
that Circe will try to practise upon you. She will mix
a mess for you to drink, and she will drug the meal with
which she makes it, but she will not be able to charm

153

you, for the virtue of the herb that I shall give you will prevent her spells from working. I will tell you all about it. When Circe strikes you with her wand, draw your sword and spring upon her as though you were going to kill her. She will then be frightened, and will desire you to go to bed with her; on this you must not point blank refuse her, for you want her to set your companions free, and to take good care also of yourself, but you must make her swear solemnly by all the blessed gods that she will plot no further mischief against you, or else when she has got you naked she will unman you and make you fit for nothing.'

302 " As he spoke he pulled the herb out of the ground and showed me what it was like. The root was black, while the flower was as white as milk; the gods call it Moly, and mortal men cannot uproot it, but the gods can do whatever they like.

307 " Then Mercury went back to high Olympus passing over the wooded island; but I fared onward to the house of Circe, and my heart was clouded with care as I walked along. When I got to the gates I stood there and called the goddess, and as soon as she heard me she came down, opened the door, and asked me to come in; so I followed her—much troubled in my mind. She set me on a richly decorated seat inlaid with silver, there was a footstool also under my feet, and she mixed a mess in a golden goblet for me to drink; but she drugged it, for she meant me mischief. When she had given it me, and I had drunk it without its charming me, she struck me with her wand. ' There now,' she cried, ' be off to the pigsty, and make your lair with the rest of them.'

321 " But I rushed at her with my sword drawn as though I would kill her, whereon she fell with a loud scream, clasped my knees, and spoke piteously, saying, ' Who

154

and whence are you? from what place and people have
you come? How can it be that my drugs have no
power to charm you? Never yet was any man able to
stand so much as a taste of the herb I gave you; you
must be spell-proof; surely you can be none other than
the bold hero Ulysses, who Mercury always said would
come here some day with his ship while on his way home
from Troy; so be it then; sheathe your sword and let
us go to bed, that we may make friends and learn to
trust each other.'

" And I answered, ' Circe, how can you expect me to 336
be friendly with you when you have just been turning
all my men into pigs? And now that you have got me
here myself, you mean me mischief when you ask me
to go to bed with you, and will unman me and make me
fit for nothing. I shall certainly not consent to go to
bed with you unless you will first take your solemn oath
to plot no further harm against me."

" So she swore at once as I had told her, and when 345
she had completed her oath then I went to bed with
her.

" Meanwhile her four servants, who are her house- 348
maids, set about their work. They are the children of
the groves and fountains, and of the holy waters that
run down into the sea. One of them spread a fair
purple cloth over a seat, and laid a carpet underneath
it. Another brought tables of silver up to the seats, and
set them with baskets of gold. A third mixed some
sweet wine with water in a silver bowl and put golden
cups upon the tables, while the fourth brought in water
and set it to boil in a large cauldron over a good fire
which she had lighted. When the water in the cauldron
was boiling,[1] she poured cold into it till it was just as I

---

[1] Il., xviii, 349. Again the writer draws from the washing the
body of Patroclus—which offends.

liked it, and then she set me in a bath and began washing me from the cauldron about the head and shoulders, to take the tire and stiffness out of my limbs. As soon as she had done washing me and anointing me with oil, she arrayed me in a good cloak and shirt and led me to a richly decorated seat inlaid with silver; there was a footstool also under my feet. A maid servant then brought me water in a beautiful golden ewer and poured it into a silver basin for me to wash my hands, and she drew a clean table beside me; an upper servant brought me bread and offered me many good things of what there was in the house, and then Circe bade me eat, but I would not, and sat without heeding what was before me, still moody and suspicious.

375 " When Circe saw me sitting there without eating, and in great grief, she came to me and said, ' Ulysses, why do you sit like that as though you were dumb, gnawing at your own heart, and refusing both meat and drink? Is it that you are still suspicious? You ought not to be, for I have already sworn solemnly that I will not hurt you.'

382 " And I said, ' Circe, no man with any sense of what is right can think of either eating or drinking in your house until you have set his friends free and let him see them. If you want me to eat and drink, you must free my men and bring them to me that I may see them with my own eyes.'

388 " When I had said this she went straight through the court with her wand in her hand and opened the pig-sty doors. My men came out like so many prime hogs and stood looking at her, but she went about among them and anointed each with a second drug, whereon the bristles that the bad drug had given them fell off, and they became men again, younger than they were before, and much taller and better looking. They knew

156

me at once, seized me each of them by the hand, and
wept for joy till the whole house was filled with the
sound of their hullabalooing, and Circe herself was
so sorry for them that she came up to me and said,
' Ulysses, noble son of Laertes, go back at once to the
sea where you have left your ship, and first draw it on
to the land. Then, hide all your ship's gear and property
in some cave, and come back here with your men.'

" I agreed to this, so I went back to the sea shore, and 406
found the men at the ship weeping and wailing most
piteously. When they saw me the silly blubbering
fellows began frisking round me as calves break out and
gambol round their mothers, when they see them coming home to be milked after they have been feeding all
day, and the homestead resounds with their lowing.
They seemed as glad to see me as though they had got
back to their own rugged Ithaca, where they had been
born and bred. ' Sir,' said the affectionate creatures,
' we are as glad to see you back as though we had got
safe home to Ithaca; but tell us all about the fate of our
comrades.'

" I spoke comfortingly to them and said, ' We must 422
draw our ship on to the land, and hide the ship's gear
with all our property in some cave; then come with me
all of you as fast as you can to Circe's house, where you
will find your comrades eating and drinking in the
midst of great abundance.'

" On this the men would have come with me at 428
once, but Eurylochus tried to hold them back and said,
' Alas, poor wretches that we are, what will become
of us? Rush not on your ruin by going to the house
of Circe, who will turn us all into pigs or wolves or
lions, and we shall have to keep guard over her house.
Remember how the Cyclops treated us when our
comrades went inside his cave, and Ulysses with them.

It was all through his sheer folly that those men lost their lives.'

438   " When I heard him I was in two minds whether or no to draw the keen blade that hung by my sturdy thigh and cut his head off in spite of his being a near relation of my own; but the men interceded for him and said, ' Sir, if it may so be, let this fellow stay here and mind the ship, but take the rest of us with you to Circe's house.'

446   " On this we all went inland, and Eurylochus was not left behind after all, but came on too, for he was frightened by the severe reprimand that I had given him.

449   " Meanwhile Circe had been seeing that the men who had been left behind were washed and anointed with olive oil; she had also given them woollen cloaks and shirts, and when we came we found them all comfortably at dinner in her house. As soon as the men saw each other face to face and knew one another, they wept for joy and cried aloud till the whole palace rang again. Thereon Circe came up to me and said, ' Ulysses, noble son of Laertes, tell your men to leave off crying; I know how much you have all of you suffered at sea, and how ill you have fared among cruel savages on the mainland, but that is over now, so stay here, and eat and drink till you are once more as strong and hearty as you were when you left Ithaca; for at present you are weakened both in body and mind; you keep all the time thinking of the hardships you have suffered during your travels, so that you have no more cheerfulness left in you.'

466   " Thus did she speak and we assented. We stayed with Circe for a whole twelvemonth feasting upon an untold quantity both of meat and wine. But when the year had passed in the waning of moons and the long days had come round, my men called me apart and said,

' Sir, it is time you began to think about going home,
if so be you are to be spared to see your house and native
country at all.'

" Thus did they speak and I assented. Thereon 475
through the livelong day to the going down of the sun
we feasted our fill on meat and wine, but when the sun
went down and it came on dark the men laid themselves
down to sleep in the covered cloisters. I, however,
after I had got into bed with Circe, besought her by her
knees, and the goddess listened to what I had got to
say. ' Circe,' said I, ' please to keep the promise you
made me about furthering me on my homeward voyage.
I want to get back and so do my men, they are always
pestering me with their complaints as soon as ever your
back is turned.'

" And the goddess answered, ' Ulysses, noble son of 487
Laertes, you shall none of you stay here any longer if
you do not want to, but there is another journey which
you have got to take before you can sail homewards.
You must go to the house of Hades and of dread
Proserpine to consult the ghost of the blind Theban
prophet Teiresias, whose reason is still unshaken. To
him alone has Proserpine left his understanding even in
death, but the other ghosts flit about aimlessly.'

" I was dismayed when I heard this. I sat up in bed 496
and wept, and would gladly have lived no longer to see
the light of the sun, but presently when I was tired of
weeping and tossing myself about, I said, ' And who
shall guide me upon this voyage—for the house of Hades
is a port that no ship can reach.'

" ' You will want no guide,' she answered; ' raise 504
your mast, set your white sails, sit quite still, and the
North Wind will blow you there of itself. When your
ship has traversed the waters of Oceanus, you will reach
the fertile shore of Proserpine's country with its groves

of tall poplars and willows that shed their fruit untimely; here beach your ship upon the shore of Oceanus, and go straight on to the dark abode of Hades. You will find it near the place where the rivers Pyriphlegethon and Cocytus (which is a branch of the river Styx) flow into Acheron, and you will see a rock near it, just where the two roaring rivers run into one another.

516 " ' When you have reached this spot, as I now tell you, dig a trench a cubit or so in length, breadth, and depth, and pour into it as a drink-offering to all the dead, first, honey mixed with milk, then wine, and in the third place water–sprinkling white barley meal over the whole. Moreover you must offer many prayers to the poor feeble ghosts, and promise them that when you get back to Ithaca you will sacrifice a barren heifer to them, the best you have, and will load the pyre with good things. More particularly you must promise that Teiresias shall have a black sheep all to himself, the finest in all your flocks.

526 " ' When you shall have thus besought the ghosts with your prayers, offer them a ram and a black ewe, bending their heads towards Erebus; but yourself turn away from them as though you would make towards the river. On this, many dead men's ghosts will come to you, and you must tell your men to skin the two sheep that you have just killed, and offer them as a burnt sacrifice with prayers to Hades and to Proserpine. Then draw your sword and sit there, so as to prevent any other poor ghost from coming near the spilt blood before Teiresias shall have answered your questions. The seer will presently come to you, and will tell you about your voyage–what stages you are to make, and how you are to sail the sea so as to reach your home.'

541 " It was day-break by the time she had done speaking, so she dressed me in my shirt and cloak. As for herself

she threw a beautiful light gossamer fabric over her shoulders, fastening it with a golden girdle round her waist, and she covered her head with a mantle. Then I went about among the men everywhere all over the house, and spoke kindly to each of them man by man: ' You must not lie sleeping here any longer,' said I to them, ' we must be going, for Circe has told me all about it.' And on this they did as I bade them.

" Even so, however, I did not get them away without 551 misadventure. We had with us a certain youth named Elpenor, not very remarkable for sense or courage, who had got drunk and was lying on the house-top away from the rest of the men, to sleep off his liquor in the cool. When he heard the noise of the men bustling about, he jumped up on a sudden and forgot all about coming down by the main staircase, so he tumbled right off the roof and broke his neck, and his soul went down to the house of Hades.

" When I had got the men together I said to them, 561 ' You think you are about to start home again, but Circe has explained to me that instead of this, we have got to go to the house of Hades and Proserpine to consult the ghost of the Theban prophet Teiresias.'

" The men were broken-hearted as they heard me, 566 and threw themselves on the ground groaning and tearing their hair, but they did not mend matters by crying. When we reached the sea shore, weeping and lamenting our fate, Circe brought the ram and the ewe, and we made them fast hard by the ship. She passed through the midst of us without our knowing it, for who can see the comings and goings of a god, if the god does not wish to be seen? 574

THEN, WHEN WE HAD GOT DOWN TO the sea shore we drew our ship into the water and got her mast and sails into her; we also put the sheep on board and took our places, weeping and in great distress of mind. Circe, that great and cunning goddess, sent us a fair wind that blew dead aft and stayed steadily with us keeping our sails all the time well filled; so we did whatever wanted doing to the ship's gear and let her go as the wind and helmsman headed her. All day long her sails were full as she held her course over the sea, but when the sun went down and darkness was over all the earth, we got into the deep waters of the river Oceanus, where lie the land and city of the Cimmerians who live enshrouded in mist and darkness which the rays of the sun never pierce neither at his rising nor as he goes down again out of the heavens, but the poor wretches live in one long melancholy night. When we got there we beached the ship, took the sheep out of her, and went along by the waters of Oceanus till we came to the place of which Circe had told us.

23 "Here Perimedes and Eurylochus held the victims, while I drew my sword and dug the trench a cubit each way. I made a drink-offering to all the dead, first with honey and milk, then with wine, and thirdly with water, and I sprinkled white barley meal over the whole, praying earnestly to the poor feckless ghosts, and promising them that when I got back to Ithaca I would sacrifice a barren heifer for them, the best I had, and would load the pyre with good things. I also particularly promised that Teiresias should have a black sheep to himself, the best in all my flocks. When I had prayed sufficiently to the dead, I cut the throats of the two sheep and let the blood run into the trench, whereon the ghosts came

[1] This visit is wholly without topographical significance.

162

trooping up from Erebus—brides,[1] young bachelors,
old men worn out with toil, maids who had been crossed
in love, and brave men who had been killed in battle,
with their armour still smirched with blood; they came
from every quarter and flitted round the trench with a
strange kind of screaming sound that made me turn pale
with fear. When I saw them coming I told the men to
be quick and flay the carcasses of the two dead sheep
and make burnt offerings of them, and at the same time
to repeat prayers to Hades and to Proserpine; but I sat
where I was with my sword drawn and would not let
the poor feckless ghosts come near the blood till
Teiresias should have answered my questions.

"The first ghost that came was that of my comrade 51
Elpenor, for he had not yet been laid beneath the earth.
We had left his body unwaked and unburied in Circe's
house, for we had had too much else to do. I was very
sorry for him, and cried when I saw him: 'Elpenor,'
said I, 'how did you come down here into this gloom
and darkness? You have got here on foot quicker than
I have with my ship.'

"'Sir,' he answered with a groan, 'it was all bad 60
luck, and my own unspeakable drunkenness. I was
lying asleep on the top of Circe's house, and never
thought of coming down again by the great staircase
but fell right off the roof and broke my neck, so my soul
came down to the house of Hades. And now I beseech
you by all those whom you have left behind you,
though they are not here, by your wife, by the father
who brought you up when you were a child, and by
Telemachus who is the one hope of your house, do
what I shall now ask you. I know that when you leave

---

[1] Brides presented themselves instinctively to the imagination
of the writer, as the phase of humanity which she found most
interesting.

this limbo you will again hold your ship for the Aeaean island. Do not go thence leaving me unwaked and unburied behind you, or I may bring heaven's anger upon you; but burn me with whatever armour I have, build a barrow for me on the sea shore, that may tell people in days to come what a poor unlucky fellow I was, and plant over my grave the oar I used to row with when I was yet alive and with my messmates.' And I said, ' My poor fellow, I will do all that you have asked of me.'

81 " Thus, then, did we sit and hold sad talk with one another, I on the one side of the trench with my sword held over the blood, and the ghost of my comrade saying all this to me from the other side. Then came the ghost of my dead mother Anticlea, daughter to Autolycus. I had left her alive when I set out for Troy and was moved to tears when I saw her, but even so, for all my sorrow I would not let her come near the blood till I had asked my questions of Teiresias.

90 " Then came also the ghost of Theban Teiresias, with his golden sceptre in his hand. He knew me and said, ' Ulysses, noble son of Laertes, why, poor man, have you left the light of day and come down to visit the dead in this sad place? Stand back from the trench and withdraw your sword that I may drink of the blood and answer your questions truly.'

97 " So I drew back, and sheathed my sword, whereon when he had drank of the blood he began with his prophecy.

100 " ' You want to know,' said he, ' about your return home, but heaven will make this hard for you. I do not think that you will escape the eye of Neptune, who still nurses his bitter grudge against you for having blinded his son. Still, after much suffering you may get home

164

if you can restrain yourself and your companions when
your ship reaches the Thrinacian island, where you will
find the sheep and cattle belonging to the sun, who sees
and gives ear to everything. If you leave these flocks
unharmed and think of nothing but of getting home,
you may yet after much hardship reach Ithaca; but if
you harm them, then I forewarn you of the destruction
both of your ship and of your men. Even though you
may yourself escape, you will return in bad plight after
losing all your men, [in another man's ship, and you
will find trouble in your house, which will be overrun
by high-handed people, who are devouring your substance under the pretext of paying court and making
presents to your wife.

" ' When you get home you will take your revenge 118
on these suitors; and after you have killed them by
force or fraud in your own house, you must take a well-
made oar and carry it on and on, till you come to a
country where the people have never heard of the sea
and do not even mix salt with their food, nor do they
know anything about ships, and oars that are as the
wings of a ship. I will give you this certain token which
cannot escape your notice. A wayfarer will meet you
and will say it must be a winnowing shovel that you
have got upon your shoulder; on this you must fix the
oar in the ground and sacrifice a ram, a bull, and a boar
to Neptune.[1] Then go home and offer hecatombs to all
the gods in heaven one after the other. As for yourself,
death shall come to you from the sea, and your life

---

[1] Ulysses was, in fact, to become a missionary and preach
Neptune to people who knew not his name. I was fortunate
enough to meet in Sicily a woman carrying one of these winnowing shovels; it was not much shorter than an oar, and I was
able at once to see what the writer of the Odyssey intended.

165

shall ebb away very gently when you are full of years
and peace of mind, and your people shall bless you. All
that I have said will come true].'[1]

138 " 'This,' I answered, 'must be as it may please
heaven, but tell me and tell me true, I see my poor
mother's ghost close by us; she is sitting by the blood
without saying a word, and though I am her own son
she does not remember me and speak to me; tell me,
Sir, how I can make her know me.'

145 " 'That,' said he, 'I can soon do. Any ghost that
you let taste of the blood will talk with you like a
reasonable being, but if you do not let them have any
blood they will go away again.'

150 " On this the ghost of Teiresias went back to the
house of Hades, for his prophecyings had now been
spoken, but I sat still where I was until my mother
came up and tasted the blood. Then she knew me at
once and spoke fondly to me, saying, ' My son, how did
you come down to this abode of darkness while you
are still alive? It is a hard thing for the living to see
these places, for between us and them there are great
and terrible waters, and there is Oceanus, which no man
can cross on foot, but he must have a good ship to take
him. Are you all this time trying to find your way home
from Troy, and have you never yet got back to Ithaca
nor seen your wife in your own house?'

163 " 'Mother,' said I, 'I was forced to come here to
consult the ghost of the Theban prophet Teiresias. I

---

[1] I suppose the lines I have enclosed in brackets to have been
added by the writer when she enlarged her original scheme by
the addition of books i–iv and xiii (from line 187)-xxiv. The
reader will observe that in the corresponding passage (xii,
137-141) the prophecy ends with "after losing all your comrades,"
and that there is no allusion to the suitors. For fuller explana-
tion see *The Authoress of the Odyssey*, pp. 265, 266.

have never yet been near the Achaean land nor set foot
on my native country, and I have had nothing but one
long series of misfortunes from the very first day that I
set out with Agamemnon for Ilius, the land of noble
steeds, to fight the Trojans. But tell me, and tell me
true, in what way did you die? Did you have a long
illness, or did heaven vouchsafe you a gentle easy
passage to eternity? Tell me also about my father, and
the son whom I left behind me; is my property still in
their hands, or has some one else got hold of it, who
thinks that I shall not return to claim it? Tell me again
what my wife intends doing, and in what mind she is;
does she live with my son and guard my estate securely,
or has she made the best match she could and married
again?'

" My mother answered, 'Your wife still remains in 180
your house, but she is in great distress of mind and
spends her whole time in tears both night and day. No
one as yet has got possession of your fine property, and
Telemachus still holds your lands undisturbed. He has
to entertain largely, as of course he must, considering
his position as a magistrate,[1] and how every one invites
him; your father remains at his old place in the country
and never goes near the town. He has no comfortable
bed nor bedding; in the winter he sleeps on the floor
in front of the fire with the men and goes about all in
rags, but in summer, when the warm weather comes on
again, he lies out in the vineyard on a bed of vine leaves
thrown anyhow upon the ground. He grieves continually about your never having come home, and
suffers more and more as he grows older. As for my

[1] The reader will remember that we are in the first year of
Ulysses' wanderings, Telemachus therefore was only eleven
years old. The same anachronism is made later on in this
book. See *The Authoress of the Odyssey*, pp. 137, 138.

own end it was in this wise: heaven did not take me swiftly and painlessly in my own house, nor was I attacked by any illness such as those that generally wear people out and kill them, but my longing to know what you were doing and the force of my affection for you—this it was that was the death of me.'[1]

204 " Then I tried to find some way of embracing my poor mother's ghost. Thrice I sprang towards her and tried to clasp her in my arms, but each time she flitted from my embrace as it were a dream or phantom, and being touched to the quick I said to her, ' Mother, why do you not stay still when I would embrace you? If we could throw our arms around one another we might find sad comfort in the sharing of our sorrows even in the house of Hades; does Proserpine want to lay a still further load of grief upon me by mocking me with a phantom only? '

215 " ' My son,' she answered, ' most ill-fated of all mankind, it is not Proserpine that is beguiling you, but all people are like this when they are dead. The sinews no longer hold the flesh and bones together; these perish in the fierceness of consuming fire as soon as life has left the body, and the soul flits away as though it were a dream. Now, however, go back to the light of day as soon as you can, and note all these things that you may tell them to your wife hereafter.'

225 " Thus did we converse, and anon Proserpine sent up the ghosts of the wives and daughters of all the most famous men. They gathered in crowds about the blood, and I considered how I might question them severally. In the end I deemed that it would be best to draw the keen blade that hung by my sturdy thigh, and keep them from all drinking the blood at once. So

[1] Tradition says that she had hanged herself. *Cf.* Odyssey, xv, 355, etc.

168

they came up one after the other, and each one as I
questioned her told me her race and lineage.

" The first I saw was Tyro. She was daughter of 235
Salmoneus and wife of Cretheus the son of Aeolus.[1]
She fell in love with the river Enipeus who is much the
most beautiful river in the whole world. Once when
she was taking a walk by his side as usual, Neptune,
disguised as her lover, lay with her at the mouth of the
river, and a huge blue wave arched itself like a mountain
over them to hide both woman and god, whereon he
loosed her virgin girdle and laid her in a deep slumber.
When the god had accomplished the deed of love, he
took her hand in his own and said, ' Tyro, rejoice in all
good will; the embraces of the gods are not fruitless,
and you will have fine twins about this time twelve
months. Take great care of them. I am Neptune, so
now go home, but hold your tongue and do not tell
any one.'

" Then he dived under the sea, and she in due course 253
bore Pelias and Neleus, who both of them served Jove
with all their might. Pelias was a great breeder of sheep
and lived in Iolcus, but the other lived in Pylos. The
rest of her children were by Cretheus, namely, Aeson,
Pheres, and Amythaon, who was a mighty warrior and
charioteer.

" Next to her I saw Antiope, daughter to Asopus, 260
who could boast of having slept in the arms of even
Jove himself, and who bore him two sons Amphion
and Zethus. These founded Thebes with its seven
gates, and built a wall all round it; for strong though
they were they could not hold Thebes till they had
walled it.

" Then I saw Alcmena, the wife of Amphitryon, who 266
also bore to Jove indomitable Hercules; and Megara

[1] Not to be confounded with Aeolus, king of the winds.

who was daughter to great King Creon, and married the redoubtable son of Amphitryon.

271 "I also saw fair Epicaste mother of king Oedipodes whose awful lot it was to marry her own son without suspecting it. He married her after having killed his father, but the gods proclaimed the whole story to the world; whereon he remained king of Thebes, in great grief for the spite the gods had borne him; but Epicaste went to the house of the mighty jailor Hades, having hanged herself for grief, and the avenging spirits haunted him as for an outraged mother—to his ruing bitterly thereafter.

281 "Then I saw Chloris, whom Neleus married for her beauty, having given priceless presents for her. She was youngest daughter to Amphion son of Iasus and king of Minyan Orchomenus, and was Queen in Pylos. She bore Nestor, Chromius, and Periclymenus, and she also bore that marvellously lovely woman Pero, who was wooed by all the country round; but Neleus would only give her to him who should raid the cattle of Iphicles from the grazing grounds of Phylace, and this was a hard task. The only man who would undertake to raid them was a certain excellent seer,[1] but the will of heaven was against him, for the rangers of the cattle caught him and put him in prison; nevertheless when a full year had passed and the same season came round again, Iphicles set him at liberty, after he had expounded all the oracles of heaven. Thus, then, was the will of Jove accomplished.

298 "And I saw Leda the wife of Tyndarus, who bore him two famous sons, Castor breaker of horses, and Pollux the mighty boxer. Both these heroes are lying under the earth, though they are still alive, for by a special dispensation of Jove, they die and come to life

[1] Melampus, *vide* book xv, 225, etc.

170

again, each one of them every other day throughout all time, and they have the rank of gods.

"After her I saw Iphimedeia wife of Aloeus who ₃₀₅ boasted the embrace of Neptune. She bore two sons Otus and Ephialtes, but both were short lived. They were the finest children that were ever born in this world, and the best looking, Orion only excepted; for at nine years old they were nine fathoms high, and measured nine cubits round the chest. They threatened to make war with the gods in Olympus, and tried to set Mount Ossa on the top of Mount Olympus, and Mount Pelion on the top of Ossa, that they might scale heaven itself, and they would have done it too if they had been grown up, but Apollo, son of Leto, killed both of them, before they had got so much as a sign of hair upon their cheeks or chin.

"Then I saw Phaedra, and Procris, and fair Ariadne ₃₂₁ daughter of the magician Minos, whom Theseus was carrying off from Crete to Athens, but he did not enjoy her, for before he could do so Diana killed her in the island of Dia on account of what Bacchus had said against her.

"I also saw Maera and Clymene and hateful Eriphyle, ₃₂₆ who sold her own husband for gold. But it would take me all night if I were to name every single one of the wives and daughters of heroes whom I saw, and it is time for me to go to bed, either on board ship with my crew, or here. As for my escort, heaven and yourselves will see to it."

Here he ended, and the guests sat all of them en- ₃₃₃ thralled and speechless throughout the covered cloister. Then Arete said to them:

"What do you think of this man, O Phaeacians? Is ₃₃₆ he not tall and good looking, and is he not clever? True, he is my own guest, but you all of you share in

171

the distinction. Do not be in a hurry to send him away, nor niggardly in the presents you make to one who is in such great need, for heaven has blessed all of you with great abundance."

342   Then spoke the aged hero Echeneus who was one of the oldest men among them, " My friends," said he, " what our august queen has just said to us is both reasonable and to the purpose, therefore be persuaded by it; but the decision whether in word or deed rests ultimately with King Alcinous."

347   " The thing shall be done," exclaimed Alcinous, " as surely as I still live and reign over the Phaeacians. Our guest is indeed very anxious to get home, still we must persuade him to remain with us until to-morrow, by which time I shall be able to get together the whole sum that I mean to give him. As regards his escort it will be a matter for you all, and mine above all others as the chief person among you."

354   And Ulysses answered, " King Alcinous, if you were to bid me to stay here for a whole twelve months, and then speed me on my way, loaded with your noble gifts, I should obey you gladly and it would redound greatly to my advantage, for I should return fuller-handed to my own people, and should thus be more respected and beloved by all who see me when I get back to Ithaca."

362   " Ulysses," replied Alcinous, " not one of us who sees you has any idea that you are a charlatan or a swindler. I know there are many people going about who tell such plausible stories that it is very hard to see through them, but there is a style about your language which assures me of your good disposition. Moreover you have told the story of your own misfortunes, and those of the Argives, as though you were a practised bard; but tell me, and tell me true, whether you saw any of the mighty heroes who went to Troy at the same

172

time with yourself, and perished there. The evenings are still at their longest, and it is not yet bed time–go on, therefore, with your divine story, for I could stay here listening till to-morrow morning, so long as you will continue to tell us of your adventures."

"Alcinous," answered Ulysses, "there is a time for 377 making speeches, and a time for going to bed; nevertheless, since you so desire, I will not refrain from telling you the still sadder tale of those of my comrades who did not fall fighting with the Trojans, but perished on their return, through the treachery of a wicked woman.

"When Proserpine had dismissed the female ghosts 385 in all directions, the ghost of Agamemnon son of Atreus came sadly up to me, surrounded by those who had perished with him in the house of Aegisthus. As soon as he had tasted the blood he knew me, and weeping bitterly stretched out his arms towards me to embrace me; but he had no strength nor substance any more, and I too wept and pitied him as I beheld him. 'How did you come by your death,' said I, 'King Agamemnon? Did Neptune raise his winds and waves against you when you were at sea, or did your enemies make an end of you on the mainland when you were cattle-lifting or sheep-stealing, or while they were fighting in defence of their wives and city?'

"'Ulysses,' he answered, 'noble son of Laertes, I 404 was not lost at sea in any storm of Neptune's raising, nor did my foes despatch me upon the mainland, but Aegisthus and my wicked wife were the death of me between them. He asked me to his house, feasted me, and then butchered me most miserably as though I were a fat beast in a slaughter house, while all around me my comrades were slain like sheep or pigs for the wedding breakfast, or picnic, or gorgeous banquet of some great nobleman. You must have seen numbers of men killed

173

either in a general engagement, or in single combat, but
you never saw anything so truly pitiable as the way in
which we fell in that cloister, with the mixing-bowl and
the loaded tables lying all about, and the ground reeking
with our blood. I heard Priam's daughter Cassandra
scream as Clytemnestra killed her close beside me. I lay
dying upon the earth with the sword in my body, and
raised my hands to kill the slut of a murderess, but she
slipped away from me; she would not even close my
lips nor my eyes when I was dying, for there is nothing
in this world so cruel and so shameless as a woman when
she has fallen into such guilt as hers was. Fancy
murdering her own husband! I thought I was going
to be welcomed home by my children and my servants,
but her abominable crime has brought disgrace on
herself and all women who shall come after—even on
the good ones.'

435 "And I said, ' In truth Jove has hated the house of
Atreus from first to last in the matter of their women's
counsels. See how many of us fell for Helen's sake, and
now it seems that Clytemnestra hatched mischief against
you too during your absence.'

441 " ' Be sure, therefore,' continued Agamemnon, ' and
not be too friendly even with your own wife. Do not
tell her all that you know perfectly well yourself. Tell
her a part only, and keep your own counsel about the
rest. Not that your wife, Ulysses, is likely to murder
you, for Penelope is a very admirable woman, and has
an excellent nature. We left her a young bride with an
infant at her breast when we set out for Troy. This
child no doubt is now grown up happily to man's
estate,[1] and he and his father will have a joyful meeting

---

[1] I have already said in a note on bk. xi, 186, that at this point
of Ulysses' voyages Telemachus could only be between eleven
and twelve years old.

and embrace one another as it is right they should do,
whereas my wicked wife did not even allow me the
happiness of looking upon my son, but killed me ere
I could do so. Furthermore I say—and lay my saying
to your heart—do not tell people when you are bringing
your ship to Ithaca, but steal a march upon them, for
after all this there is no trusting women. But now tell
me, and tell me true, can you give me any news of my
son Orestes? Is he in Orchomenus, or at Pylos, or is he
at Sparta with Menelaus—for I presume that he is still
living.'

"And I said, 'Agamemnon, why do you ask me? I 462
do not know whether your son is alive or dead, and it is
not right to talk when one does not know.'

"As we two sat weeping and talking thus sadly with 465
one another the ghost of Achilles came up to us with
Patroclus, Antilochus, and Ajax who was the finest and
goodliest man of all the Danaans after the son of Peleus.
The fleet descendant of Aeacus knew me and spoke
piteously, saying, 'Ulysses, noble son of Laertes, what
deed of daring will you undertake next, that you venture
down to the house of Hades among us silly dead, who
are but the ghosts of them that can labour no more?'

"And I said, 'Achilles, son of Peleus, foremost 477
champion of the Achaeans, I came to consult Teiresias,
and see if he could advise me about my return home to
Ithaca, for I have never yet been able to get near the
Achaean land, nor to set foot in my own country, but
have been in trouble all the time. As for you, Achilles,
no one was ever yet so fortunate as you have been, nor
ever will be, for you were adored by all us Argives as
long as you were alive, and now that you are here you
are a great prince among the dead. Do not, therefore,
take it so much to heart even if you are dead.'

" 'Say not a word,' he answered, 'in death's favour; 487

175

I would rather be a paid servant in a poor man's house and be above ground than king of kings among the dead. But give me news about my son; is he gone to the wars and will he be a great soldier, or is this not so? Tell me also if you have heard anything about my father Peleus—does he still rule among the Myrmidons, or do they show him no respect throughout Hellas and Phthia now that he is old and his limbs fail him? Could I but stand by his side, in the light of day, with the same strength that I had when I killed the bravest of our foes upon the plain of Troy—could I but be as I then was and go even for a short time to my father's house, any one who tried to do him violence or supersede him would soon rue it.'

504   " ' I have heard nothing,' I answered, ' of Peleus, but I can tell you all about your son Neoptolemus, for I took him in my own ship from Scyros with the Achaeans. In our councils of war before Troy he was always first to speak, and his judgement was unerring. Nestor and I were the only two who could surpass him; and when it came to fighting on the plain of Troy, he would never remain with the body of his men, but would dash on far in front, foremost of them all in valour. Many a man did he kill in battle—I cannot name every single one of those whom he slew while fighting on the side of the Argives, but will only say how he killed that valiant hero Eurypylus son of Telephus, who was the handsomest man I ever saw except Memnon; many others also of the Ceteians fell around him by reason of a woman's bribes. Moreover, when all the bravest of the Argives went inside the horse that Epeus had made, and it was left to me to settle when we should either open the door of our ambuscade, or close it, though all the other leaders and chief men among the Danaans were drying their eyes

176

and quaking in every limb, I never once saw him turn
pale nor wipe a tear from his cheek; he was all the time
urging me to break out from the horse—grasping the
handle of his sword and his bronze-shod spear, and
breathing fury against the foe. Yet when we had
sacked the city of Priam he got his handsome share of
the prize money and went on board (such is the fortune
of war) without a wound upon him, neither from a
thrown spear nor in close combat, for the rage of Mars
is a matter of great chance.'

"When I had told him this, the ghost of Achilles 538
strode off across a meadow full of asphodel, exulting
over what I had said concerning the prowess of his son.

"The ghosts of other dead men stood near me and 541
told me each his own melancholy tale; but that of Ajax
son of Telamon alone held aloof—still angry with me
for having won the cause in our dispute about the
armour of Achilles. Thetis had offered it as a prize, but
the Trojan prisoners and Minerva were the judges.
Would that I had never gained the day in such a contest,
for it cost the life of Ajax, who was foremost of all the
Danaans after the son of Peleus, alike in stature and
prowess.

"When I saw him I tried to pacify him and said, 552
'Ajax, will you not forget and forgive even in death,
but must the judgement about that hateful armour still
rankle with you? It cost us Argives dear enough to
lose such a tower of strength as you were to us. We
mourned you as much as we mourned Achilles son of
Peleus himself, nor can the blame be laid on anything
but on the spite which Jove bore against the Danaans,
for it was this that made him counsel your destruction—
come hither, therefore, bring your proud spirit into
subjection, and hear what I can tell you.'

"He would not answer, but turned away to Erebus 563

and to the other ghosts; nevertheless, I should have made him talk to me in spite of his being so angry, or I should have gone on talking to him,[1] only that there were still others among the dead whom I desired to see.

568 "Then I saw Minos son of Jove with his golden sceptre in his hand sitting in judgement on the dead, and the ghosts were gathered sitting and standing round him in the spacious house of Hades, to learn his sentences upon them.

572 "After him I saw huge Orion in a meadow full of asphodel driving the ghosts of the wild beasts that he had killed upon the mountains, and he had a great bronze club in his hand, unbreakable for ever and ever.

576 "And I saw Tityus son of Gaia stretched upon the plain and covering some nine acres of ground. Two vultures on either side of him were digging their beaks into his liver, and he kept on trying to beat them off with his hands, but could not; for he had violated Jove's mistress Leto as she was going through Panopeus on her way to Pytho.

582 "I saw also the dreadful fate of Tantalus, who stood in a lake that reached his chin; he was dying to quench his thirst, but could never reach the water, for whenever the poor creature stooped to drink, it dried up and vanished, so that there was nothing but dry ground—parched by the spite of heaven. There were tall trees, moreover, that shed their fruit over his head—pears, pomegranates, apples, sweet figs and juicy olives, but whenever the poor creature stretched out his hand to take some, the wind tossed the branches back again to the clouds.

593 "And I saw Sisyphus at his endless task raising his prodigious stone with both his hands. With hands and feet he tried to roll it up to the top of the hill, but

[1] Is the writer a man or a woman?

178

always, just before he could roll it over on to the other side, its weight would be too much for him, and the pitiless stone[1] would come thundering down again on to the plain. Then he would begin trying to push it up hill again, and the sweat ran off him and the steam rose after him.

" After him I saw mighty Hercules, but it was his 601 phantom only, for he is feasting ever with the immortal gods, and has lovely Hebe to wife, who is daughter of Jove and Juno. The ghosts were screaming round him like scared birds flying all whithers. He looked black as night with his bare bow in his hands and his arrow on the string, glaring around as though ever on the point of taking aim. About his breast there was a wondrous golden belt adorned in the most marvellous fashion with bears, wild boars, and lions with gleaming eyes; there was also war, battle, and death. The man who made that belt, do what he might, would never be able to make another like it. Hercules knew me at once when he saw me, and spoke piteously, saying, ' My poor Ulysses, noble son of Laertes, are you too leading the same sorry kind of life that I did when I was above ground? I was son of Jove, but I went through an infinity of suffering, for I became bondsman to one who was far beneath me—a low fellow who set me all manner of labours. He once sent me here to fetch the hell-hound—for he did not think he could find anything harder for me than this, but I got the hound out of

---

[1] *Cf.* Il., iv, 521, ἀμφοτέρω δὲ τένοντε καὶ ὀστέα λᾶας ἀναιδὴς ἄχρις ἀπηλοίηςεν. The Odyssean line reads, αὖτις ἔπειτα πέδονδε κυλίνδετο λᾶας ἀναιδής. The famous dactylism, therefore, of the Odyssean line was probably suggested by that of the Iliadic rather than by a desire to accommodate sound to sense. At any rate the double coincidence of a dactylic line, and an ending λᾶας ἀναιδής, seems conclusive as to the familiarity of the writer of the Odyssey with the Iliadic line.

Hades and brought him to him, for Mercury and
Minerva helped me.'

627   " On this Hercules went down again into the house
of Hades, but I stayed where I was in case some other
of the mighty dead should come to me. And I should
have seen still other of them that are gone before, whom
I would fain have seen – Theseus and Pirithous –
glorious children of the gods, but so many thousands of
ghosts came round me and uttered such appalling cries,
that I was panic stricken lest Proserpine should send
up from the house of Hades the head of that awful
monster Gorgon. On this I hastened back to my ship
and ordered my men to go on board at once and loose
the hawsers; so they embarked and took their places,
whereon the ship went down the stream of the river
Oceanus. We had to row at first, but presently a fair
640 wind sprang up.

"AFTER WE WERE CLEAR OF THE RIVER
Oceanus, and had got out into the open sea,
we went on till we reached the Aeaean island
where there is dawn and sunrise as in other
places. We then drew our ship on to the sands and
got out of her on to the shore, where we went to sleep
and waited till day should break.

"Then, when the child of morning, rosy-fingered 8
Dawn, appeared, I sent some men to Circe's house to
fetch the body of Elpenor. We cut firewood from a
wood where the headland jutted out into the sea, and
after we had wept over him and lamented him we performed his funeral rites. When his body and armour
had been burned to ashes, we raised a cairn, set a stone
over it, and at the top of the cairn we fixed the oar that
he had been used to row with.

"While we were doing all this, Circe, who knew that 16
we had got back from the house of Hades, dressed
herself and came to us as fast as she could; and her
maid servants came with her bringing us bread, meat,
and wine. Then she stood in the midst of us and said,
'You have done a bold thing in going down alive to
the house of Hades, and you will have died twice, to
other people's once; now, then, stay here for the rest
of the day, feast your fill, and go on with your voyage
at daybreak to-morrow morning. In the meantime I
will tell Ulysses about your course, and will explain
everything to him so as to prevent your suffering from
misadventure either by land or sea.'

"We agreed to do as she had said, and feasted 28
through the livelong day to the going down of the sun,
but when the sun had set and it came on dark, the men
laid themselves down to sleep by the stern cables of the
ship. Then Circe took me by the hand and bade me be

181

seated away from the others, while she reclined by my
side and asked me all about our adventures.

37   " ' So far so good,' said she, when I had ended my
ﬆory, ' and now pay attention to what I am about to
tell you—heaven itself, indeed, will recall it to your
recolleﬅion. Firﬆ you, will come to the Sirens who
enchant all who come near them. If any one unwarily
draws in too close and hears the singing of the Sirens,
his wife and children will never welcome him home
again, for they sit in a green field and warble him to
death with the sweetness of their song. There is a great
heap of dead men's bones lying all around, with the
flesh ﬆill rotting off them. Therefore pass these Sirens
by, and ﬆop your men's ears with wax that none of them
may hear; but if you like you can liﬆen yourself, for
you may get the men to bind you as you ﬆand upright
on a cross-piece half way up the maﬆ,[1] and they muﬆ
lash the rope's ends to the maﬆ itself, that you may have
the pleasure of liﬆening. If you beg and pray the men
to unloose you, then they muﬆ bind you faﬆer.

55   " ' When your crew have taken you paﬆ these Sirens,
I cannot give you coherent direﬅions[2] as to which of

[1] Off the coaﬆ of Sicily and South Italy, in the month of May,
I have seen men faﬆened half way up a boat's maﬆ with their
feet reﬆing on a cross-piece, just large enough to support them.
From this point of vantage they spear sword-fish. When I
saw men thus employed I could hardly doubt that the writer of
the Odyssey had seen others like them, and had them in her
mind when describing the binding of Ulysses. I have therefore
with some diffidence ventured to depart from the received
translation of ιϲτοπέλη (*cf.* Alcaeus, frag. 18, where, however,
it is very hard to say what ιϲτοπέλαν means). In Sophocles'
Lexicon I find a reference to Chrysoﬆom (I, 242, A. Ed. Bene-
diﬅine, Paris, 1834-1839) for the word ιϲτοπόλη, which is probably the same as ιϲτοπέλη, but I have looked for the passage in
vain.

[2] The writer is at fault here and tries to put it off on Circe.

182

two courses you are to take; I will lay the two alternatives before you, and you must consider them for yourself. On the one hand there are some overhanging rocks against which the deep blue waves of Amphitrite beat with terrific fury; the blessed gods call these rocks the Wanderers. Here not even a bird may pass, no, not even the timid doves that bring ambrosia to Father Jove, but the sheer rock always carries off one of them, and Father Jove has to send another to make up their number; no ship that ever yet came to these rocks has got away again, but the waves and whirlwinds of fire are freighted with wreckage and with the bodies of

When Ulysses comes to take the route prescribed by Circe, he ought to pass either the Wanderers or some other difficulty of which we are not told, but he does not do so. The Planctae, or Wanderers, merge into Scylla and Charybdis, and the alternative between them and something untold merges into the alternative whether Ulysses had better choose Scylla or Charybdis. Yet from line 260 it seems we are to consider the Wanderers as having been passed by Ulysses ; this appears even more plainly from xxiii, 327, in which Ulysses expressly mentions the Wandering rocks as having been between the Sirens and Scylla and Charybdis. The writer, however, is evidently aware that she does not quite understand her own story; her difficulty was perhaps due to the fact that though Trapanese sailors had given her a fair idea as to where all her other localities really were, no one in those days more than in our own could localize the Planctae, which in fact, as Buttmann has argued, were derived not from any particular spot, but from sailors' tales about the difficulties of navigating the group of the Aeolian islands as a whole (see note on Od., x, 3). Still, the matter of the poor doves caught her fancy, so she would not forgo them. The whirlwind of fire and smoke that hangs on Scylla suggests allusion to Stromboli and perhaps even Etna. Scylla is on the Italian side, and therefore may be said to look West. It is about eight miles thence to the Sicilian coast, so Ulysses may be perfectly well told that after passing Scylla he will come to the Thrinacian island or Sicily. Charybdis is transposed to a site some few miles to the north of its actual position.

183

dead men. The only vessel that ever sailed and got
through, was the famous Argo on her way from the
house of Aeetes, and she too would have gone againSt
these great rocks, only that Juno piloted her paSt them
for the love she bore to Jason.

73   " ' Of these two rocks the one reaches heaven and its
peak is loSt in a dark cloud. This never leaves it, so
that the top is never clear not even in summer and early
autumn. No man though he had twenty hands and
twenty feet could get a foothold on it and climb it, for
it runs sheer up, as smooth as though it had been
polished. In the middle of it there is a large cavern,
looking WeSt and turned towards Erebus; you muSt
take your ship this way, but the cave is so high up that
not even the StouteSt archer could send an arrow into it.
Inside it Scylla sits and yelps with a voice that you
might take to be that of a young hound, but in truth
she is a dreadful monSter and no one—not even a god—
could face her without being terror-Struck. She has
twelve mis-shapen feet, and six necks of the moSt
prodigious length; and at the end of each neck she has
a frightful head with three rows of teeth in each, all set
very close together, so that they would crunch any one
to death in a moment, and she sits deep within her shady
cell thruSting out her heads and peering all round the
rock, fishing for dolphins or dogfish or any larger
monSter that she can catch, of the thousands with which
Amphitrite teems. No ship ever yet got paSt her without losing some men, for she shoots out all her heads
at once, and carries off a man in each mouth.

101   " ' You will find the other rock lie lower, but they
are so close together that there is not more than a bow-
shot between them. [A large fig tree in full leaf¹ grows

¹ I suppose this line to have been intercalated by the author
when lines 426–446 were added.

184

upon it], and under it lies the sucking whirlpool of
Charybdis. Three times in the day does she vomit
forth her waters, and three times she sucks them down
again; see that you be not there when she is sucking,
for if you are, Neptune himself could not save you; you
must hug the Scylla side and drive your ship by as fast
as you can, for you had better lose six men than your
whole crew.'

" ' Is there no way,' said I, ' of escaping Charybdis, 111
and at the same time keeping Scylla off when she is
trying to harm my men? '

" ' You dare-devil,' replied the goddess, ' you are 115
always wanting to fight somebody or something; you
will not let yourself be beaten even by the immortals.
For Scylla is not mortal; moreover she is savage,
extreme, rude, cruel and invincible. There is no help
for it; your best chance will be to get by her as fast
as ever you can, for if you dawdle about her rock while
you are putting on your armour, she may catch you
with a second cast of her six heads, and snap up another
half dozen of your men; so drive your ship past her at
full speed, and roar out lustily to Crataiis who is Scylla's
dam, bad luck to her; she will then stop her from
making a second raid upon you.

" ' You will now come to the Thrinacian island, and 127
here you will see many herds of cattle and flocks of
sheep belonging to the sun-god—seven herds of cattle
and seven flocks of sheep, with fifty head in each flock.
They do not breed, nor do they become fewer in number, and they are tended by the goddesses Phaethusa
and Lampetie, who are children of the sun-god Hyperion
by Neaera. Their mother when she had borne them
and had done suckling them sent them to the Thrinacian
island, which was a long way off, to live there and look
after their father's flocks and herds. If you leave these

185

flocks unharmed, and think of nothing but getting home, you may yet after much hardship reach Ithaca; but if you harm them, then I forewarn you of the destruction both of your ship and of your comrades; and even though you may yourself escape, you will return late, in bad plight, after losing all your men.'

142 " Here she ended, and dawn enthroned in gold began to show in heaven, whereon she returned inland. I then went on board and told my men to loose the ship from her moorings; so they at once got into her, took their places, and began to smite the grey sea with their oars. Presently the great and cunning goddess Circe befriended us with a fair wind that blew dead aft, and stayed steadily with us, keeping our sails well filled, so we did whatever wanted doing to the ship's gear, and let her go as wind and helmsman headed her.

153 " Then, being much troubled in mind, I said to my men, ' My friends, it is not right that one or two of us alone should know the prophecies that Circe has made me, I will therefore tell you about them, so that whether we live or die we may do so with our eyes open. First she said we were to keep clear of the Sirens, who sit and sing most beautifully in a field of flowers; but she said I might hear them myself so long as no one else did. Therefore, take me and bind me to the crosspiece half way up the mast; bind me as I stand upright, with a bond so fast that I cannot possibly break away, and lash the rope's ends to the mast itself. If I beg and pray you to set me free, then bind me more tightly still.'

165 " I had hardly finished telling everything to the men before we reached the island of the two Sirens,[1] for the

---

[1] For the reasons which enable us to identify the island of the two Sirens with the Lipari island, now Salinas—the ancient Didyme, or " twin " island—see *The Authoress of the Odyssey*, pp. 205, 206. The two Sirens doubtless were, as their name

wind had been very favourable. Then all of a sudden
it fell dead calm; there was not a breath of wind nor a
ripple upon the water, so the men furled the sails and
stowed them; then taking to their oars they whitened
the water with the foam they raised in rowing. Meanwhile I look a large wheel of wax and cut it up small
with my sword. Then I kneaded the wax in my strong
hands till it became soft, which it soon did between the
kneading and the rays of the sun-god son of Hyperion.
Then I stopped the ears of all my men, and they bound
me hands and feet to the mast as I stood upright on the
cross-piece; but they went on rowing themselves.
When we had got within earshot of the land, and the
ship was going at a good rate, the Sirens saw that we
were getting in shore and began with their singing.

" ' Come here,' they sang, ' renowned Ulysses, 184
honour to the Achaean name, and listen to our two
voices. No one ever sailed past us without staying to
hear the enchanting sweetness of our song—and he who
listens will go on his way not only charmed, but wiser,
for we know all the ills that the gods laid upon the
Argives and Trojans before Troy, and can tell you
everything that is going to happen over the whole
world.'

" They sang these words most musically, and as I 192
longed to hear them further I made signs by frowning
to my men that they should set me free; but they
quickened their stroke, and Eurylochus and Perimedes
bound me with still stronger bonds till we had got out
of hearing of the Sirens' voices. Then my men took
the wax from their ears and unbound me.

suggests, the whistling gusts, or avalanches of air that at
times descend without a moment's warning from the two lofty
mountains of Salinas—as also from all high points in the
neighbourhood.

201 " Immediately after we had got past the island I saw
a great wave from which spray was rising, and I heard
a loud roaring sound. The men were so frightened
that they loosed hold of their oars, for the whole sea
resounded with the rushing of the waters,[1] but the ship
stayed where it was, for the men had left off rowing.
I went round, therefore, and exhorted them man by
man not to lose heart.

208 " ' My friends,' said I, ' this is not the first time that
we have been in danger, and we are in nothing like so
bad a case as when the Cyclops shut us up in his cave;
nevertheless, my courage and wise counsel saved us
then, and we shall live to look back on all this as well.
Now, therefore, let us all do as I say, trust in Jove and
row on with might and main. As for you, coxswain,
these are your orders; attend to them, for the ship is
in your hands; turn her head away from these steaming
rapids and hug the rock, or she will give you the slip
and be over.yonder before you know where you are,
and you will be the death of us.'

222 " So they did as I told them; but I said nothing
about the awful monster Scylla, for I knew the men
would not go on rowing if I did, but would huddle
together in the hold. In one thing only did I disobey
Circe's strict instructions – I put on my armour. Then
seizing two strong spears I took my stand on the ship's
bows, for it was there that I expected first to see the
monster of the rock, who was to do my men so much
harm; but I could not make her out anywhere, though
I strained my eyes with looking the gloomy rock all
over and over.

234 " Then we entered the Straits in great fear of mind,
for on the one hand was Scylla, and on the other dread

[1] See Admiral Smyth on the currents in the Straits of Messina,
quoted in *The Authoress of the Odyssey*, p. 207.

Charybdis kept sucking up the salt water. As she vomited it up, it was like the water in a cauldron when it is boiling over upon a great fire, and the spray reached the top of the rocks on either side. When she began to suck again, we could see the water all inside whirling round and round, and it made a deafening sound as it broke against the rocks. We could see the bottom of the whirlpool all black with sand and mud, and the men were at their wits ends for fear. While we were taken up with this, and were expecting each moment to be our last, Scylla pounced down suddenly upon us and snatched up my six best men. I was looking at once after both ship and men, and in a moment I saw their hands and feet ever so high above me, struggling in the air as Scylla was carrying them off, and I heard them call out my name in one last despairing cry. As a fisherman, seated, spear in hand, upon some jutting rock [1] throws bait into the water to deceive the poor little fishes, and spears them with the ox's horn with which his spear is shod, throwing them gasping on to the land as he catches them one by one— even so did Scylla land these panting creatures on her rock and munch them up at the mouth of her den, while they screamed and stretched out their hands to me in their mortal agony. This was the most sickening sight that I saw throughout all my voyages.

" When we had passed the [Wandering] rocks, with ₂₆₀ Scylla and terrible Charybdis, we reached the noble island of the sun-god, where were the goodly cattle and sheep belonging to the sun Hyperion. While still at sea in my ship I could hear the cattle lowing as they came

---

[1] In the islands of Favognana and Marettimo off Trapani I have seen men fish exactly as here described. They chew bread into a paste and throw it into the sea to attract the fish, which they then spear. No line is used.

home to the yards, and the sheep bleating. Then I remembered what the blind Theban prophet Teiresias had told me, and how carefully Aeaean Circe had warned me to shun the island of the blessed sun-god. So being much troubled I said to the men, 'My men, I know you are hard pressed, but listen while I tell you the prophecy that Teiresias made me, and how carefully Aeaean Circe warned me to shun the island of the blessed sun-god, for it was here, she said, that our worst danger would lie. Head the ship, therefore, away from the island.'

277 " The men were in despair at this, and Eurylochus at once gave me an insolent answer. ' Ulysses,' said he, ' you are cruel; you are very strong yourself and never get worn out; you seem to be made of iron, and now, though your men are exhausted with toil and want of sleep, you will not let them land and cook themselves a good supper upon this island, but bid them put out to sea and go faring fruitlessly on through the watches of the flying night. It is by night that the winds blow hardest and do so much damage; how can we escape should one of those sudden squalls spring up from South West or West, which so often wreck a vessel when our lords the gods are unpropitious? Now, therefore, let us obey the behests of night and prepare our supper here hard by the ship; to-morrow morning we will go on board again and put out to sea.'

294 " Thus spoke Eurylochus, and the men approved his words. I saw that heaven meant us a mischief and said, ' You force me to yield, for you are many against one, but at any rate each one of you must take his solemn oath that if he meet with a herd of cattle or a large flock of sheep, he will not be so mad as to kill a single head of either, but will be satisfied with the food that Circe has given us.'

" They all swore as I bade them, and when they had 303
completed their oath we made the ship fast in a harbour
that was near a stream of fresh water, and the men went
ashore and cooked their suppers. As soon as they had
had enough to eat and drink, they began talking about
their poor comrades whom Scylla had snatched up and
eaten; this set them weeping, and they went on crying
till they fell off into a sound sleep.

" In the third watch of the night when the stars had 312
shifted their places, Jove raised a great gale of wind that
blew a hurricane so that land and sea were covered with
thick clouds, and night sprang forth out of the heavens.
When the child of morning, rosy-fingered Dawn,
appeared, we brought the ship to land and drew her
into a cave wherein the sea-nymphs hold their courts
and dances, and I called the men together in council.

" ' My friends,' said I, ' we have meat and drink in 320
the ship, let us mind, therefore, and not touch the cattle,
or we shall suffer for it; for these cattle and sheep
belong to the mighty sun, who sees and gives ear to
everything.' And again they promised that they would
obey.

" For a whole month the wind blew steadily from the 325
South, and there was no other wind, but only South and
East.¹ As long as corn and wine held out the men did
not touch the cattle when they were hungry; when,
however, they had eaten all there was in the ship, they
were forced to go further afield, fishing with hook and
line, catching birds, and taking whatever they could lay
their hands on; for they were starving. One day,
therefore, I went up inland that I might pray heaven to
show me some means of getting away. When I had

¹ The writer evidently regards Ulysses as on a coast that looked
East at no great distance south of the Straits of Messina somewhere, say, near Tauromenium, now Taormina.

gone far enough to be clear of all my men, and had
found a place that was well sheltered from the wind, I
washed my hands and prayed to all the gods in Olympus
till by and by they sent me off into a sweet sleep.

339 "Meanwhile Eurylochus had been giving evil
counsel to the men, 'Listen to me,' said he, 'my poor
comrades. All deaths are bad enough, but there is none
so bad as famine. Why should not we drive in the best
of these cows and offer them in sacrifice to the immortal
gods? If we ever get back to Ithaca, we can build a fine
temple to the sun-god and enrich it with every kind of
ornament; if, however, he is determined to sink our
ship out of revenge for these horned cattle, and the
other gods are of the same mind, I for one would rather
drink salt water once for all and have done with it, than
be starved to death by inches in such a desert island as
this is.'

352 "Thus spoke Eurylochus, and the men approved his
words. Now the cattle, so fair and goodly, were
feeding not far from the ship; the men, therefore, drove
in the best of them, and they all stood round them saying
their prayers, and using young oak-shoots instead of
barley-meal, for there was no barley left. When they
had done praying they killed the cows and dressed their
carcasses; they cut out the thigh bones, wrapped them
round in two layers of fat, and set some pieces of raw
meat on the top of them. They had no wine with
which to make drink-offerings over the sacrifice while
it was cooking, so they kept pouring on a little water
from time to time while the inward meats were being
grilled; then, when the thigh bones were burned and
they had tasted the inward meats, they cut the rest up
small and put the pieces upon the spits.

366 "By this time my deep sleep had left me, and I
turned back to the ship and to the sea shore. As I drew

near I began to smell hot roaſt meat, so I groaned out a prayer to the immortal gods. 'Father Jove,' I exclaimed, ' and all you other gods who live in everlasting bliss, you have done me a cruel mischief by the sleep into which you have sent me; see what fine work these men of mine have been making in my absence.'

" Meanwhile Lampetie went ſtraight off to the sun 374 and told him we had been killing his cows, whereon he flew into a great rage, and said to the immortals, ' Father Jove, and all you other gods who live in everlasting bliss, I muſt have vengeance on the crew of Ulysses' ship: they have had the insolence to kill my cows, which were the one thing I loved to look upon, whether I was going up heaven or down again. If they do not square accounts with me about my cows, I will go down to Hades and shine there among the dead.'

" ' Sun,' said Jove, ' go on shining upon us gods and 384 upon mankind over the fruitful earth. I will shiver their ship into little pieces with a bolt of white lightning as soon as they get out to sea.'

" I was told all this by Calypso, who said she had 389 heard it from the mouth of Mercury.

" As soon as I got down to my ship and to the sea 391 shore I rebuked each one of the men separately, but we could see no way out of it, for the cows were dead already. And indeed the gods began at once to show signs and wonders among us, for the hides of the cattle crawled about, and the joints upon the spits began to low like cows, and the meat, whether cooked or raw, kept on making a noise juſt as cows do.

" For six days my men kept driving in the beſt cows 397 and feaſting upon them, but when Jove the son of Saturn had added a seventh day, the fury of the gale abated; we therefore went on board, raised our maſts, spread sail, and put out to sea. As soon as we were well

away from the island, and could see nothing but sky and
sea, the son of Saturn raised a black cloud over our
ship, and the sea grew dark beneath it. We did not
get on much further, for in another moment we were
caught by a terrific squall from the West that snapped
the forestays of the mast so that it fell aft, while all the
ship's gear tumbled about at the bottom of the vessel.
The mast fell upon the head of the helmsman in the
ship's stern, so that the bones of his head were crushed
to pieces, and he fell overboard as though he were
diving, with no more life left in him.

415 "Then Jove let fly with his thunderbolts, and the
ship went round and round, and was filled with fire and
brimstone as the lightning struck it. The men all fell
into the sea; they were carried about in the water
round the ship, looking like so many sea-gulls, but the
god presently deprived them of all chance of getting
home again.

420 "I stuck to the ship till the sea knocked her sides
from her keel (which drifted about by itself) and struck
the mast out of her in the direction of the keel; but
there was a backstay of stout ox-thong still hanging
about it, and with this I lashed the mast and keel
together, and getting astride of them was carried wherever the winds chose to take me.

426 "[The gale from the West had now spent its force,
and the wind got into the South again, which frightened
me lest I should be taken back to the terrible whirlpool
of Charybdis. This indeed was what actually happened,
for I was borne along by the waves all night, and by
sunrise had reached the rock of Scylla, and the whirlpool. She was then sucking down the salt sea water,[1]

[1] Surely there must be a line missing here to tell us that the
keel and mast were carried down into Charybdis. Besides, the
aorist ἀνερροίβδησε in its present surrounding is perplexing. I

194

but I was carried aloft toward the fig tree, which I caught hold of and clung on to like a bat. I could not plant my feet anywhere so as to stand securely, for the roots were a long way off and the boughs that overshadowed the whole pool were too high, too vast, and too far apart for me to reach them; so I hung patiently on, waiting till the pool should discharge my mast and raft again—and a very long while it seemed. A juryman is not more glad to get home to supper, after having been long detained in court by troublesome cases, than I was to see my raft beginning to work its way out of the whirlpool again. At last I let go with my hands and feet, and fell heavily into the sea, hard by my raft on to which I then got, and began to row with my hands. As for Scylla, the father of gods and men would not let her get further sight of me—otherwise I should have certainly been lost.] [1]

" Hence I was carried along for nine days till on the tenth night the gods stranded me on the Ogygian island, where dwells the great and powerful goddess Calypso. She took me in and was kind to me, but I need say no more about this, for I told you and your noble wife all about it yesterday, and I hate saying the same thing over and over again."   453

have translated it as though it were an imperfect ; I see Messrs. Butcher and Lang translate it as a pluperfect, but surely Charybdis was in the act of sucking down the water when Ulysses arrived.

[1] I suppose the passage within brackets to have been an afterthought but to have been written by the same hand as the rest of the poem. I suppose xii, 103, to have been also added by the writer when she decided on sending Ulysses back to Charybdis. The simile suggests the hand of the wife or daughter of a magistrate who had often seen her father come in cross and tired.

THUS DID HE SPEAK, AND THEY ALL
held their peace throughout the covered cloister,
enthralled by the charm of his story, till presently
Alcinous began to speak.

3 " Ulysses," said he, " now that you have reached my
house I doubt not you will get home without further
misadventure no matter how much you have suffered in
the past. To you others, however, who come here
night after night to drink my choicest wine and listen
to my bard, I would insist as follows. Our guest has
already packed up the clothes, wrought gold,[1] and other
valuables which you have brought for his acceptance;
let us now, therefore, present him further, each one of
us, with a large tripod and a cauldron. We will recoup
ourselves by the levy of a general rate; for private
individuals cannot be expected to bear the burden of
such a handsome present."

16 Every one approved of this, and then they went
home to bed each in his own abode. When the child of
morning, rosy-fingered Dawn, appeared, they hurried
down to the ship and brought their cauldrons with
them. Alcinous went on board and saw everything so
securely stowed under the ship's benches that nothing
could break adrift and injure the rowers. Then they
went to the house of Alcinous to get dinner, and he
sacrificed a bull for them in honour of Jove who is the
lord of all. They set the steaks to grill and made an
excellent dinner, after which the inspired bard, Demodocus, who was a favourite with every one, sang to
them; but Ulysses kept on turning his eyes towards the
sun, as though to hasten his setting, for he was longing

---

[1] Gr. πολγλαίΔαλος. This puts coined money out of the question, but nevertheless implies that the gold had been worked into
ornaments of some kind.

to be on his way. As one who has been all day ploughing a fallow field with a couple of oxen keeps thinking
about his supper and is glad when night comes that he
may go and get it, for it is all his legs can do to carry
him, even so did Ulysses rejoice when the sun went
down, and he at once said to the Phaeacians, addressing
himself more particularly to King Alcinous:

"Sir, and all of you, farewell. Make your drink- 38
offerings and send me on my way rejoicing, for you
have fulfilled my heart's desire by giving me an escort,
and making me presents, which heaven grant that I may
turn to good account; may I find my admirable wife
living in peace among friends,[1] and may you whom I
leave behind me give satisfaction to your wives and
children;[2] may heaven vouchsafe you every good grace,
and may no evil thing come among your people."

Thus did he speak. His hearers all of them approved 47
his saying and agreed that he should have his escort
inasmuch as he had spoken reasonably. Alcinous
therefore said to his servant, "Pontonous, mix some
wine and hand it round to everybody, that we may
offer a prayer to father Jove, and speed our guest upon
his way."

Pontonous mixed the wine and handed it to every one 53
in turn; the others each from his own seat made a
drink-offering to the blessed gods that live in heaven,
but Ulysses rose and placed the double cup in the hands
of queen Arete.

---

[1] I suppose Teiresias' prophecy of bk. xi, 114-120, had made no
impression on Ulysses. More probably the prophecy was an
afterthought, intercalated, as I have already said, by the authoress
when she changed her scheme.

[2] A male writer would have made Ulysses say, not "may you
give satisfaction to your wives," but "may your wives give
satisfaction to you."

59 " Farewell, queen," said he, " henceforward and for ever, till age and death, the common lot of mankind, lay their hands upon you. I now take my leave; be happy in this house with your children, your people, and with king Alcinous."

63 As he spoke he crossed the threshold, and Alcinous sent a man to conduct him to his ship and to the sea shore. Arete also sent some maid servants with him— one with a clean shirt and cloak, another to carry his strong-box, and a third with corn and wine. When they got to the water side the crew took these things and put them on board, with all the meat and drink; but for Ulysses they spread a rug and a linen sheet on deck that he might sleep soundly in the stern of the ship. Then he too went on board and lay down without a word, but the crew took every man his place and loosed the hawser from the pierced stone to which it had been bound. Thereon, when they began rowing out to sea, Ulysses fell into a deep, sweet, and almost deathlike slumber.[1]

81 The ship bounded forward on her way as a four in hand chariot flies over the course when the horses feel the whip. Her prow curveted as it were the neck of a stallion, and a great wave of dark blue water seethed in her wake. She held steadily on her course, and even a falcon, swiftest of all birds, could not have kept pace with her. Thus, then, she cut her way through the water, carrying one who was as cunning as the gods, but who was now sleeping peacefully, forgetful of all that he had suffered both on the field of battle and by the waves of the weary sea.

93 When the bright star that heralds the approach of dawn began to show, the ship drew near to land.[2] Now

[1] See note on vii, 318.
[2] The land was in reality the shallow inlet, now the salt works of S. Cusumano–the neighbourhood of Trapani and Mt. Eryx

there is in Ithaca a haven of the old merman Phorcys, which lies between two points that break the line of the sea and shut the harbour in. These shelter it from the storms of wind and sea that rage outside, so that, when once within it, a ship may lie without being even moored. At the head of this harbour there is a large olive tree, and at no great distance a fine overarching cavern sacred to the nymphs who are called Naiads.[1] There are mixing-bowls within it and wine-jars of stone, and the bees hive there. Moreover, there are great looms of stone on which the nymphs weave their robes of sea purple—very curious to see—and at all times there is water within it. It has two entrances, one facing North by which mortals can go down into the cave, while the other comes from the South and is more mysterious; mortals cannot possibly get in by it, it is the way taken by the gods.

Into this harbour, then, they took their ship, for they 113 knew the place.[2] She had so much way upon her that she ran half her own length on to the shore;[3] when, however, they had landed, the first thing they did was to lift Ulysses with his rug and linen sheet out of the ship, and lay him down upon the sand still fast asleep. Then

being made to do double duty, both as Scheria and Ithaca. Hence the necessity for making Ulysses set out after dark, fall instantly into a profound sleep, and wake up on a morning so foggy that he could not see anything till the interviews between Neptune and Jove and between Ulysses and Minerva should have given the audience time to accept the situation. See illustrations and map near the end of bks. v and vi respectively.

[1] This cave, which is identifiable with singular completeness, is now called the "grotta del toro," probably a corruption of "tesoro," for it is held to contain a treasure. See *The Authoress of the Odyssey*, pp. 175-178.

[2] Probably they would.

[3] Then it had a shallow shelving bottom.

they took out the presents which Minerva had persuaded the Phaeacians to give him when he was setting out on his voyage homewards. They put these all together by the root of the olive tree, away from the road, for fear some passer by[1] might come and steal them before Ulysses awoke; and then they made the best of their way home again.

125 But Neptune did not forget the threats with which he had already threatened Ulysses, so he took counsel with Jove. "Father Jove," said he, " I shall no longer be held in any sort of respect among you gods, if mortals like the Phaeacians, who are my own flesh and blood, show such small regard for me. I said I would let Ulysses get home when he had suffered sufficiently. I did not say that he should never get home at all, for I knew you had already nodded your head about it, and promised that he should do so; but now they have brought him in a ship fast asleep and have landed him in Ithaca after loading him with more magnificent presents of bronze, gold, and raiment than he would ever have brought back from Troy, if he had had his share of the spoil and got home without misadventure."

139 And Jove answered, "What, O Lord of the Earthquake, are you talking about? The gods are by no means wanting in respect for you. It would be monstrous were they to insult one so old and honoured as you are. As regards mortals, however, if any of them is indulging in insolence and treating you disrespectfully, it will always rest with yourself to deal with him as you may think proper, so do just as you please."

146 " I should have done so at once," replied Neptune,

---

[1] Doubtless the road would pass the harbour in Odyssean times as it passes the salt works now ; indeed, if there is to be a road at all there is no other level ground which it could take. See map above referred to.

" if I were not anxious to avoid anything that might displease you; now, therefore, I should like to wreck the Phaeacian ship as it is returning from its escort. This will stop them from escorting people in future; and I should also like to bury their city under a huge mountain."

" My good friend," answered Jove, " I should 153 recommend you at the very moment when the people from the city are watching the ship on her way, to turn it into a rock near the land and looking like a ship. This will astonish everybody, and you can then bury their city under the mountain."

When earth-encircling Neptune heard this he went 159 to Scheria where the Phaeacians live, and stayed there till the ship, which was making rapid way, had got close in. Then he went up to it, turned it into stone, and drove it down with the flat of his hand so as to root it in the ground. After this he went away.

The Phaeacians then began talking among themselves, 165 and one would turn towards his neighbour, saying, " Bless my heart, who is it that can have rooted the ship in the sea just as she was getting into port? We could see the whole of her only a moment ago."

This was how they talked, but they knew nothing 170 about it; and Alcinous said, " I remember now the old prophecy of my father. He said that Neptune would be angry with us for taking every one so safely over the sea, and would one day wreck a Phaeacian ship as it was returning from an escort, and bury our city under a high mountain. This was what my old father used to say, and now it is all coming true.[1] Now therefore let us all

[1] The rock at the end of the Northern harbour of Trapani, to which I suppose the writer of the Odyssey to be here referring, still bears the name Malconsiglio–" the rock of evil counsel." There is a legend that it was a ship of Turkish pirates who were

do as I say; in the first place we must leave off giving
people escorts when they come here, and in the next let
us sacrifice twelve picked bulls to Neptune that he may
have mercy upon us, and not bury our city under the
high mountain." When the people heard this they
were afraid and got ready the bulls.

185   Thus did the chiefs and rulers of the Phaeacians pray
to king Neptune, standing round his altar; and at the
same time [1] Ulysses woke up once more upon his own
soil. He had been so long away that he did not know it
again; moreover, Jove's daughter Minerva had made
it a foggy day, so that people might not know of his
having come, and that she might tell him everything
without either his wife or his fellow citizens and friends
recognizing him [2] until he had taken his revenge upon
the wicked suitors. Everything, therefore, seemed
quite different to him—the long straight tracks, the
harbours, the precipices, and the goodly trees, appeared
all changed as he started up and looked upon his native
land. So he smote his thighs with the flat of his hands
and cried aloud despairingly.

200   " Alas," he exclaimed, " among what manner of

intending to attack Trapani, but the " Madonna di Trapani "
crushed them under this rock just as they were coming into port.
My friend Cavaliere Giannitrapani of Trapani told me that his
father used to tell him when he was a boy that if he would drop
exactly three drops of oil on to the water near the rock, he would
see the ship still at the bottom. The legend is evidently a
Christianized version of the Odyssean story, while the name
supplies the additional detail that the disaster happened in
consequence of an evil counsel.

[1] It would seem then that the ship had got all the way back
from Ithaca in about a quarter of an hour.

[2] And may we not add " and also to prevent his recognizing
that he was only in the place where he had met Nausicaa two days
earlier."

people am I fallen? Are they savage and uncivilized
or hospitable and humane? Where shall I put all this
treasure, and which way shall I go? I wish I had ſtayed
over there with the Phaeacians; or I could have gone
to some other great chief who would have been good to
me and given me an escort. As it is I do not know
where to put my treasure, and I cannot leave it here for
fear somebody else should get hold of it. In good truth
the chiefs and rulers of the Phaeacians have not been
dealing fairly by me, and have left me in the wrong
country; they said they would take me back to Ithaca
and they have not done so: may Jove the protector of
suppliants chaſtise them, for he watches over everybody
and punishes those who do wrong. Still, I suppose I
muſt count my goods and see if the crew have gone off
with any of them."

He counted his goodly coppers and cauldrons, his 217
gold and all his clothes, but there was nothing missing;
ſtill he kept grieving about not being in his own
country, and wandered up and down by the shore of the
sounding sea bewailing his hard fate. Then Minerva
came up to him disguised as a young shepherd of
delicate and princely mien, with a good cloak folded
double about her shoulders; she had sandals on her
comely feet and held a javelin in her hand. Ulysses was
glad when he saw her, and went ſtraight up to her.

"My friend," said he, "you are the firſt person 228
whom I have met with in this country; I salute you,
therefore, and beg you to be well disposed towards me.
Protect these my goods, and myself too, for I embrace
your knees and pray to you as though you were a god.
Tell me, then, and tell me truly, what land and country
is this? Who are its inhabitants? Am I on an island,
or is this the sea board of some continent?"

Minerva answered, "Stranger, you muſt be very 236

simple, or mu&t have come from somewhere a long way
off, not to know what country this is. It is a very
celebrated place, and everybody knows it both Ea&t and
We&t. It is rugged and not a good driving country, but
it is by no means a bad island for what there is of it. It
grows any quantity of corn and also wine, for it is
watered both by rain and dew; it breeds cattle also and
goats; all kinds of timber grow here, and there are
watering places where the water never runs dry; so, sir,
the name of Ithaca is known even as far as Troy, which
I under&tand to be a long way off from this Achaean
country."

250   Ulysses was glad at finding himself, as Minerva told
him, in his own country, and he began to answer, but
he did not speak the truth, and made up a lying &tory
in the in&tin&tive wiliness of his heart.

256   " I heard of Ithaca," said he, " when I was in Crete
beyond the seas, and now it seems I have reached it with
all these treasures. I have left as much more behind me
for my children, but am flying because I killed Orsilochus
son of Idomeneus, the fleete&t runner in Crete. I killed
him because he wanted to rob me of the spoils I had got
from Troy with so much trouble and danger both on
the field of battle and by the waves of the weary sea;
he said I had not served his father loyally at Troy as
vassal, but had set myself up as an independent ruler,
so I lay in wait for him with one of my followers by the
road side, and speared him as he was coming into town
from the country. It was a very dark night and nobody
saw us; it was not known, therefore, that I had killed
him, but as soon as I had done so I went to a ship and
besought the owners, who were Phoenicians, to take
me on board and set me in Pylos or in Elis where the
Epeans rule, giving them as much spoil as satisfied them.
They meant no guile, but the wind drove them off their

204

course, and we sailed on till we came hither by night.
It was all we could do to get inside the harbour, and
none of us said a word about supper though we wanted
it badly, but we all went on shore and lay down just as
we were. I was very tired and fell asleep directly, so
they took my goods out of the ship, and placed them
beside me where I was lying upon the sand. Then they
sailed away to Sidonia, and I was left here in great
distress of mind."

Such was his story, but Minerva smiled and caressed ₂₈₇
him with her hand. Then she took the form of a
woman, fair, stately, and wise, " He must be indeed a
shifty lying fellow," said she, " who could surpass you
in all manner of craft even though you had a god for
your antagonist. Dare-devil that you are, full of guile,
unwearying in deceit, can you not drop your tricks and
your instinctive falsehood, even now that you are in
your own country again? We will say no more, however, about this, for we can both of us deceive upon
occasion—you are the most accomplished counsellor
and orator among all mankind, while I for diplomacy
and subtlety have no equal among the gods. Did you
not know Jove's daughter Minerva—me, who have
been ever with you, who kept watch over you in all
your troubles, and who made the Phaeacians take so
great a liking to you? And now, again, I am come here
to talk things over with you, and help you to hide the
treasure I made the Phaeacians give you; I want to tell
you about the troubles that await you in your own house;
you have got to face them, but tell no one, neither man
nor woman, that you have come home again. Bear
everything, and put up with every man's insolence,
without a word."

And Ulysses answered, " A man, goddess, may know ₃₁₁
a great deal, but you are so constantly changing your

205

appearance that when he meets you it is a hard matter for him to know whether it is you or not. This much, however, I know exceedingly well; you were very kind to me as long as we Achaeans were fighting before Troy, but from the day on which we went on board ship after having sacked the city of Priam, and heaven dispersed us—from that day, Minerva, I saw no more of you, and cannot ever remember your coming to my ship to help me in a difficulty; I had to wander on sick and sorry till the gods delivered me from evil and I reached the city of the Phaeacians, where you encouraged me and took me into the town.[1] And now, I beseech you in your father's name, tell me the truth, for I do not believe I am really back in Ithaca. I am in some other country and you are mocking me and deceiving me in all you have been saying. Tell me then truly, have I really got back to my own country? "

329 " You are always taking something of that sort into your head," replied Minerva, " and that is why I cannot desert you in your afflictions; you are so plausible, shrewd, and shifty. Any one but yourself on returning from so long a voyage would at once have gone home to see his wife and children, but you do not seem to care about asking after them or hearing any news about them till you have exploited your wife, who remains at home vainly grieving for you, and having no peace night or day for the tears she sheds on your behalf. As for my not coming near you, I was never uneasy about you, for I was certain you would get back safely though you would lose all your men, and I did not wish to quarrel with my uncle Neptune, who never forgave you for

---

[1] All this is to excuse the entire absence of Minerva from books ix-xii, which I suppose had been written already, before the authoress had determined on making Minerva so prominent a character.

having blinded his son.[1] I will now, however, point
out to you the lie of the land, and you will then perhaps
believe me. This is the haven of the old merman
Phorcys, and here is the olive tree that grows at the
head of it; [near it is the cave sacred to the Naiads;] [2]
here too is the overarching cavern in which you have
offered many an acceptable hecatomb to the nymphs,
and this is the wooded mountain Neritum."

As she spoke the goddess dispersed the mist and the 352
land appeared. Then Ulysses rejoiced at finding himself again in his own land, and kissed the bounteous
soil; he lifted up his hands and prayed to the nymphs,
saying, " Naiad nymphs, daughters of Jove, I made sure
that I was never again to see you, now therefore I greet
you with all loving salutations, and I will bring you
offerings as in the old days, if Jove's redoubtable
daughter will grant me life, and bring my son to manhood."

" Take heart, and do not trouble yourself about that," 362
rejoined Minerva, " let us rather set about stowing your
things at once in the cave, where they will be quite safe.
Let us see how we can best manage it all."

Therewith she went down into the cave to look for 366

[1] We have met with this somewhat lame attempt to cover the
writer's change of scheme at the end of bk. vi.

[2] I take the following from *The Authoress of the Odyssey*,
pp. 175, 176: " It is clear from the text that there were two [caves]
not one, but some one has enclosed in brackets the two lines in
which the second cave is mentioned, I presume because he found
himself puzzled by having a second cave sprung upon him
when up to this point he had only been told of one.

" I venture to think that if he had known the ground he would
not have been puzzled, for there are two caves, distant about 80
or 100 yards from one another." The cave in which Ulysses
hid his treasure is, as I have already said, identifiable with singular completeness. The other cave presents no special features,.
neither in the poem nor in nature.

the safest hiding places, while Ulysses brought up all the treasure of gold, bronze, and good clothing which the Phaeacians had given him. They stowed everything carefully away, and Minerva set a stone against the door of the cave. Then the two sat down by the root of the great olive, and consulted how to compass the destruction of the wicked suitors.

375 " Ulysses," said Minerva, " noble son of Laertes, think how you can lay hands on these disreputable people who have been lording it in your house these three years, courting your wife and making wedding presents to her, while she does nothing but lament your absence, giving hope and sending encouraging messages [1] to every one of them, but meaning the very opposite of all she says."

382 And Ulysses answered, " In good truth, goddess, it seems I should have come to much the same bad end in my own house as Agamemnon did, if you had not given me such timely information. Advise me how I shall best avenge myself. Stand by my side and put your courage into my heart as on the day when we loosed Troy's fair 'diadem from her brow. Help me now as you did then, and I will fight three hundred men, if you, goddess, will be with me."

393 " Trust me for that," said she, " I will not lose sight of you when once we set about it, and I imagine that some of those who are devouring your substance will then bespatter the pavement with their blood and brains. I will begin by disguising you so that no human being shall know you; I will cover your body with wrinkles; you shall lose all your yellow hair; I will

---

[1] There is no attempt to disguise the fact that Penelope had long given encouragement to the suitors. The only defence set up is that she did not really mean to encourage them. Would it not have been wiser to have tried a little discouragement?

clothe you in a garment that shall fill all who see it with loathing; I will blear your fine eyes for you, and make you an unseemly object in the sight of the suitors, of your wife, and of the son whom you left behind you. Then go at once to the swineherd who is in charge of your pigs; he has been always well affected towards you, and is devoted to Penelope and your son; you will find him feeding his pigs near the rock that is called Raven[1] by the fountain Arethusa, where they are fattening on beechmast and spring water after their manner. Stay with him and find out how things are going, while I proceed to Sparta and see your son, who is with Menelaus at Lacedaemon, where he has gone to try and find out whether you are still alive."[2]

"But why," said Ulysses, "did you not tell him, for you knew all about it? Did you want him too to go sailing about amid all kinds of hardship while others are eating up his estate?" 416

Minerva answered, "Never mind about him, I sent him that he might be well spoken of for having gone. He is in no sort of difficulty, but is staying quite comfortably with Menelaus, and is surrounded with abundance of every kind. The suitors have put out to sea and are lying in wait for him, for they mean to kill him before he can get home. I do not much think they will succeed, but rather that some of those who are now eating up your estate will first find a grave themselves." 420

As she spoke Minerva touched him with her wand 429

[1] See map near the end of bk. vi. *Ruccazzù dei corvi* of course means "the rock of the ravens." Both name and ravens still exist.

[2] See *The Authoress of the Odyssey*, pp. 146, 147. The real reason for sending Telemachus to Pylos and Lacedaemon was that the authoress might get Helen of Troy into her poem. He was sent at the only point in the story at which he could be sent, so he must have gone then or not at all.

and covered him with wrinkles, took away all his yellow
hair, and withered the flesh over his whole body; she
bleared his eyes, which were naturally very fine ones;
she changed his clothes and threw an old rag of a wrap
about him, and a tunic, tattered, filthy, and begrimed
with smoke; she also gave him an undressed deer skin
as an outer garment, and furnished him with a staff and
a wallet all in holes, with a twisted thong for him to
sling it over his shoulder.

439 When the pair had thus laid their plans they parted,
and the goddess went straight to Lacedaemon to fetch
440 Telemachus.

ULYSSES NOW LEFT THE HAVEN, AND took the rough track up through the wooded country and over the crest of the mountain till he reached the place where Minerva had said that he would find the swineherd, who was the most thrifty servant he had. He found him sitting in front of his hut, which was by the yards that he had built on a site which could be seen from far.[1] He had made them spacious and fair to see, with a free run for the pigs all round them; he had built them during his master's absence, of stones which he had gathered out of the ground, without saying anything to Penelope or Laertes, and he had fenced them on top with thorn bushes. Outside the yard he had run a strong fence of oaken posts, split, and set pretty close together, while inside he had built twelve sties near one another for the sows to lie in. There were fifty pigs wallowing in each sty, all of them breeding sows; but the boars slept outside and were much fewer in number, for the suitors kept on eating them, and the swineherd had to send them the best he had continually. There were three hundred and sixty boar pigs, and the herdsman's four hounds, which were as fierce as wolves, slept always with them. The swineherd was at that moment cutting out a[2] pair of sandals from a good stout ox hide. Three of his men were out herding the pigs in one place or another, and he had sent the fourth to town with a boar that he had

[1] The site I assign to Eumaeus's hut, close to the *Ruccazzù dei corvi*, is about 2,000 feet above the sea, and commands an extensive view.

[2] Sandals such as Eumaeus was making are still worn in the Abruzzi and elsewhere. An oblong piece of leather forms the sole : holes are cut at the four corners, and through these holes leathern straps are passed, which are bound round the foot and cross-gartered up the calf.

211

been forced to send the suitors that they might sacrifice
it and have their fill of meat.

29 When the hounds saw Ulysses they set up a furious
barking and flew at him, but Ulysses was cunning
enough to sit down and loose his hold of the stick that
he had in his hand: still, he would have been torn by
them in his own homestead had not the swineherd
dropped his ox hide, rushed full speed through the gate
of the yard and driven the dogs off by shouting and
throwing stones at them. Then he said to Ulysses,
" Old man, the dogs were likely to have made short
work of you, and then you would have got me into
trouble. The gods have given me quite enough worries
without that, for I have lost the best of masters, and am
in continual grief on his account. I have to attend swine
for other people to eat, while he, if he yet lives to see
the light of day, is starving in some distant land. But
come inside, and when you have had your fill of bread
and wine, tell me where you come from, and all about
your misfortunes."

48 On this the swineherd led the way into the hut and
bade him sit down. He strewed a good thick bed of
rushes upon the floor, and on the top of this he threw
the shaggy chamois skin–a great thick one–on which
he used to sleep by night. Ulysses was pleased at being
made thus welcome, and said " May Jove, sir, and the
rest of the gods grant you your heart's desire in return
for the kind way in which you have received me."

55 To this you answered, O swineherd Eumaeus,
" Stranger, though a still poorer man should come here,
it would not be right for me to insult him, for all
strangers and beggars are from Jove. You must take
what you can get and be thankful, for servants live in
fear when they have young lords for their masters;
and this is my misfortune now, for heaven has hindered

the return of him who would have been always good
to me and given me something of my own—a house,
a piece of land, a good looking wife, and all else that a
liberal master allows a servant who has worked hard
for him, and whose labour the gods have prospered as
they have mine in the situation which I hold. If my
master had grown old here he would have done great
things by me, but he is gone, and I wish that Helen's
whole race were utterly destroyed, for she has been the
death of many a good man. It was this matter that
took my master to Ilius, the land of noble steeds, to
fight the Trojans in the cause of king Agamemnon."

As he spoke he bound his girdle round him and went 72
to the sties where the young sucking pigs were penned.
He picked out two which he brought back with him
and sacrificed. He singed them, cut them up, and
spitted them; when the meat was cooked he brought it
all in and set it before Ulysses, hot and still on the spit,
whereon Ulysses sprinkled it over with white barley
meal. The swineherd then mixed wine in a bowl of
ivy-wood, and taking a seat opposite Ulysses told him
to begin.

"Fall to, stranger," said he, "on a dish of servant's 80
pork. The fat pigs have to go to the suitors, who eat
them up without shame or scruple; but the blessed
gods love not such shameful doings, and respect those
who do what is lawful and right. Even the fierce free-
booters who go raiding on other people's land, and
Jove gives them their spoil—even they, when they have
filled their ships and got home again live conscience-
stricken, and look fearfully for judgement; but some god
seems to have told these people that Ulysses is dead and
gone; they will not, therefore, go back to their own
homes and make their offers of marriage in the usual
way, but waste his estate by force, without fear or stint.

Not a day or night comes out of heaven, but they sacrifice not one victim nor two only, and they take the run of his wine, for he was exceedingly rich. No other great man either in Ithaca or on the mainland is as rich as he was; he had as much as twenty men put together. I will tell you what he had. There are twelve herds of cattle upon the mainland, and as many flocks of sheep, there are also twelve droves of pigs, while his own men and hired strangers feed him twelve widely spreading herds of goats. Here in Ithaca he runs eleven large flocks of goats on the far end of the island, and they are in the charge of excellent goatherds. Each one of these sends the suitors the best goat in the flock every day. As for myself, I am in charge of the pigs that you see here, and I have to keep picking out the best I have and sending it to them."

109   This was his story, but Ulysses went on eating and drinking ravenously without a word, brooding his revenge. When he had eaten enough and was satisfied, the swineherd took the bowl from which he usually drank, filled it with wine, and gave it to Ulysses, who was pleased, and said as he took it in his hands, " My friend, who was this master of yours that bought you and paid for you, so rich and so powerful as you tell me? You say he perished in the cause of King Agamemnon; tell me who he was, in case I may have met with such a person. Jove and the other gods know, but I may be able to give you news of him, for I have travelled much."

121   Eumaeus answered, " Old man, no traveller who comes here with news will get Ulysses' wife and son to believe his story. Nevertheless, tramps in want of a lodging keep coming with their mouths full of lies, and not a word of truth; every one who finds his way to Ithaca goes to my mistress and tells her falsehoods,

whereon she takes them in, makes much of them, and asks them all manner of questions, crying all the time as women will when they have lost their husbands. And you too, old man, for a shirt and cloak would doubtless make up a very pretty story. But the wolves and birds of prey have long since torn Ulysses to pieces, or the fishes of the sea have eaten him, and his bones are lying buried deep in sand upon some foreign shore; he is dead and gone, and a bad business it is for all his friends—for me especially; go where I may I shall never find so good a master, not even if I were to go home to my father and mother where I was bred and born. I do not so much care, however, about my parents now, though I should dearly like to see them again in my own country; it is the loss of Ulysses that grieves me most; I cannot speak of him without reverence though he is here no longer, for he was very fond of me, and took such care of me that wherever he may be I shall always honour his memory."

"My friend," replied Ulysses, "you are very positive, 148 and very hard of belief about your master's coming home again, nevertheless I will not merely say, but will swear, that he is coming. Do not give me anything for my news till he has actually come, you may then give me a shirt and cloak of good wear if you will. I am in great want, but I will not take anything at all till then, for I hate a man, even as I hate hell fire, who lets his poverty tempt him into lying. I swear by king Jove, by the rites of hospitality, and by that hearth of Ulysses to which I have now come, that all will surely happen as I have said it will. Ulysses will return in this self same year; with the end of this moon and the beginning of the next he will be here to do vengeance on all those who are ill treating his wife and son."

To this you answered, O swineherd Eumaeus, "Old 165

215

man, you will neither get paid for bringing good news, nor will Ulysses ever come home; drink your wine in peace, and let us talk about something else. Do not keep on reminding me of all this; it always pains me when any one speaks about my honoured master. As for your oath we will let it alone, but I only wish he may come, as do Penelope, his old father Laertes, and his son Telemachus. I am terribly unhappy too about this same boy of his; he was running up fast into manhood, and bade fare to be no worse man, face and figure, than his father, but some one, either god or man, has been unsettling his mind, so he has gone off to Pylos to try and get news of his father, and the suitors are lying in wait for him as he is coming home, in the hope of leaving the house of Arceisius without a name in Ithaca. But let us say no more about him, and leave him to be taken, or else to escape if the son of Saturn holds his hand over him to protect him. And now, old man, tell me your own story; tell me also, for I want to know, who you are and where you come from. Tell me of your town and parents, what manner of ship you came in, how your crew brought you to Ithaca, and from what country they professed to come—for you cannot have come by land."

191 And Ulysses answered, "I will tell you all about it. If there were meat and wine enough, and we could stay here in the hut with nothing to do but to eat and drink while the others go to their work, I could easily talk on for a whole twelve months without ever finishing the story of the sorrows with which it has pleased heaven to visit me.

199 "I am by birth a Cretan; my father was a well-to-do man, who had many sons born in marriage, whereas I was the son of a slave whom he had purchased for a concubine; nevertheless, my father Castor son of

216

Hylax (whose lineage I claim, and who was held in the
highest honour among the Cretans for his wealth,
prosperity, and the valour of his sons) put me on the
same level with my brothers who had been born in
wedlock. When, however, death took him to the
house of Hades, his sons divided his estate and cast lots
for their shares, but to me they gave a holding and little
else; nevertheless, my valour enabled me to marry
into a rich family, for I was not given to bragging, or
shirking on the field of battle. It is all over now; still,
if you look at the straw you can see what the ear was,
for I have had trouble enough and to spare. Mars and
Minerva made me doughty in war; when I had picked
my men to surprise the enemy with an ambuscade I
never gave death so much as a thought, but was the
first to leap forward and spear all whom I could overtake. Such was I in battle, but I did not care about farm
work, nor the frugal home life of those who would
bring up children. My delight was in ships, fighting,
javelins, and arrows—things that most men shudder to
think of; but one man likes one thing and another
another, and this was what I was most naturally inclined
to. Before the Achaeans went to Troy, nine times was
I in command of men and ships on foreign service, and
I amassed much wealth. I had my pick of the spoil in
the first instance, and much more was allotted to me
later on.

"My house grew apace and I became a great man 233
among the Cretans, but when Jove counselled that
terrible expedition, in which so many perished, the
people required me and Idomeneus to lead their ships
to Troy, and there was no way out of it, for they
insisted on our doing so. There we fought for nine
whole years, but in the tenth we sacked the city of
Priam and sailed home again as heaven dispersed us.

Then it was that Jove devised evil against me. I spent but one month happily with my children, wife, and property, and then I conceived the idea of making a descent on Egypt, so I fitted out a fine fleet and manned it. I had nine ships, and the people flocked to fill them. For six days I and my men made feast, and I found them many victims both for sacrifice to the gods and for themselves, but on the seventh day we went on board and set sail from Crete with a fair North wind behind us though we were going down a river. Nothing went ill with any of our ships, and we had no sickness on board, but sat where we were and let the ships go as the wind and steersmen took them. On the fifth day we reached the river Aegyptus; there I stationed my ships in the river, bidding my men stay by them and keep guard over them while I sent out scouts to reconnoitre from every point of vantage.

262   "But the men disobeyed my orders, took to their own devices, and ravaged the land of the Egyptians, killing the men, and taking their wives and children captive. The alarm was soon carried to the city, and when they heard the war cry, the people came out at daybreak till the plain was filled with horsemen and foot soldiers and with the gleam of armour. Then Jove spread panic among my men, and they would no longer face the enemy, for they found themselves surrounded. The Egyptians killed many of us, and took the rest alive to do forced labour for them. Jove, however, put it in my mind to do thus—and I wish I had died then and there in Egypt instead, for there was much sorrow in store for me—I took off my helmet and shield and dropped my spear from my hand; then I went straight up to the king's chariot, clasped his knees and kissed them, whereon he spared my life, bade me get into his chariot, and took me weeping to his own home.

Many made at me with their ashen spears and tried to kill me in their fury, but the king protected me, for he feared the wrath of Jove the protector of strangers, who punishes those who do evil.

"I stayed there for seven years and got together 285 much money among the Egyptians, for they all gave me something; but when it was now going on for eight years there came a certain Phoenician, a cunning rascal, who had already committed all sorts of villainy, and this man talked me over into going with him to Phoenicia, where his house and his possessions lay. I stayed there for a whole twelve months, but at the end of that time when months and days had gone by till the same season had come round again, he set me on board a ship bound for Libya, on a pretence that I was to take a cargo along with him to that place, but really that he might sell me as a slave and take the money I fetched. I suspected his intention, but went on board with him, for I could not help it.

"The ship ran before a fresh North wind till we had 299 reached the sea that lies between Crete and Libya; there, however, Jove counselled their destruction, for as soon as we were well out from Crete and could see nothing but sea and sky, he raised a black cloud over our ship and the sea grew dark beneath it. Then Jove let fly with his thunderbolts and the ship went round and round and was filled with fire and brimstone as the lightning struck it. The men fell all into the sea; they were carried about in the water round the ship looking like so many sea-gulls, but the god presently deprived them of all chance of getting home again. I was all dismayed; Jove, however, sent the ship's mast within my reach, which saved my life, for I clung to it, and drifted before the fury of the gale. Nine days did I drift but in the darkness of the tenth night a great wave bore

219

me on to the Thesprotian coast. There Pheidon king
of the Thesprotians entertained me hospitably without
charging me anything at all—for his son found me when
I was nearly dead with cold and fatigue, whereon he
raised me by the hand, took me to his father's house and
gave me clothes to wear.

321 " There it was that I heard news of Ulysses, for the
king told me he had entertained him, and shown him
much hospitality while he was on his homeward journey. He showed me also the treasure of gold, bronze,
and wrought iron that Ulysses had got together. There
was enough to keep his family for ten generations, so
much had he left in the house of king Pheidon. But the
king said Ulysses had gone to Dodona that he might
learn Jove's mind from the god's high oak tree, and
know whether after so long an absence he should
return to Ithaca openly, or in secret. Moreover the
king swore in my presence, making drink-offerings in
his own house as he did so, that the ship was by the
water side, and the crew found, that should take him to
his own country. He sent me off however before
Ulysses returned, for there happened to be a Thesprotian ship sailing for the wheat-growing island of
Dulichium, and he told those in charge of her to be sure
and take me safely to King Acastus.

337 " These men hatched a plot against me that would
have reduced me to the very extreme of misery, for
when the ship had got some way out from land they
resolved on selling me as a slave. They stripped me of
the shirt and cloak that I was wearing, and gave me
instead the tattered old clouts in which you now see me;
then, towards nightfall, they reached the tilled lands
of Ithaca, and there they bound me with a strong rope
fast in the ship, while they went on shore to get supper
by the sea side. But the gods soon undid my bonds

for me, and having drawn my rags over my head I slid down the rudder into the sea, where I struck out and swam till I was well clear of them, and came ashore near a thick wood in which I lay concealed. They were very angry at my having escaped and went searching about for me, till at last they thought it was no further use and went back to their ship. The gods, having hidden me thus easily, then took me to a good man's door—for it seems that I am not to die yet awhile."

To this you answered, O swineherd Eumaeus, ₃₆₀ "Poor unhappy stranger, I have found the story of your misfortunes extremely interesting, but that part about Ulysses is not right; and you will never get me to believe it. Why should a man like you go about telling lies in this way? I know all about the return of my master. The gods one and all of them detest him, or they would have taken him before Troy, or let him die with friends around him when the days of his fighting were done; for then the Achaeans would have built a mound over his ashes and his son would have been heir to his renown, but now the storm winds have spirited him away we know not whither.

" As for me I live out of the way here with the pigs, ₃₇₂ and never go to the town unless when Penelope sends for me on the arrival of some news about Ulysses. Then they all sit round and ask questions, both those who grieve over the king's absence, and those who rejoice at it because they can eat up his property without paying for it. For my own part I have never cared about asking any one else since the time when I was taken in by an Aetolian, who had killed a man and come a long way till at last he reached my station, and I was very kind to him. He said he had seen Ulysses with Idomeneus among the Cretans, refitting his ships which had been damaged in a gale. He said Ulysses would return in the following summer or autumn with his men, and that he would bring back much wealth. And now you, you unfortunate old man, since fate has brought you to my door, do not try to flatter me in this way with vain hopes. It is not for any such reason that I shall treat you kindly, but only out of respect for Jove the god of hospitality, as fearing him and pitying you."

390   Ulysses answered, " I see that you are of an unbelieving mind; I have given you my oath, and yet you will not credit me; let us then make a bargain, and call all the gods in heaven to witness it. If your master comes home, give me a cloak and shirt of good wear, and send me to Dulichium where I want to go; but if he does not come as I say he will, set your men on to me, and tell them to throw me from yonder precipice, as a warning to tramps not to go about the country telling lies."

401   " And a pretty figure I should cut then," replied Eumaeus, " both now and hereafter, if I were to kill you after receiving you into my hut and showing you hospitality. I should have to say my prayers in good earnest if I did; but it is just supper time and I hope my men will come in directly, that we may cook something savoury for supper."

409   Thus did they converse, and presently the swineherds came up with the pigs, which were then shut up for the night in their sties, and a tremendous squealing they made as they were being driven into them. But Eumaeus called to his men and said, " Bring in the best pig you have, that I may sacrifice him for this stranger, and we will take toll of him ourselves. We have had trouble enough this long time feeding pigs, while others reap the fruit of our labour."

418   On this he began chopping firewood, while the others brought in a fine fat five year old boar pig, and set it at the altar. Eumaeus did not forget the gods, for he was

a man of good principles, so the first thing he did was
to cut bristles from the pig's face and throw them into
the fire, praying to all the gods as he did so that Ulysses
might return home again.   Then he clubbed the pig
with a billet of oak which he had kept back when he was
chopping the firewood, and stunned it, while the others
slaughtered and singed it.   Then they cut it up, and
Eumaeus began by putting raw pieces from each joint
on to some of the fat; these he sprinkled with barley
meal, and laid upon the embers; they cut the rest of the
meat up small, put the pieces upon the spits and roasted
them till they were done; when they had taken them
off the spits they threw them on to the dresser in a heap.
The swineherd, who was a most equitable man, then
stood up to give every one his share.   He made seven
portions; one of these he set apart for Mercury the son
of Maia and the nymphs, praying to them as he did so;
the others he dealt out to the men man by man.   He
gave Ulysses some slices cut lengthways down the loin
as a mark of especial honour, and Ulysses was much
pleased.   " I hope, Eumaeus," said he, " that Jove will
be as well disposed towards you as I am, for the respect
you are showing to an outcast like myself."

To this you answered, O swineherd Eumaeus, " Eat, 441
my good fellow, and enjoy your supper, such as it is.
God grants this, and withholds that, just as he thinks
right, for he can do whatever he chooses."

As he spoke he cut off the first piece and offered it as a 446
burnt sacrifice to the immortal gods; then he made
them a drink-offering, put the cup in the hands of
Ulysses, and sat down to his own portion.   Mesaulius
brought them their bread; the swineherd had bought
this man on his own account from among the Taphians
during his master's absence, and had paid for him with
his own money without saying anything either to his

mistress or Laertes. They then laid their hands upon the good things that were before them, and when they had had enough to eat and drink, Mesaulius took away what was left of the bread, and they all went to bed after having made a hearty supper.

457   Now the night came on stormy and very dark, for there was no moon. It poured without ceasing, and the wind blew strong from the West, which is a wet quarter, so Ulysses thought he would see whether Eumaeus, in the excellent care he took of him, would take off his own cloak and give it him, or make one of his men give him one. "Listen to me," said he, "Eumaeus and the rest of you; when I have said a prayer I will tell you something. It is the wine that makes me talk in this way; wine will make even a wise man fall to singing; it will make him chuckle and dance and say many a word that he had better leave unspoken; still, as I have begun, I will go on. Would that I were still young and strong as when we got up an ambuscade before Troy. Menelaus and Ulysses were the leaders, but I was in command also, for the other two would have it so. When we had come up to the wall of the city we crouched down beneath our armour and lay there under cover of the reeds and thick brushwood that grew about the swamp. It came on to freeze with a North wind blowing; the snow fell small and fine like hoar frost, and our shields were coated thick with rime. The others had all got cloaks and shirts, and slept comfortably enough with their shields about their shoulders, but I had carelessly left my cloak behind me, not thinking that I should be too cold, and had gone off in nothing but my shirt and shield. When the night was two-thirds through and the stars had shifted their places, I nudged Ulysses who was close to me with my elbow, and he at once gave me his ear.

224

" ' Ulysses,' said I, ' this cold will be the death of me, 486
for I have no cloak; some god fooled me into setting
off with nothing on but my shirt, and I do not know
what to do.'

" Ulysses, who was as crafty as he was valiant, hit 490
upon the following plan:

" ' Keep still,' said he in a low voice, ' or the others 493
will hear you.' Then he raised his head on his elbow.

" ' My friends,' said he, ' I have had a dream from 495
heaven in my sleep. We are a long way from the ships;
I wish some one would go down and tell Agamemnon
to send us up more men at once.'

" On this Thoas son of Andraemon threw off his 499
cloak and set out running to the ships, whereon I took
the cloak and lay in it comfortably enough till morning.
Would that I were still young and strong as I was in
those days, for then some one of you swineherds would
give me a cloak both out of good will and for the respect
due to a brave soldier; but now people look down upon
me because my clothes are shabby."

And Eumaeus answered, " Old man, you have told 507
us an excellent story, and have said nothing so far but
what is quite satisfactory; for the present, therefore,
you shall want neither clothing nor anything else that a
stranger in distress may reasonably expect, but to-
morrow morning you will have to shake your own old
rags about your body again, for we have not many
spare cloaks nor shirts up here, but every man has only
one. When Ulysses' son comes home again he will give
you both cloak and shirt, and send you wherever you
may want to go."

With this he got up and made a bed for Ulysses by 518
throwing some goatskins and sheepskins on the
ground in front of the fire. Here Ulysses lay down, and
Eumaeus covered him over with a great heavy cloak

that he kept for a change in case of extraordinarily bad weather.

523 Thus did Ulysses sleep, and the young men slept beside him. But the swineherd did not like sleeping away from his pigs, so he got ready to go outside, and Ulysses was glad to see that he looked after his property during his master's absence. First he slung his sword over his brawny shoulders and put on a thick cloak to keep out the wind. He also took the skin of a large and well fed goat, and a javelin in case of attack from men or dogs. Thus equipped he went to his rest where the pigs were camping under an overhanging rock that 533 gave them shelter from the North wind.

BUT MINERVA WENT TO THE FAIR CITY of Lacedaemon to tell Ulysses' son that he was to return at once. She found him and Pisistratus sleeping in the forecourt of Menelaus's house; Pisistratus was fast asleep, but Telemachus could get no rest all night for thinking of his unhappy father, so Minerva went close up to him and said:

"Telemachus, you should not remain so far away from home any longer, nor leave your property with such dangerous people in your house; they will eat up everything you have among them, and you will have been on a fool's errand. Ask Menelaus to send you home at once if you wish to find your excellent mother still there when you get back. Her father and brothers are already urging her to marry Eurymachus, who has given her more than any of the others, and has been greatly increasing his wedding presents. I hope nothing valuable may have been taken from the house in spite of you, but you know what women are—they always want to do the best they can for the man who marries them, and never give another thought to the children of their first husband, nor to their father either when he is dead and done with. Go home, therefore, and put everything in charge of the most respectable woman servant that you have, until it shall please heaven to send you a wife of your own. Let me tell you also of another matter which you had better attend to. The chief men among the suitors are lying in wait for you in the Strait[1] between Ithaca and Samos, and they mean to kill you before you can reach home. I do not much think they will succeed; it is more likely that some of

[1] See note on Od., ix, 26.

those who are now eating up your property will find a grave themselves. Sail night and day, and keep your ship well away from the islands; the god who watches over you and protects you will send you a fair wind. As soon as you get to Ithaca send your ship and men on to the town, but yourself go straight to the swine-herd who has charge of your pigs; he is well disposed towards you, stay with him, therefore, for the night, and then send him to Penelope to tell her that you have got back safe from Pylos."

43   Then she went back to Olympus; but Telemachus stirred Pisistratus with his heel to rouse him, and said, "Wake up Pisistratus, and yoke the horses to the chariot, for we must set off home."[1]

48   But Pisistratus said, "No matter what hurry we are in we cannot drive in the dark. It will be morning soon; wait till Menelaus has brought his presents and put them in the chariot for us; and let him say good-bye to us in the usual way. So long as he lives a guest should never forget a host who has shown him kindness."

56   As he spoke day began to break, and Menelaus, who had already risen, leaving Helen in bed, came towards them. When Telemachus saw him he put on his shirt as fast as he could, threw a great cloak over his shoulders, and went out to meet him. "Menelaus," said he, "let me go back now to my own country, for I want to get home."

67   And Menelaus answered, "Telemachus, if you insist on going I will not detain you. I do not like to see a host either too fond of his guest or too rude to him. Moderation is best in all things, and not letting a man go when he wants to do so is as bad as telling him to go if he would like to stay. One should treat a guest well

---

[1] Telemachus, like many another good young man, seems to expect every one to fetch and carry for him.

as long as he is in the house and speed him when he wants to leave it. Wait, then, till I can get your beautiful presents into your chariot, and till you have yourself seen them. I will tell the women to prepare a sufficient dinner for you of what there may be in the house; it will be at once more proper and cheaper for you to get your dinner before setting out on such a long journey. If, moreover, you have a fancy for making a tour in Hellas or in the Peloponnese, I will yoke my horses, and will conduct you myself through all our principal cities. No one will send us away empty handed; every one will give us something–a bronze tripod, a couple of mules, or a gold cup."

"Menelaus," replied Telemachus, "I want to go 86 home at once, for when I came away I left my property without protection, and fear that while looking for my father I shall come to ruin myself, or find that something valuable has been stolen during my absence."

When Menelaus heard this he immediately told his 92 wife and servants to prepare a sufficient dinner from what there might be in the house. At this moment Eteoneus joined him, for he lived close by and had just got up; so Menelaus told him to light the fire and cook some meat, which he at once did. Then Menelaus went down into his fragrant store room,[1] not alone, but Helen went too, with Megapenthes. When he reached the place where the treasures of his house were kept, he selected a double cup, and told his son Megapenthes to bring also a silver mixing-bowl. Meanwhile Helen went to the chest where she kept the lovely dresses which she had made with her own hands, and took out one that was largest and most beautifully enriched with embroidery; it glittered like a star, and lay at the

[1] Il., vi, 288. The store room was fragrant because it was made of cedar wood. See Il., xxiv, 192.

229

very bottom of the chest.[1] Then they all came back through the house again till they got to Telemachus, and Menelaus said, " Telemachus, may Jove, the mighty husband of Juno, bring you safely home according to your desire. I will now present you with the finest and most precious piece of plate in all my house. It is a mixing-bowl of pure silver, except the rim, which is inlaid with gold, and it is the work of Vulcan. Phaedimus king of the Sidonians made me a present of it in the course of a visit that I paid him while I was on my return home. I should like to give it to you."

120 With these words he placed the double cup in the hands of Telemachus, while Megapenthes brought the beautiful mixing-bowl and set it before him. Hard by stood lovely Helen with the robe ready in her hand.

125 " I too, my son," said she, " have something for you as a keepsake from the hand of Helen; it is for your bride to wear upon her wedding day. Till then, get your dear mother to keep it for you; thus may you go back rejoicing to your own country and to your home."

130 So saying she gave the robe over to him and he received it gladly. Then Pisistratus put the presents into the chariot, and admired them all as he did so. Presently Menelaus took Telemachus and Pisistratus into the house, and they both of them sat down to table. A maid servant brought them water in a beautiful golden ewer, and poured it into a silver basin for them to wash their hands, and she drew a clean table beside them; an upper servant brought them bread and offered

---

[1] *Cf.* Il., vi, 289 and 293-296. The dress was kept at the bottom of the chest as one that would only be wanted on the greatest occasions ; but surely the marriage of Hermione and of Megapenthes (bk. iv, *ad init.*) might have induced Helen to wear it on the preceding evening, in which case it could hardly have got back. We find no hint here of Megapenthes' recent marriage.

them many good things of what there was in the house. Eteoneus carved the meat and gave them each their portions, while Megapenthes poured out the wine. Then they laid their hands upon the good things that were before them, but as soon as they had had enough to eat and drink Telemachus and Pisistratus yoked the horses, and took their places in the chariot. They drove out through the inner gateway and under the echoing gatehouse of the outer court, and Menelaus came after them with a golden goblet of wine in his right hand that they might make a drink-offering before they set out. He stood in front of the horses and pledged them, saying, " Farewell to both of you; see that you tell Nestor how I have treated you, for he was as kind to me as any father could be while we Achaeans were fighting before Troy."

" We will be sure, sir," answered Telemachus, " to 154 tell him everything as soon as we see him. I wish I were as certain of finding Ulysses returned when I get back to Ithaca, that I might tell him of the very great kindness you have shown me and of the many beautiful presents I am taking with me."

As he was thus speaking a bird flew by on his right 160 hand—an eagle with a great white goose in its talons which it had carried off from the farm yard—and all the men and women were running after it and shouting. It came quite close up to them and flew away on their right hands in front of the horses. When they saw it they were glad, and their hearts took comfort within them, whereon Pisistratus said, " Tell me, Menelaus, has heaven sent this omen for us or for you? "

Menelaus was thinking what would be the most 169 proper answer for him to make, but Helen was too quick for him and said, " I will read this matter as heaven has put it in my heart, and as I doubt not that it will come to pass. The eagle came from the mountain where it was bred and has its nest, and in like manner Ulysses, after having travelled far and suffered much, will return to take his revenge–if indeed he is not back already and hatching mischief for the suitors."

179 "May Jove so grant it," replied Telemachus; " if it should prove to be so, I will make vows to you as though you were a god, even when I am at home."

182 As he spoke he lashed his horses and they started off at full speed through the town towards the open country. They swayed the yoke upon their necks and travelled the whole day long till the sun set and darkness was over all the land. Then they reached Pherae, where Diocles lived who was son of Ortilochus, the son of Alpheus. There they passed the night and were treated hospitably. When the child of morning, rosy-fingered Dawn, appeared, they again yoked their horses and took their places in the chariot. They drove out through the inner gateway and under the echoing gatehouse of the outer court. Then Pisistratus lashed his horses on and they flew forward nothing loath; ere long they came to Pylos, and then Telemachus said:

195 " Pisistratus, I hope you will promise to do what I am going to ask you. You know our fathers were old friends before us; moreover, we are both of an age, and this journey has brought us together still more closely; do not, therefore, take me past my ship, but leave me there, for if I go to your father's house he will try to keep me in the warmth of his good will towards me, and I must go home at once."

202 Pisistratus thought how he should do as he was asked, and in the end he deemed it best to turn his horses towards the ship, and put Menelaus's beautiful presents of gold and raiment in the stern of the vessel. Then he said, " Go on board at once and tell your men to do so

232

also before I can reach home to tell my father. I know
how obstinate he is, and am sure he will not let you go;
he will come down here to fetch you, and he will not
go back without you. But he will be very angry."

With this he drove his goodly steeds back to the 215
city of the Pylians and soon reached his home, but
Telemachus called the men together and gave his orders.
" Now, my men," said he, " get everything in order on
board the ship, and let us set out home."

Thus did he speak, and they went on board even as 220
he had said. But as Telemachus was thus busied,
praying also and sacrificing to Minerva in the ship's
stern, there came to him a man from a distant country,
a seer, who was flying from Argos because he had killed
a man. He was descended from Melampus, who used
to live in Pylos, the land of sheep; he was rich and
owned a great house, but he was driven into exile by the
great and powerful king Neleus. Neleus seized his
goods and held them for a whole year, during which he
was a close prisoner in the house of king Phylacus, and
in much distress of mind both on account of the daughter
of Neleus and because he was haunted by a great sorrow
that dread Erinys had laid upon him. In the end, however, he escaped with his life, drove the cattle from
Phylace to Pylos, avenged the wrong that had been
done him, and gave the daughter of Neleus to his
brother. Then he left the country and went to Argos,
where it was ordained that he should reign over much
people. There he married, established himself, and had
two famous sons Antiphates and Mantius. Antiphates
became father of Oicleus, and Oicleus of Amphiaraus,
who was dearly loved both by Jove and by Apollo, but
he did not live to old age, for he was killed in Thebes
by reason of a woman's gifts. His sons were Alcmaeon
and Amphilochus. Mantius, the other son of Melampus,

233

was father to Polypheides and Cleitus. Aurora, throned
in gold, carried off Cleitus for his beauty's sake, that he
might dwell among the immortals, but Apollo made
Polypheides the greatest seer in the whole world now
that Amphiaraus was dead. He quarrelled with his
father and went to live in Hyperesia, where he remained
and prophesied for all men.

256 His son, Theoclymenus, it was who now came up to
Telemachus as he was making drink-offerings and
praying in his ship. "Friend," said he, "now that I
find you sacrificing in this place, I beseech you by your
sacrifices themselves, and by the god to whom you
make them, I pray you also by your own head and by
those of your followers, tell me the truth and nothing
but the truth. Who and whence are you? Tell me
also of your town and parents."

265 Telemachus said, "I will answer you quite truly. I
am from Ithaca, and my father is Ulysses, as surely as
that he ever lived. But he has come to some miserable
end. Therefore I have taken this ship and got my crew
together to see if I can hear any news of him, for he has
been away a long time."

271 "I too," answered Theoclymenus, "am an exile, for
I have killed a man of my own race. He has many
brothers and kinsmen in Argos, and they have great
power among the Argives. I am flying to escape death
at their hands, and am thus doomed to be a wanderer
on the face of the earth. I am your suppliant; take me,
therefore, on board your ship that they may not kill
me, for I know they are in pursuit."

279 "I will not refuse you," replied Telemachus, "if you
wish to join us. Come, therefore, and in Ithaca we will
treat you hospitably according to what we have."

282 On this he received Theoclymenus' spear and laid it
down on the deck of the ship. He went on board and

sat in the stern, bidding Theoclymenus sit beside him;
then the men let go the hawsers. Telemachus told them
to catch hold of the ropes, and they made all haste to do
so. They set the mast in its socket in the cross plank,
raised it and made it fast with the forestays, and they
hoisted their white sails with sheets of twisted ox hide.
Minerva sent them a fair wind that blew fresh and
strong to take the ship on her course as fast as possible.
Thus then they passed by Crouni and Chalcis.

Presently the sun set and darkness was over all the 296
land. The vessel made a quick passage to Pheae and
thence on to Elis, where the Epeans rule. Telemachus
then headed her for the flying islands,[1] wondering
within himself whether he should escape death or
should be taken prisoner.

Meanwhile Ulysses and the swineherd were eating 301
their supper in the hut, and the men supped with them.
As soon as they had had enough to eat and drink,
Ulysses began trying to prove the swineherd and see
whether he would continue to treat him kindly, and
ask him to stay on at the station or pack him off to the
city; so he said:

"Eumaeus, and all of you, to-morrow I want to go 307
away and begin begging about the town, so as to be no
more trouble to you or to your men. Give me your
advice therefore, and let me have a good guide to go
with me and show me the way. I will go the round of
the city begging as I needs must, to see if any one will
give me a drink and a piece of bread. I should like also
to go to the house of Ulysses and bring news of her
husband to Queen Penelope. I could then go about
among the suitors and see if out of all their abundance
they will give me a dinner. I should soon make them
an excellent servant in all sorts of ways. Listen and

[1] See note on Od., x, 3.

235

believe when I tell you that by the blessing of Mercury who gives grace and good name to the works of all men, there is no one living who would make a more handy servant than I should – to put fresh wood on the fire, chop fuel, carve, cook, pour out wine, and do all those services that poor men have to do for their betters."

325 The swineherd was very much disturbed when he heard this. "Heaven help me," he exclaimed, "whatever can have put such a notion as that into your head? If you go near the suitors you will be undone to a certainty, for their pride and insolence reach the very heavens. They would never think of taking a man like you for a servant. Their servants are all young men, well dressed, wearing good cloaks and shirts, with well looking faces and their hair always tidy, the tables are kept quite clean and are loaded with bread, meat, and wine. Stay where you are, then; you are not in anybody's way; I do not mind your being here, no more do any of the others, and when Telemachus comes home he will give you a shirt and cloak and will send you wherever you want to go."

340 Ulysses answered, "I hope you may be as dear to the gods as you are to me, for having saved me from going about and getting into trouble; there is nothing worse than being always on the tramp; still, when men have once got low down in the world they will go through a great deal on behalf of their miserable bellies. Since, however, you press me to stay here and await the return of Telemachus, tell me about Ulysses' mother, and his father whom he left on the threshold of old age when he set out for Troy. Are they still living or are they already dead and in the house of Hades?"

351 "I will tell you all about them," replied Eumaeus, "Laertes is still living and prays heaven to let him

236

depart peacefully in his own house, for he is terribly
distressed about the absence of his son, and also about
the death of his wife, which grieved him greatly and
aged him more than anything else did. She came to an
unhappy end[1] through sorrow for her son: may no
friend or neighbour who has dealt kindly by me come
to such an end as she did. As long as she was still
living, though she was always grieving, I used to like
seeing her and asking her how she did, for she brought
me up along with her daughter Ctimene, the youngest
of her children; we were boy and girl together, and
she made little difference between us. When, however,
we both grew up, they sent Ctimene to Same and
received a splendid dowry for her. As for me, my
mistress gave me a good shirt and cloak with a pair of
sandals for my feet, and sent me off into the country,
but she was just as fond of me as ever. This is all over
now. Still it has pleased heaven to prosper my work
in the situation which I now hold. I have enough to
eat and drink, and can find something for any respectable stranger who comes here; but there is no getting
a kind word or deed out of my mistress, for the house
has fallen into the hands of wicked people. Servants
want sometimes to see their mistress and have a talk
with her; they like to have something to eat and drink
at the house, and something too to take back with them
into the country. This is what will keep servants in a
good humour."

Ulysses answered, " Then you must have been a very 380
little fellow, Eumaeus, when you were taken so far
away from your home and parents. Tell me, and tell
me true, was the city in which your father and mother
lived sacked and pillaged, or did some enemies carry
you off when you were alone tending sheep or cattle,

[1] *Cf.* Od., xi, 196, etc.

237

ship you off here, and sell you for whatever your master gave them? "

389 " Stranger," replied Eumaeus, " as regards your question: sit still, make yourself comfortable, drink your wine, and listen to me. The nights are now at their longest; there is plenty of time both for sleeping and sitting up talking together; you ought not to go to bed till bed time, too much sleep is as bad as too little; if any one of the others wishes to go to bed let him leave us and do so; he can then take my master's pigs out when he has done breakfast in the morning. We two will sit here eating and drinking in the hut, and telling one another stories about our misfortunes; for when a man has suffered much, and been buffeted about in the world, he takes pleasure in recalling the memory of sorrows that have long gone by. As regards your question, then, my tale is as follows:

403 " You may have heard of an island called Syra that lies over above Ortygia,[1] where the land begins to turn round and look in another direction.[2] It is not very thickly peopled, but the soil is good, with much pasture fit for cattle and sheep, and it abounds with wine and wheat. Dearth never comes there, nor are the people plagued by any sickness, but when they grow old Apollo comes with Diana and kills them with his painless shafts. It contains two communities, and the whole

[1] The names Syra and Ortygia, on which island a great part of the Doric Syracuse was originally built, suggest that even in Odyssean times there was a prehistoric Syracuse, the existence of which was known to the writer of the poem.

[2] Literally " where are the turnings of the sun." Assuming, as we may safely do, that the Syra and Ortygia of the Odyssey refer to Syracuse, it is the fact that not far to the South of these places the land turns sharply round, so that mariners following the coast would find the sun upon the other side of their ship to that on which they had had it hitherto.

Mr. A. S. Griffith has kindly called my attention to Herod. iv,

238

country is divided between these two.¹ My father
Ctesius son of Ormenus, a man comparable to the gods,
reigned over both.

" Now to this place there came some cunning traders ₄₁₅
from Phoenicia (for the Phoenicians are great mariners)
in a ship which they had freighted with gewgaws of all
kinds. There happened to be a Phoenician woman in
my father's house, very tall and comely, and an excellent
servant; these scoundrels got hold of her one day when
she was washing near their ship, seduced her, and
cajoled her in ways that no woman can resist, no matter
how good she may be by nature. The man who had
seduced her asked her who she was and where she came
from, and on this she told him her father's name. ' I
come from Sidon,' said she, ' and am daughter to
Arybas, a man rolling in wealth. One day as I was
coming into the town from the country some Taphian
pirates seized me and took me here over the sea, where
they sold me to the man who owns this house, and he
gave them their price for me.'

" The man who had seduced her then said, ' Would ₄₃₀

42, where, speaking of the circumnavigation of Africa by
Phoenician mariners under Necos, he writes :

" On their return they declared–I for my part do not believe
them, but perhaps others may–that in sailing round Libya
[*i.e.,* Africa] they had the sun upon their right hand. In this
way was the extent of Libya first discovered."

I take it that Eumaeus was made to have come from Syracuse
because the writer thought she rather ought to have made something happen at Syracuse during her account of the voyages of
Ulysses. She could not, however, break his long drift from
Charybdis to the island of Pantellaria ; she therefore resolved to
make it up to Syracuse in another way.

¹ Modern excavations establish the existence of two and only
two pre-Dorian communities at Syracuse ; they were, so Dr. Orsi
informed me, at Plemmirio and Cozzo Pantano. See *The
Authoress of the Odyssey,* pp. 221-223.

you like to come along with us to see the house of your parents and your parents themselves? They are both alive and are said to be well off.'

434   " 'I will do so gladly,' answered she, 'if you men will first swear me a solemn oath that you will do me no harm by the way.'

437   " They all swore as she told them, and when they had completed their oath the woman said, 'Hush; and if any of your men meets me in the street or at the well, do not let him speak to me, for fear some one should go and tell my master, in which case he would suspect something. He would put me in prison, and would have all of you murdered; keep your own counsel therefore; buy your merchandise as fast as you can, and send me word when you have done loading. I will bring as much gold as I can lay my hands on, and there is something else also that I can do towards paying my fare. I am nurse to the son of the good man of the house, a funny little fellow just able to run about. I will carry him off in your ship, and you will get a great deal of money for him if you take him and sell him in foreign parts.'

454   " On this she went back to the house. The Phoenicians stayed a whole year till they had loaded their ship with much precious merchandise, and then, when they had got freight enough, they sent to tell the woman. Their messenger, a very cunning fellow, came to my father's house bringing a necklace of gold with amber beads strung among it; and while my mother and the servants had it in their hands admiring it and bargaining about it, he made a sign quietly to the woman and then went back to the ship, whereon she took me by the hand and led me out of the house. In the fore part of the house she saw the tables set with the cups of guests who had been feasting with my father, as being in

attendance on him; these were now all gone to a
meeting of the public assembly, so she snatched up three
cups and carried them off in the bosom of her dress,
while I followed her, for I knew no better. The sun
was now set, and darkness was over all the land, so
we hurried on as fast as we could till we reached the
harbour, where the Phoenician ship was lying. When
they had got on board they sailed their ways over the
sea, taking us with them, and Jove sent them a fair
wind; six days did we sail both night and day, but on
the seventh day Diana struck the woman and she fell
heavily down into the ship's hold as though she were a
sea gull alighting on the water; so they threw her overboard to the seals and fishes, and I was left all sorrowful
and alone. Presently the winds and waves took the
ship to Ithaca, where Laertes gave sundry of his chattels
for me, and thus it was that ever I came to set eyes upon
this country."

Ulysses answered, " Eumaeus, I have heard the story 485
of your misfortunes with the most lively interest and
pity, but Jove has given you good as well as evil, for
in spite of everything you have a good master, who
sees that you always have enough to eat and drink; and
you lead a good life, whereas I am still going about
begging my way from city to city."

Thus did they converse, and they had only a very 493
little time left for sleep, for it was soon daybreak. In
the meantime Telemachus and his crew were nearing
land, so they loosed the sails, took down the mast, and
rowed the ship into the harbour.[1] They cast out their
mooring stones and made fast the hawsers; they then
got out upon the sea shore, mixed their wine, and got

[1] This harbour is again evidently the harbour in which Ulysses
had landed, *i.e.*, the harbour that is now the salt works of
S. Cusumano.

dinner ready. As soon as they had had enough to eat and drink Telemachus said, " Take the ship on to the town, but leave me here, for I want to look after the herdsmen on one of my farms. In the evening, when I have seen all I want, I will come down to the city, and to-morrow morning in return for your trouble I will give you all a good dinner with meat and wine." [1]

508 Then Theoclymenus said, ' And what, my dear young friend, is to become of me? To whose house, among all your chief men, am I to repair? or shall I go straight to your own house and to your mother? "

512 " At any other time," replied Telemachus, " I should have bidden you go to my own house, for you would find no want of hospitality; at the present moment, however, you would not be comfortable there, for I shall be away, and my mother will not see you; she does not often show herself even to the suitors, but sits at her loom weaving in an upper chamber, out of their way; but I can tell you a man whose house you can go to—I mean Eurymachus the son of Polybus, who is held in the highest estimation by every one in Ithaca. He is much the best man and the most persistent wooer, of all those who are paying court to my mother and trying to take Ulysses' place. Jove, however, in heaven alone knows whether or no they will come to a bad end before the marriage takes place."

525 As he was speaking a bird flew by upon his right hand—a hawk, Apollo's messenger. It held a dove in its talons, and the feathers, as it tore them off,[2] fell to the

---

[1] This never can have been anything but very niggardly pay for some eight or nine days' service. I suppose the crew were to consider the pleasure of having had a trip to Pylos as a set off. There is no trace of the dinner as having been actually given, either on the following or any other morning.

[2] No hawk can tear its prey while it is on the wing.

ground midway between Telemachus and the ship.
On this Theoclymenus called him apart and caught him
by the hand. " Telemachus," said he, " that bird did
not fly on your right hand without having been sent
there by some god. As soon as I saw it I knew it was
an omen; it means that you will remain powerful and
that there will be no house in Ithaca more royal than
your own."

" I wish it may prove so," answered Telemachus. 535
" If it does, I will show you so much good will and
give you so many presents that all who meet you will
congratulate you."

Then he said to his friend Piraeus, " Piraeus, son of 539
Clytius, you have throughout shown yourself the most
willing to serve me of all those who have accompanied
me to Pylos; I wish you would take this stranger to
your own house and entertain him hospitably till I can
come for him."

And Piraeus answered, " Telemachus, you may stay 544
away as long as you please, but I will look after him for
you, and he shall find no lack of hospitality."

As he spoke he went on board, and bade the others 547
do so also and loose the hawsers, so they took their
places in the ship. But Telemachus bound on his
sandals, and took a long and doughty spear with a head
of sharpened bronze from the deck of the ship. Then
they loosed the hawsers, thrust the ship off from land,
and made on towards the city as they had been told to
do, while Telemachus strode on as fast as he could, till
he reached the homestead where his countless herds of
swine were feeding, and where dwelt the excellent
swineherd, who was so devoted a servant to his master. 557

MEANWHILE ULYSSES AND THE swineherd had lit a fire in the hut and were getting breakfast ready at daybreak, for they had sent the men out with the pigs. When Telemachus came up, the dogs did not bark but fawned upon him, so Ulysses, hearing the sound of feet and noticing that the dogs did not bark, said to Eumaeus:

8 "Eumaeus, I hear footsteps; I suppose one of your men or some one of your acquaintance is coming here, for the dogs are fawning upon him and not barking."

11 The words were hardly out of his mouth before his son stood at the door. Eumaeus sprang to his feet, and the bowls in which he was mixing wine fell from his hands, as he made towards his master. He kissed his head and both his beautiful eyes, and wept for joy. A father could not be more delighted at the return of an only son, the child of his old age, after ten years' absence in a foreign country and after having gone through much hardship. He embraced him, kissed him all over as though he had come back from the dead, and spoke fondly to him saying:

23 "So you are come, Telemachus, light of my eyes that you are. When I heard you had gone to Pylos I made sure I was never going to see you any more. Come in, my dear child, and sit down, that I may have a good look at you now you are home again; it is not very often you come into the country to see us herdsmen; you stick pretty close to the town generally. I suppose you think it better to keep an eye on what the suitors are doing."

30 "So be it, old friend," answered Telemachus, "but I am come now because I want to see you, and to learn whether my mother is still at her old home or whether some one else has married her, so that the bed of Ulysses is without bedding and covered with cobwebs."

"She is still at the house," replied Eumaeus, "griev- 36 ing and breaking her heart, and doing nothing but weep, both night and day continually."

As he spoke he took Telemachus' spear, whereon he 40 crossed the stone threshold and came inside. Ulysses rose from his seat to give him place as he entered, but Telemachus checked him; "Sit down, stranger," said he, "I can easily find another seat, and there is one here who will lay it for me."

Ulysses went back to his own place, and Eumaeus 46 strewed some green brushwood on the floor and threw a sheepskin on top of it for Telemachus to sit upon. Then the swineherd brought them platters of cold meat, the remains from what they had eaten the day before, and he filled the bread baskets with bread as fast as he could. He mixed wine also in bowls of ivy-wood, and took his seat facing Ulysses. Then they laid their hands on the good things that were before them, and as soon as they had had enough to eat and drink Telemachus said to Eumaeus, "Old friend, where does this stranger come from? How did his crew bring him to Ithaca, and who were they?—for assuredly he did not come here by land."

To this you answered, O swineherd Eumaeus, "My 60 son, I will tell you the real truth. He says he is a Cretan, and that he has been a great traveller. At this moment he is running away from a Thesprotian ship, and has taken refuge at my station, so I will put him into your hands. Do whatever you like with him, only remember that he is your suppliant."

"I am very much distressed," said Telemachus, "by 68 what you have just told me. How can I take this stranger into my house? I am as yet young, and am not strong enough to hold my own if any man attacks me. My mother cannot make up her mind whether to stay

245

where she is and look after the house out of respect for
public opinion and the memory of her husband, or
whether the time is now come for her to take the best
man of those who are wooing her, and the one who will
make her the most advantageous offer; still, as the
stranger has come to your station I will find him a cloak
and shirt of good wear, with a sword and sandals, and
will send him wherever he wants to go. Or if you like
you can keep him here at the station, and I will send
him clothes and food that he may be no burden on you
and on your men; but I will not have him go near the
suitors, for they are very insolent, and are sure to ill-
treat him in a way that would greatly grieve me; no
matter how valiant a man may be he can do nothing
against numbers, for they will be too strong for him."

90   Then Ulysses said, " Sir, it is right that I should say
something myself. I am much shocked by what you
have said about the insolent way in which the suitors are
behaving in despite of such a man as you are. Tell me,
do you submit to such treatment tamely, or has some
god set your people against you? May you not complain of your brothers—for it is to these that a man may
look for support, however great his quarrel may be?
I wish I were as young as you are and in my present
mind; if I were son to Ulysses, or, indeed, Ulysses
himself, I would rather some one came and cut my head
off, but I would go to the house and be the bane of
every one of these men.[1] If they were too many for
me—I being single-handed—I would rather die fighting
in my own house than see such disgraceful sights day
after day, strangers grossly maltreated, and men dragging the women servants about the house in an unseemly

[1] The text is here apparently corrupt, and will not make sense
as it stands. I follow Messrs. Butcher and Lang in omitting line
101.

way, wine drawn recklessly, and bread wasted all to no
purpose for an end that shall never be accomplished."

And Telemachus answered, " I will tell you truly 112
everything. There is no enmity between me and my
people, nor can I complain of brothers, to whom a man
may look for support however great his quarrel may be.
Jove has made us a race of only sons. Laertes was the
only son of Arceisius, and Ulysses only son of Laertes.
I am myself the only son of Ulysses who left me behind
him when he went away, so that I have never been of
any use to him. Hence it comes that my house is in the
hands of numberless marauders; for the chiefs from all
the neighbouring islands, Dulichium, Same, Zacynthus,
as also all the principal men of Ithaca itself, are eating
up my house under the pretext of paying court to my
mother, who will neither say point blank that she will
not marry, nor yet bring matters to an end, so they are
making havoc of my estate, and before long will do so
with myself into the bargain. The issue, however,
rests with heaven. But do you, old friend Eumaeus, go
at once and tell Penelope that I am safe and have
returned from Pylos. Tell it to herself alone, and then
come back here without letting any one else know, for
there are many who are plotting mischief against me."

" I understand and heed you," replied Eumaeus; 135
" you need instruct me no further, only as I am going
that way say whether I had not better let poor Laertes
know that you are returned. He used to superintend
the work on his farm in spite of his bitter sorrow about
Ulysses, and he would eat and drink at will along with
his servants; but they tell me that from the day on
which you set out for Pylos he has neither eaten nor
drunk as he ought to do, nor does he look after his
farm, but sits weeping and wasting the flesh from off his
bones."

146 "More's the pity," answered Telemachus, "I am
sorry for him, but we muSt leave him to himself juSt
now. If people could have everything their own way,
the firSt thing I should choose would be the return of
my father; but go, and give your message; then make
haSte back again, and do not turn out of your way to tell
Laertes. Tell my mother to send one of her women
secretly with the news at once, and let him hear it from
her."

154 Thus did he urge the swineherd; Eumaeus, therefore, took his sandals, bound them to his feet, and
Started for the town. Minerva watched him well off
the Station, and then came up to it in the form of a
woman–fair, Stately, and wise. She Stood againSt the
side of the entry, and revealed herself to Ulysses, but
Telemachus could not see her, and knew not that
she was there, for the gods do not let themselves be
seen by everybody. Ulysses saw her, and so did the
dogs, for they did not bark, but went scared and whining off to the other side of the yards. She nodded her
head and motioned to Ulysses with her eyebrows;
whereon he left the hut and Stood before her outside
the main wall of the yards. Then she said to him:

167 "Ulysses, noble son of Laertes, it is now time for you
to tell your son: do not keep him in the dark any longer,
but lay your plans for the deStruction of the suitors, and
then make for the town. I will not be long in joining
you, for I too am eager for the fray."

172 As she spoke she touched him with her golden wand.
FirSt she threw a fair clean shirt and cloak about his
shoulders; then she made him younger and of more
imposing presence; she gave him back his colour, filled
out his cheeks, and let his beard become dark again.
Then she went away and Ulysses came back inside the
hut. His son was aStounded when he saw him, and

248

turned his eyes away for fear he might be looking upon
a god.

"Stranger," said he, "how suddenly you have 181
changed from what you were a moment or two ago.
You are dressed differently and your colour is not the
same. Are you some one or other of the gods that live
in heaven? If so, be propitious to me till I can make
you due sacrifice and offerings of wrought gold. Have
mercy upon me."

And Ulysses said, "I am no god, why should you take 186
me for one? I am your father, on whose account you
grieve and suffer so much at the hands of lawless men."

As he spoke he kissed his son, and a tear fell from his 190
cheek on to the ground, for he had restrained all tears
till now. But Telemachus could not yet believe that it
was his father, and said:

"You are not my father, but some god is flattering 194
me with vain hopes that I may grieve the more hereafter; no mortal man could of himself contrive to do
as you have been doing, and make yourself old and
young at a moment's notice, unless a god were with
him. A second ago you were old and all in rags, and
now you are like some god come down from heaven."

Ulysses answered, "Telemachus, you ought not to
be so immeasurably astonished at my being really here.
There is no other Ulysses who will come hereafter.
Such as I am, it is I, who after long wandering and much
hardship have got home in the twentieth year to my
own country. What you wonder at is the work of the
redoubtable goddess Minerva, who does with me whatever she will, for she can do what she pleases. At one
moment she makes me like a beggar, and the next I am
a young man with good clothes on my back; it is an
easy matter for the gods who live in heaven to make any
man look either rich or poor."

213 As he spoke he sat down, and Telemachus threw his arms about his father and wept. They were both so much moved that they cried aloud like eagles or vultures with crooked talons that have been robbed of their half fledged young by peasants. Thus piteously did they weep, and the sun would have gone down upon their mourning if Telemachus had not suddenly said, " In what ship, my dear father, did your crew bring you to Ithaca? Of what nation did they declare themselves to be–for you cannot have come by land? "

226 " I will tell you the truth, my son," replied Ulysses. " It was the Phaeacians who brought me here. They are great sailors, and are in the habit of giving escorts to any one who reaches their coasts. They took me over the sea while I was fast asleep, and landed me in Ithaca, after giving me many presents in bronze, gold, and raiment. These things by heaven's mercy are lying concealed in a cave, and I am now come here on the suggestion of Minerva that we may consult about killing our enemies. First, therefore, give me a list of the suitors, with their number, that I may learn who, and how many, they are. I can then turn the matter over in my mind, and see whether we two can fight the whole body of them ourselves, or whether we must find others to help us."

240 To this Telemachus answered, " Father, I have always heard of your renown both in the field and in council, but the task you talk of is a very great one: I am awed at the mere thought of it; two men cannot stand against many and brave ones. There are not ten suitors only, nor twice ten, but ten many times over; you shall learn their number at once. There are fifty-two chosen youths from Dulichium, and they have six servants; from Same there are twenty-four; twenty young Achaeans from Zacynthus, and twelve from

Ithaca itself, all of them well born. They have with them a servant Medon, a bard, and two men who can carve at table. If we face such numbers as this, you may have bitter cause to rue your coming, and your revenge. See whether you cannot think of some one who would be willing to come and help us."

" Listen to me," replied Ulysses, " and think whether 257 Minerva and her father Jove may seem sufficient, or whether I am to try and find some one else as well."

" Those whom you have named," answered Tele- 262 machus, " are a couple of good allies, for though they dwell high up among the clouds they have power over both gods and men."

" These two," continued Ulysses, " will not keep 266 long out of the fray, when the suitors and we join fight in my house. Now, therefore, return home early to-morrow morning, and go about among the suitors as before. Later on the swineherd will bring me to the city disguised as a miserable old beggar. If you see them ill-treating me, steel your heart against my sufferings; even though they drag me feet foremost out of the house, or throw things at me, look on and do nothing beyond gently trying to make them behave more reasonably; but they will not listen to you, for the day of their reckoning is at hand. Furthermore I say, and lay my saying to your heart, when Minerva shall put it in my mind, I will nod my head to you, and on seeing me do this you must collect all the armour that is in the house and hide it in the strong store room. Make some excuse when the suitors ask you why you are removing it; say that you have taken it to be out of the way of the smoke, inasmuch as it is no longer what it was when Ulysses went away, but has become soiled and begrimed with soot. Add to this more particularly that you are afraid Jove may set them on to quarrel over their wine,

and that they may do each other some harm which may
disgrace both banquet and wooing, for the sight of arms
sometimes tempts people to use them. But leave a
sword and a spear apiece for yourself and me, and a
couple of oxhide shields so that we can snatch them up
at any moment; Jove and Minerva will then soon quiet
these people. There is also another matter; if you are
indeed my son and my blood runs in your veins, let no
one know that Ulysses is within the house—neither
Laertes, nor yet the swineherd, nor any of the servants,
nor even Penelope herself. Let you and me exploit the
women alone, and let us also make trial of some other
of the men servants, to see who is on our side and
whose hand is against us."

308 "Father," replied Telemachus, "you will come to
know me by and by, and when you do you will find
that I can keep your counsel. I do not think, however,
the plan you propose will turn out well for either of us.
Think it over. It will take us a long time to go the
round of the farms and exploit the men, and all the
time the suitors will be wasting your estate with im-
punity and without compunction. Prove the women
by all means, to see who are disloyal and who guiltless,
but I am not in favour of going round and trying the
men. We can attend to that later on, if you really have
some sign from Jove that he will support you."

321 Thus did they converse, and meanwhile the ship
which had brought Telemachus and his crew from
Pylos had reached the town of Ithaca. When they had
come inside the harbour they drew the ship on to the
land; their servants came and took their armour from
them, and they left all the presents at the house of
Clytius. Then they sent a servant to tell Penelope that
Telemachus had gone into the country, but had sent the
ship to the town to prevent her from being alarmed and

made unhappy. This servant and Eumaeus happened
to meet when they were both on the same errand of
going to tell Penelope. When they reached the house,
the servant stood up and said to the queen in the
presence of the waiting women, " Your son, Madam,
is now returned from Pylos "; but Eumaeus went close
up to Penelope, and said privately all that her son had
bidden him tell her. When he had given his message
he left the house with its outbuildings and went back
to his pigs again.

The suitors were surprised and angry at what had 342
happened, so they went outside the great wall that ran
round the outer court, and held a council near the main
entrance. Eurymachus, son of Polybus, was the first to
speak.

" My friends," said he, " this voyage of Telemachus's 346
is a very serious matter; we had made sure that it
would come to nothing. Now, however, let us draw
a ship into the water, and get a crew together to send
after the others and tell them to come back as fast as
they can."

He had hardly done speaking when Amphinomus 351
turned in his place and saw the ship inside the harbour,
with the crew lowering her sails, and putting by their
oars; so he laughed, and said to the others, " We need
not send them any message, for they are here. Some
god must have told them, or else they saw the ship go
by, and could not overtake her."

On this they rose and went to the water side. The 358
crew then drew the ship on shore; their servants took
their armour from them, and they went up in a body to
the place of assembly, but they would not let any one
old or young sit along with them, and Antinous, son
of Eupeithes, spoke first.

" Good heavens," said he, " see how the gods have 364

253

saved this man from destruction. We kept a succession
of scouts upon the headlands all day long, and when the
sun was down we never went on shore to sleep, but
waited in the ship all night till morning in the hope of
capturing and killing him; but some god has conveyed
him home in spite of us. Let us consider how we can
make an end of him. He must not escape us; our affair
is never likely to come off while he is alive, for he is very
shrewd, and public feeling is by no means all on our
side. We must make haste before he can call the Achaeans in assembly; he will lose no time in doing so, for he
will be furious with us, and will tell all the world how
we plotted to kill him, but failed to take him. The
people will not like this when they come to know of it;
we must see that they do us no hurt, nor drive us from
our own country into exile. Let us try and lay hold of
him either on his farm away from the town, or on the
road hither. Then we can divide up his property
amongst us, and let his mother and the man who marries
her have the house. If this does not please you, and
you wish Telemachus to live on and hold his father's
property, then we must not gather here and eat up his
goods in this way, but must make our offers to Penelope
each from his own house, and she can marry the man
who will give the most for her, and whose lot it is to
win her."

393   They all held their peace until Amphinomus rose to
speak. He was the son of Nisus, who was son to king
Aretias, and he was foremost among all the suitors from
the wheat-growing and well grassed island of Dulichium;
his conversation, moreover, was more agreeable to
Penelope than that of any of the other suitors, for he was
a man of good natural disposition. "My friends," said
he, speaking to them plainly and in all honesty, " I am
not in favour of killing Telemachus. It is a heinous

thing to kill one who is of noble blood. Let us first take counsel of the gods, and if the oracles of Jove advise it, I will both help to kill him myself, and will urge everyone else to do so; but if they dissuade us, I would have you hold your hands."

Thus did he speak, and his words pleased them well, 406 so they rose forthwith and went to the house of Ulysses, where they took their accustomed seats.

Then Penelope resolved that she would show herself 409 to the suitors. She knew of the plot against Telemachus, for the servant Medon had overheard their counsels and had told her; she went down therefore to the court attended by her maidens, and when she reached the suitors she stood by one of the bearing-posts supporting the roof of the cloister holding a veil before her face, and rebuked Antinous saying:

"Antinous, insolent and wicked schemer, they say 417 you are the best speaker and counsellor of any man your own age in Ithaca, but you are nothing of the kind. Madman, why should you try to compass the death of Telemachus, and take no heed of suppliants, whose witness is Jove himself? It is not right for you to plot thus against one another. Do you not remember how your father fled to this house in fear of the people, who were enraged against him for having gone with some Taphian pirates and plundered the Thesprotians who were at peace with us? They wanted to tear him in pieces and eat up everything he had, but Ulysses stayed their hands although they were infuriated, and now you devour his property without paying for it, and break my heart by wooing his wife and trying to kill his son. Leave off doing so, and stop the others also."

To this Eurymachus son of Polybus answered, 434 "Take heart, Queen Penelope daughter of Icarius, and do not trouble yourself about these matters. The man

is not yet born, nor never will be, who shall lay hands
upon your son Telemachus, while I yet live to look upon
the face of the earth. I say–and it shall surely be–that
my spear shall be reddened with his blood; for many a
time has Ulysses taken me on his knees, held wine up
to my lips to drink, and put pieces of meat into my
hands. Therefore Telemachus is much the dearest
friend I have, and has nothing to fear from the hands
of us suitors. Of course, if death comes to him from
the gods, he cannot escape it." He said this to quiet
her, but in reality he was plotting against Telemachus.

449 Then Penelope went upstairs again and mourned her
husband till Minerva shed sleep over her eyes. In the
evening Eumaeus got back to Ulysses and his son, who
had just sacrificed a young pig of a year old and were
helping one another to get supper ready; Minerva
therefore came up to Ulysses, turned him into an old
man with a stroke of her wand, and clad him in his old
clothes again, for fear that the swineherd might recognize
him and not keep the secret, but go and tell Penelope.

460 Telemachus was the first to speak. " So you have
got back, Eumaeus," said he. " What is the news of the
town? Have the suitors returned, or are they still
waiting over yonder, to take me on my way home? "

464 " I did not think of asking about that," replied
Eumaeus, " when I was in the town. I thought I
would give my message and come back as soon as I
could. I met a man sent by those who had gone with
you to Pylos, and he was the first to tell the news to
your mother, but I can say what I saw with my own
eyes; I had just got on to the crest of the hill of Mercury
above the town when I saw a ship coming into harbour
with a number of men in her. They had many shields
and spears, and I thought it was the suitors, but I cannot
be sure."

256

In the Hut

On hearing this Telemachus smiled to his father, but 476
so that Eumaeus could not see him.

Then, when they had finished their work and the 478
meal was ready, they ate it, and every man had his full
share so that all were satisfied. As soon as they had had
enough to eat and drink, they laid down to rest and
enjoyed the boon of sleep. 481

BOOK SEVENTEEN: TELEMACHUS AND HIS MOTHER MEET,
ULYSSES AND EUMAEUS COME DOWN TO THE TOWN, AND
ULYSSES IS INSULTED BY MELANTHIUS, HE IS RECOGNIZED
BY THE DOG ARGOS, HE IS INSULTED AND PRESENTLY
STRUCK BY ANTINOUS WITH A STOOL, PENELOPE DESIRES
THAT HE SHALL BE SENT TO HER

WHEN THE CHILD OF MORNING, ROSY-fingered Dawn, appeared, Telemachus bound on his sandals and took a strong spear that suited his hands, for he wanted to go into the city. " Old friend," said he to the swineherd, " I will now go to the town and show myself to my mother, for she will never leave off grieving till she has seen me. As for this unfortunate stranger, take him to the town and let him beg there of any one who will give him a drink and a piece of bread. I have trouble enough of my own, and cannot be burdened with other people. If this makes him angry so much the worse for him, but I like to say what I mean."

16   Then Ulysses said, " Sir, I do not want to stay here; a beggar can always do better in town than country, for any one who likes can give him something. I am too old to care about remaining here at the beck and call of a master. Therefore let this man do as you have just told him, and take me to the town as soon as I have had a warm by the fire, and the day has got a little heat in it. My clothes are wretchedly thin, and this frosty morning I shall be perished with cold, for you say the city is some way off."

26   On this Telemachus strode off through the yards, brooding his revenge upon the suitors. When he reached home he stood his spear against a bearing-post of the cloister, crossed the stone floor of the cloister itself, and went inside.

31   Nurse Euryclea saw him long before any one else did. She was putting the fleeces on to the seats, and she

burst out crying as she ran up to him; all the other
maids came up too, and covered his head and shoulders
with their kisses. Penelope came out of her room
looking like Diana or Venus, and wept as she flung her
arms about her son. She kissed his forehead and both
his beautiful eyes, " Light of my eyes," she cried as she
spoke fondly to him, " so you are come home again; I
made sure I was never going to see you any more. To
think of your having gone off to Pylos without saying
anything about it or obtaining my consent. But come,
tell me what you saw."

" Do not scold me, mother," answered Telemachus, 45
" nor vex me, seeing what a narrow escape I have had,
but wash your face, change your dress, go upstairs with
your maids, and promise full and sufficient hecatombs
to all the gods if Jove will only grant us our revenge
upon the suitors. I must now go to the place of
assembly to invite a stranger who has come back with
me from Pylos. I sent him on with my crew, and told
Piraeus to take him home and look after him till I could
come for him myself."

She heeded her son's words, washed her face, changed 57
her dress, and vowed full and sufficient hecatombs to all
the gods if they would only vouchsafe her revenge upon
the suitors.

Telemachus went through, and out of, the cloisters 61
spear in hand–not alone, for his two fleet dogs went
with him. Minerva endowed him with a presence of
such divine comeliness that all marvelled at him as he
went by, and the suitors gathered round him with
fair words in their mouths and malice in their hearts;
but he avoided them, and went to sit with Mentor,
Antiphus, and Halitherses, old friends of his father's
house, and they made him tell them all that had happened to him. Then Piraeus came up with Theocly-

menus, whom he had escorted through the town to the place of assembly, whereon Telemachus at once joined them. Piraeus was first to speak: "Telemachus," said he, "I wish you would send some of your women to my house to take away the presents Menelaus gave you."

77   "We do not know, Piraeus," answered Telemachus, "what may happen. If the suitors kill me in my own house and divide my property among them, I would rather you had the presents than that any of those people should get hold of them. If on the other hand I manage to kill them, I shall be much obliged if you will kindly bring me my presents."

84   With these words he took Theoclymenus to his own house. When they got there they laid their cloaks on the benches and seats, went into the baths, and washed themselves. When the maids had washed and anointed them, and had given them cloaks and shirts, they took their seats at table. A maid servant then brought them water in a beautiful golden ewer, and poured it into a silver basin for them to wash their hands; and she drew a clean table beside them. An upper servant brought them bread and offered them many good things of what there was in the house. Opposite them sat Penelope, reclining on a couch by one of the bearing-posts of the cloister, and spinning. Then they laid their hands on the good things that were before them, and as soon as they had had enough to eat and drink Penelope said:

101   "Telemachus, I shall go upstairs and lie down on that sad couch, which I have not ceased to water with my tears, from the day Ulysses set out for Troy with the sons of Atreus. You failed, however, to make it clear to me before the suitors came back to the house, whether or no you had been able to hear anything about the return of your father."

" I will tell you the truth," replied her son. " We 106
went to Pylos and saw Nestor, who took me to his
house and treated me as hospitably as though I were a
son of his own who had just returned after a long
absence; so also did his sons; but he said he had not
heard a word from any human being about Ulysses,
whether he was alive or dead. He sent me, therefore,
with a chariot and horses to Menelaus. There I saw
Helen, for whose sake so many, both Argives and
Trojans, were in heaven's wisdom doomed to suffer.
Menelaus asked me what it was that had brought me to
Lacedaemon, and I told him the whole truth, whereon
he said, ' So, then, these cowards would usurp a brave
man's bed? A hind might as well lay her new-born
young in the lair of a lion, and then go off to feed in the
forest or in some grassy dell. The lion, when he comes
back to his lair, will make short work with the pair of
them, and so will Ulysses with these suitors. By father
Jove, Minerva, and Apollo, if Ulysses is still the man
that he was when he wrestled with Philomeleides in
Lesbos, and threw him so heavily that all the Greeks
cheered him—if he is still such, and were to come near
these suitors, they would have a short shrift and a sorry
wedding. As regards your question, however, I will
not prevaricate nor deceive you, but what the old man
of the sea told me, so much will I tell you in full. He
said he could see Ulysses on an island sorrowing bitterly
in the house of the nymph Calypso, who was keeping
him prisoner, and he could not reach his home, for he
had no ships nor sailors to take him over the sea.'
This was what Menelaus told me, and when I had heard
his story I came away; the gods then gave me a fair
wind and soon brought me safe home again."

With these words he moved the heart of Penelope. 150
Then Theoclymenus said to her:

152 " Madam, wife of Ulysses, Telemachus does not understand these things; listen therefore to me, for I can divine them surely, and will hide nothing from you. May Jove the king of heaven be my witness, and the rites of hospitality, with that hearth of Ulysses to which I now come, that Ulysses himself is even now in Ithaca, and, either going about the country or staying in one place, is enquiring into all these evil deeds and preparing a day of reckoning for the suitors. I saw an omen when I was on the ship which meant this, and I told Telemachus about it."

162 " May it be even so," answered Penelope; " if your words come true, you shall have such gifts and such good will from me that all who see you shall congratulate you."

166 Thus did they converse. Meanwhile the suitors were throwing discs, or aiming with spears at a mark on the levelled ground in front of the house, and behaving with all their old insolence. But when it was now time for dinner, and the flock of sheep and goats had come into the town from all the country round,[1] with their shepherds as usual, then Medon, who was their favourite servant, and who waited upon them at table, said, " Now then, my young masters, you have had enough sport, so come inside that we may get dinner ready. Dinner is not a bad thing, at dinner time."

177 They left their sports as he told them, and when they were within the house, they laid their cloaks on the benches and seats inside, and then sacrificed some sheep, goats, pigs, and a heifer, all of them fat and well grown.[2]

---

[1] *I.e.*, to be milked, as in South Italian and Sicilian towns at the present day.

[2] The butchering and making ready the carcasses took place partly in the outer yard and partly in the open part of the inner court.

Thus they made ready for their meal. In the meantime Ulysses and the swineherd were about starting for the town, and the swineherd said, " Stranger, I suppose you still want to go to town to-day, as my master said you were to do; for my own part I should have liked you to stay here as a station hand, but I must do as my master tells me, or he will scold me later on, and a scolding from one's master is a very serious thing. Let us then be off, for it is now broad day; it will be night again directly and then you will find it colder." [1]

" I know, and understand you," replied Ulysses; 192 " you need say no more. Let us be going, but if you have a stick ready cut, let me have it to walk with, for you say the road is a very rough one."

As he spoke he threw his shabby old tattered wallet 197 over his shoulders, by the cord from which it hung, and Eumaeus gave him a stick to his liking. The two then started, leaving the station in charge of the dogs and herdsmen who remained behind; the swineherd led the way and his master followed after, looking like some broken-down old tramp as he leaned upon his staff, and his clothes were all in rags. When they had got over the rough steep ground and were nearing the city, they reached the fountain from which the citizens drew their water. This had been made by Ithacus, Neritus, and Polyctor. There was a grove of water-loving poplars planted in a circle all round it, and the clear cold water

---

[1] These words cannot mean that it would be afternoon soon after they were spoken. Ulysses and Eumaeus reached the town which was " some way off " (xvii, 25) in time for the suitors' early meal (xvii, 170 and 176) say at ten or eleven o'clock. The context of the rest of the book shows this. Eumaeus and Ulysses, therefore, cannot have started later than eight or nine, and Eumaeus's words must be taken as an exaggeration for the purpose of making Ulysses bestir himself.

came down to it from a rock high up,[1] while above the
fountain there was an altar to the nymphs, at which all
wayfarers used to sacrifice. Here Melanthius son of
Dolius overtook them as he was driving down some
goats, the beſt in his flock, for the suitors' dinner, and
there were two shepherds with him. When he saw
Eumaeus and Ulysses he reviled them with outrageous
and unseemly language, which made Ulysses very angry.
217   " There you go," cried he, " and a precious pair you
are. See how heaven brings birds of the same feather
to one another. Where, pray, maſter swineherd, are
you taking this poor miserable objeƈt? It would make
any one sick to see such a creature at table. A fellow
like this never won a prize for anything in his life, but
will go about rubbing his shoulders againſt every man's
door poſt, and begging, not for swords and cauldrons [2]
like a man, but only for a few scraps not worth begging
for. If you would give him to me for a hand on my
ſtation, he might do to clean out the folds, or bring a
bit of sweet feed to the kids, and he could fatten his
thighs as much as he pleased on whey; but he has taken
to bad ways and will not go about any kind of work;
he will do nothing but beg viƈtuals all the town over, to
feed his insatiable belly. I say, therefore–and it shall
surely be–if he goes near Ulysses' house he will get his

----

[1] I imagine the fountain to have been somewhere about where
the church of the Madonna di Trapani now ſtands, and to have
been fed with water from what is now called the Fontana Diffali
on Mt. Eryx.

[2] From this and other passages in the Odyssey it appears that
we are in an age anterior to the use of coined money—an age
when cauldrons, tripods, swords, cattle, chattels of all kinds,
measures of corn, wine, or oil, etc., etc., not to say pieces of gold,
silver, bronze, or even iron, wrought more or less, but unſtamped,
were the neareſt approach to a currency that had as yet been
reached.

head broken by the stools they will fling at him, till they
turn him out."

On this, as he passed, he gave Ulysses a kick on the 233
hip out of pure wantonness, but Ulysses stood firm, and
did not budge from the path. For a moment he
doubted whether or no to fly at Melanthius and kill him
with his staff, or fling him to the ground and beat his
brains out; he resolved, however, to endure it and keep
himself in check, but the swineherd looked straight at
Melanthius and rebuked him, lifting up his hands and
praying to heaven as he did so.

" Fountain nymphs," he cried, " children of Jove, 240
if ever Ulysses burned you thigh bones covered with fat
whether of lambs or kids, grant my prayer that heaven
may send him home. He would soon put an end to the
swaggering threats with which such men as you go
about insulting people—gadding all over the town
while your flocks are going to ruin through bad shepherding."

Then Melanthius the goatherd answered, " You ill- 247
conditioned cur, what are you talking about? Some
day or other I will put you on board ship and take you
to a foreign country, where I can sell you and pocket
the money you will fetch. I wish I were as sure that
Apollo would strike Telemachus dead this very day, or
that the suitors would kill him, as I am that Ulysses will
never come home again."

With this he left them to come on at their leisure, 254
while he went quickly forward and soon reached the
house of his master. When he got there he went in and
took his seat among the suitors opposite Eurymachus,
who liked him better than any of the others. The
servants brought him a portion of meat, and an upper
woman servant set bread before him that he might eat.
Presently Ulysses and the swineherd came up to the

house and stood by it, amid a sound of music, for Phemius was just beginning to sing to the suitors. Then Ulysses took hold of the swineherd's hand, and said:

264 "Eumaeus, this house of Ulysses is a very fine place. No matter how far you go you will find few like it. One building keeps following on after another. The outer court has a wall with battlements all round it; the doors are double folding, and of good workmanship; it would be a hard matter to take it by force of arms. I perceive, too, that there are many people banqueting within it, for there is a smell of roast meat, and I hear a sound of music, which the gods have made to go along with feasting."

272 Then Eumaeus said, "You have perceived aright, as indeed you generally do; but let us think what will be our best course. Will you go inside first and join the suitors, leaving me here behind you, or will you wait here and let me go in first? But do not wait long, or some one may see you loitering about outside, and throw something at you. Consider this matter I pray you."

280 And Ulysses answered, "I understand and heed. Go in first and leave me here where I am. I am quite used to being beaten and having things thrown at me. I have been so much buffeted about in war and by sea that I am case-hardened, and this too may go with the rest. But a man cannot hide away the cravings of a hungry belly; this is an enemy which gives much trouble to all men; it is because of this that ships are fitted out to sail the seas, and to make war upon other people."

290 As they were thus talking, a dog that had been lying asleep raised his head and pricked up his ears. This was Argos, whom Ulysses had bred before setting out for Troy, but he had never had any work out of him. In

the old days he used to be taken out by the young men
when they went hunting wild goats, or deer, or hares,
but now that his master was gone he was lying neglected
on the heaps of mule and cow dung that lay in front of
the stable doors till the men should come and draw it
away to manure the great close; and he was full of fleas.
As soon as he saw Ulysses standing there, he dropped
his ears and wagged his tail, but he could not get close
up to his master. When Ulysses saw the dog on the
other side of the yard, he dashed a tear from his eyes
without Eumaeus seeing it, and said:

" Eumaeus, what a noble hound that is over yonder 306
on the manure heap: his build is splendid; is he as fine
a fellow as he looks, or is he only one of those dogs that
come begging about a table, and are kept merely for
show? "

" This hound," answered Eumaeus, " belonged to 311
him who has died in a far country. If he were what he
was when Ulysses left for Troy, he would soon show
you what he could do. There was not a wild beast
in the forest that could get away from him when he was
once on its tracks. But now he has fallen on evil times,
for his master is dead and gone, and the women take
no care of him. Servants never do their work when
their master's hand is no longer over them, for Jove
takes half the goodness out of a man when he makes a
slave of him."

As he spoke he went inside the buildings to the 324
cloister where the suitors were, but Argos died as soon
as he had recognized his master.

Telemachus saw Eumaeus long before any one else 328
did, and beckoned him to come and sit beside him; so
he looked about and saw a seat lying near where the
carver sat serving out their portions to the suitors; he
picked it up, brought it to Telemachus's table, and sat

down opposite him. Then the servant brought him his portion, and gave him bread from the bread-basket.

336 Immediately afterwards Ulysses came inside, looking like a poor miserable old beggar, leaning on his staff and with his clothes all in rags. He sat down upon the threshold of ash-wood just inside the doors leading from the outer to the inner court, and against a bearing-post of cypress-wood which the carpenter had skilfully planed, and had made to join truly with rule and line. Telemachus took a whole loaf from the bread-basket, with as much meat as he could hold in his two hands, and said to Eumaeus, " Take this to the stranger, and tell him to go the round of the suitors, and beg from them; a beggar must not be shamefaced."

348 So Eumaeus went up to him and said, " Stranger, Telemachus sends you this, and says you are to go the round of the suitors begging, for beggars must not be shamefaced."

353 Ulysses answered, " May King Jove grant all happiness to Telemachus, and fulfil the desire of his heart."

356 Then with both hands he took what Telemachus had sent him, and laid it on the dirty old wallet at his feet. He went on eating it while the bard was singing, and had just finished his dinner as he left off. The suitors applauded the bard, whereon Minerva went up to Ulysses and prompted him to beg pieces of bread from each one of the suitors, that he might see what kind of people they were, and tell the good from the bad; but come what might she was not going to save a single one of them. Ulysses, therefore, went on his round, going from left to right, and stretched out his hands to beg as though he were a real beggar. Some of them pitied him, and were curious about him, asking one another who he was and where he came from; whereon the goatherd Melanthius said, " Suitors of my noble

mistress, I can tell you something about him, for I have
seen him before.   The swineherd brought him here,
but I know nothing about the man himself, nor where
he comes from."

On this Antinous began to abuse the swineherd. 374
" You precious idiot," he cried, " what have you
brought this man to town for?   Have we not tramps
and beggars enough already to pester us as we sit at
meat?   Do you think it a small thing that such people
gather here to waste your master's property – and must
you needs bring this man as well? "

And Eumaeus answered, " Antinous, your birth is 380
good but your words evil.   It was no doing of mine
that he came here.   Who is likely to invite a stranger
from a foreign country, unless it be one of those who
can do public service as a seer, a healer of hurts, a
carpenter, or a bard who can charm us with his singing?
Such men are welcome all the world over, but no one
is likely to ask a beggar who will only worry him.   You
are always harder on Ulysses' servants than any of the
other suitors are, and above all on me, but I do not care
so long as Telemachus and Penelope are alive and here."

But Telemachus said, " Hush, do not answer him; 392
Antinous has the bitterest tongue of all the suitors, and
he makes the others worse."

Then turning to Antinous he said, " Antinous, you 396
take as much care of my interests as though I were your
son.   Why should you want to see this stranger turned
out of the house?   Heaven forbid; take something and
give it him yourself; I do not grudge it; I bid you take
it.   Never mind my mother, nor any of the other
servants in the house; but I know you will not do what
I say, for you are more fond of eating things yourself
than of giving them to other people."

" What do you mean, Telemachus," replied Antinous, 405

" by this swaggering talk? If all the suitors were to give him as much as I will, he would not come here again for another three months."

409   As he spoke he drew the stool on which he rested his dainty feet from under the table, and made as though he would throw it at Ulysses, but the other suitors all gave him something, and filled his wallet with bread and meat; he was about, therefore, to go back to the threshold and eat what the suitors had given him, but he first went up to Antinous and said:

415   " Sir, give me something; you are not, surely, the poorest man here; you seem to be a chief, foremost among them all; therefore you should be the better giver, and I will tell far and wide of your bounty. I too was a rich man once, and had a fine house of my own; in those days I gave to many a tramp such as I now am, no matter who he might be nor what he wanted. I had any number of servants, and all the other things which people have who live well and are accounted wealthy, but it pleased Jove to take all away from me. He sent me with a band of roving robbers to Egypt; it was a long voyage and I was undone by it. I stationed my ships in the river Aegyptus, and bade my men stay by them and keep guard over them, while I sent out scouts to reconnoitre from every point of vantage.

431   " But the men disobeyed my orders, took to their own devices, and ravaged the land of the Egyptians, killing the men, and taking their wives and children captives. The alarm was soon carried to the city, and when they heard the war-cry, the people came out at daybreak till the plain was filled with soldiers horse and foot, and with the gleam of armour. Then Jove spread panic among my men, and they would no longer face the enemy, for they found themselves surrounded. The Egyptians killed many of us, and took the rest alive to

do forced labour for them; as for myself, they gave me
to a friend who met them, to take to Cyprus, Dmetor
by name, son of Iasus, who was a great man in Cyprus.
Thence I am come hither in a state of great misery."

Then Antinous said, " What god can have sent such 445
a pestilence to plague us during our dinner? Get out,
into the open part of the court,[1] or I will give you Egypt
and Cyprus over again for your insolence and importunity; you have begged of all the others, and they
have given you lavishly, for they have abundance
round them, and it is easy to be free with other people's
property when there is plenty of it."

On this Ulysses began to move off, and said, " Your 453
looks, my fine sir, are better than your breeding; if you
were in your own house you would not spare a poor
man so much as a pinch of salt, for though you are in
another man's, and surrounded with abundance, you
cannot find it in you to give him even a piece of
bread."

This made Antinous very angry, and he scowled at 458
him saying, " You shall pay for this before you get clear
of the court." With these words he threw a footstool
at him, and hit him on the right shoulder-blade near the
top of his back. Ulysses stood firm as a rock and the
blow did not even stagger him, but he shook his head
in silence as he brooded on his revenge. Then he went
back to the threshold and sat down there, laying his
well-filled wallet at his feet.

" Listen to me," he cried, " you suitors of Queen 468
Penelope, that I may speak even as I am minded. A
man knows neither ache nor pain if he gets hit while
fighting for his money, or for his sheep or his cattle;
and even so Antinous has hit me while in the service of
my miserable belly, which is always getting people into

[1] Gr. ἐc μέccon.

271

trouble. Still, if the poor have gods and avenging deities at all, I pray them that Antinous may come to a bad end before his marriage."

477   " Sit where you are, and eat your victuals in silence, or be off elsewhere," shouted Antinous. " If you say more I will have you dragged hand and foot through the courts, and the servants shall flay you alive."

481   The other suitors were much displeased at this, and one of the young men said, " Antinous, you did ill in striking that poor wretch of a tramp: it will be worse for you if he should turn out to be some god—and we know the gods go about disguised in all sorts of ways as people from foreign countries, and travel about the world to see who do amiss and who righteously." [1]

488   Thus said the suitors, but Antinous paid them no heed. Meanwhile Telemachus was furious about the blow that had been given to his father, and though no tear fell from him, he shook his head in silence and brooded on his revenge.

492   Now when Penelope heard that the beggar had been struck in the banqueting-cloister, she said before her maids, " Would that Apollo would so strike you, Antinous," and her waiting woman Eurynome answered, " If our prayers were answered not one of the suitors would ever again see the sun rise." Then Penelope said, " Nurse,[2] I hate every single one of them, for they mean nothing but mischief, but I hate Antinous like the darkness of death itself. A poor unfortunate tramp has come begging about the house for sheer want. Every one else has given him something to put in his wallet,

---

[1] I correct these proofs abroad and am not within reach of Hesiod, but surely this passage suggests acquaintance with the *Works and Days*, though it by no means compels it.

[2] It would seem as though Eurynome and Euryclea were the same person. See note on xx, 4.

but Antinous has hit him on the right shoulder-blade with a footstool."

Thus did she talk with her maids as she sat in her own 505 room, and in the meantime Ulysses was getting his dinner. Then she called for the swineherd and said, "Eumaeus, go and tell the stranger to come here, I want to see him and ask him some questions. He seems to have travelled much, and he may have seen or heard something of my unhappy husband."

To this you answered, O swineherd Eumaeus, "If 512 these Achaeans, Madam, would only keep quiet, you would be charmed with the history of his adventures. I had him three days and three nights with me in my hut, which was the first place he reached after running away from his ship, and he has not yet completed the story of his misfortunes. If he had been the most heaven-taught minstrel in the whole world, on whose lips all hearers hang entranced, I could not have been more charmed as I sat in my hut and listened to him. He says there is an old friendship between his house and that of Ulysses, and that he comes from Crete where the descendants of Minos live, after having been driven hither and thither by every kind of misfortune; he also declares that he has heard of Ulysses as being alive and near at hand among the Thesprotians, and that he is bringing great wealth home with him."

"Call him here, then," said Penelope, "that I too 528 may hear his story. As for the suitors, let them take their pleasure indoors or out as they will, for they have nothing to fret about. Their corn and wine remain un-wasted in their houses with none but servants to consume them, while they keep hanging about our house day after day, sacrificing our oxen, sheep, and fat goats for their banquets, and never giving so much as a thought to the quantity of wine they drink. No estate can stand such recklessness, for we have now no Ulysses to protect us. If he were to come again, he and his son would soon have their revenge."

541 As she spoke Telemachus sneezed so loudly that the whole house resounded with it. Penelope laughed when she heard this, and said to Eumaeus, " Go and call the stranger; did you not hear how my son sneezed just as I was speaking? This can only mean that all the suitors are going to be killed, and that not one of them shall escape. Furthermore I say, and lay my saying to your heart: if I am satisfied that the stranger is speaking the truth I shall give him a shirt and cloak of good wear."

551 When Eumaeus heard this he went straight to Ulysses and said, " Father stranger, my mistress Penelope, mother of Telemachus, has sent for you; she is in great grief, but she wishes to hear anything you can tell her about her husband, and if she is satisfied that you are speaking the truth, she will give you a shirt and cloak, which are the very things that you are most in want of. As for bread, you can get enough of that to fill your belly, by begging about the town, and letting those give that will."

560 " I will tell Penelope," answered Ulysses, " nothing but what is strictly true. I know all about her husband, and have been partner with him in affliction, but I am afraid of passing through this crowd of cruel suitors, for their pride and insolence reach heaven. Just now, moreover, as I was going about the house without doing any harm, a man gave me a blow that hurt me very much, but neither Telemachus nor any one else defended me. Tell Penelope, therefore, to be patient and wait till sundown. Let her give me a seat close up to the fire, for my clothes are worn very thin—you know they are, for you have seen them ever since I first

asked you to help me—she can then ask me about the
return of her husband."

The swineherd went back when he heard this, and 574
Penelope said as she saw him cross the threshold,
"Why do you not bring him here, Eumaeus? Is he
afraid that some one will ill-treat him, or is he shy of
coming inside the house at all? Beggars should not be
shamefaced."

To this you answered, O swineherd Eumaeus, "The 579
stranger is quite reasonable. He is avoiding the suitors,
and is only doing what any one else would do. He asks
you to wait till sundown, and it will be much better,
madam, that you should have him all to yourself, when
you can hear him and talk to him as you will."

"The man is no fool," answered Penelope, "it 585
would very likely be as he says, for there are no such
abominable people in the whole world as these men are."

When she had done speaking Eumaeus went back to 589
the suitors, for he had explained everything. Then he
went up to Telemachus and said in his ear so that none
could overhear him, "My dear sir, I will now go back
to the pigs, to see after your property and my own
business. You will look to what is going on here, but
above all be careful to keep out of danger, for there are
many who bear you ill will. May Jove bring them to a
bad end before they do us a mischief."

"Very well," replied Telemachus, "go home when 598
you have had your dinner, and in the morning come
here with the victims we are to sacrifice for the day.
Leave the rest to heaven and me."

On this Eumaeus took his seat again, and when he 602
had finished his dinner he left the courts and the cloister
with the men at table, and went back to his pigs. As for
the suitors, they presently began to amuse themselves
with singing and dancing, for it was now getting on
towards evening.   606

NOW THERE CAME A CERTAIN COMMON tramp who used to go begging all over the city of Ithaca, and was notorious as an incorrigible glutton and drunkard. This man had no strength nor stay in him, but he was a great hulking fellow to look at; his real name, the one his mother gave him, was Arnaeus, but the young men of the place called him Irus, because he used to run errands for any one who would send him.[1] As soon as he came he began to insult Ulysses, and to try and drive him out of his own house.

10 " Be off, old man," he cried, " from the doorway, or you shall be dragged out neck and heels. Do you not see that they are all giving me the wink, and wanting me to turn you out by force, only I do not like to do so? Get up then, and go of yourself, or we shall come to blows."

14 Ulysses frowned on him and said, " My friend, I do you no manner of harm; people give you a great deal, but I am not jealous. There is room enough in this doorway for the pair of us, and you need not grudge me things that are not yours to give. You seem to be just such another tramp as myself, but perhaps the gods will give us better luck by and by. Do not, however, talk too much about fighting, or you will incense me, and old though I am, I shall cover your mouth and chest with blood. I shall have more peace to-morrow if I do, for you will not come to the house of Ulysses any more."

25 Irus was very angry and answered, " You filthy

---

[1] It is plain, therefore, that Iris was commonly accepted as the messenger of the gods, though our authoress will never permit her to fetch or carry for any one.

276

glutton, you run on trippingly like an old fish-fag. I
have a good mind to lay both hands about you, and
knock your teeth out of your head like so many boar's
tusks. Get ready, therefore, and let these people here
stand by and look on. You will never be able to fight
one who is so much younger than yourself."

Thus roundly did they rate one another on the 32
smooth pavement in front of the doorway,[1] and when
Antinous saw what was going on he laughed heartily
and said to the others, "This is the finest sport that
you ever saw; heaven never yet sent anything like it
into this house. The stranger and Irus have quarrelled
and are going to fight, let us set them on to do so at
once."

The suitors all came up laughing, and gathered round 40
the two ragged tramps. "Listen to me," said Antinous,
"there are some goats' paunches down at the fire,
which we have filled with blood and fat, and set aside
for supper; he who is victorious and proves himself to
be the better man shall have his pick of the lot; he shall
be free of our table and we will not allow any other
beggar about the house at all."

The others all agreed, but Ulysses, to throw them off 50
the scent, said, "Sirs, an old man like myself, worn out
with suffering, cannot hold his own against a young one;
but my irrepressible belly urges me on, though I know
it can only end in my getting a drubbing. You must
swear, however, that none of you will give me a foul
blow to favour Irus and secure him the victory."

They swore as he told them, and when they had com- 58
pleted their oath Telemachus put in a word and said,
"Stranger, if you have a mind to settle with this fellow,
you need not be afraid of any one here. Whoever
strikes you will have to fight more than one. I am host,

[1] *I.e.*, the doorway leading from the inner to the outer court.

277

and the other chiefs, Antinous and Eurymachus, both of them men of understanding, are of the same mind as I am."

66   Every one assented, and Ulysses girded his old rags about his loins, thus baring his stalwart thighs, his broad chest and shoulders, and his mighty arms; but Minerva came up to him and made his limbs even stronger still.   The suitors were beyond measure astonished, and one would turn towards his neighbour saying, " The stranger has brought such a thigh out of his old rags that there will soon be nothing left of Irus."

75   Irus began to be very uneasy as he heard them, but the servants girded him by force, and brought him [into the open part of the court] in such a fright that his limbs were all of a tremble.   Antinous scolded him and said, " You swaggering bully, you ought never to have been born at all if you are afraid of such an old broken-down creature as this tramp is.   I say, therefore–and it shall surely be–if he beats you and proves himself the better man, I shall pack you off on board ship to the mainland and send you to king Echetus, who kills every one that comes near him.   He will cut off your nose and ears, and draw out your entrails for the dogs to eat."

88   This frightened Irus still more, but they brought him into the middle of the court, and the two men raised their hands to fight.   Then Ulysses considered whether he should let drive so hard at him as to make an end of him then and there, or whether he should give him a lighter blow that should only knock him down; in the end he deemed it best to give the lighter blow for fear the Achaeans should begin to suspect who he was. Then they began to fight, and Irus hit Ulysses on the right shoulder; but Ulysses gave Irus a blow on the neck under the ear that broke in the bones of his skull,

278

and the blood came gushing out of his mouth; he fell
groaning in the dust, gnashing his teeth and kicking on
the ground, but the suitors threw up their hands and
nearly died of laughter, as Ulysses caught hold of him
by the foot and dragged him into the outer court as far
as the gate-house. There he propped him up against
the wall and put his staff in his hands. " Sit here," said
he, " and keep the dogs and pigs off; you are a pitiful
creature, and if you try to make yourself king of the
beggars any more you shall fare still worse."

Then he threw his dirty old wallet, all tattered and 108
torn, over his shoulder with the cord by which it hung,
and went back to sit down upon the threshold; but the
suitors went within the cloisters, laughing and saluting
him, " May Jove, and all the other gods," said they,
" grant you whatever you want for having put an end
to the importunity of this insatiable tramp. We will
take him over to the mainland presently, to king
Echetus, who kills every one that comes near him."

Ulysses hailed this as of good omen, and Antinous 117
set a great goat's paunch before him filled with blood
and fat. Amphinomus took two loaves out of the
bread-basket and brought them to him, pledging him
as he did so in a golden goblet of wine. " Good luck
to you," he said, " father stranger, you are very badly
off at present, but I hope you will have better times by
and by."

To this Ulysses answered, " Amphinomus, you seem 124
to be a man of good understanding, as indeed you may
well be, seeing whose son you are. I have heard your
father well spoken of; he is Nisus of Dulichium, a man
both brave and wealthy. They tell me you are his son,
and you appear to be a considerable person; listen,
therefore, and take heed to what I am saying. Man is
the vainest of all creatures that have their being upon

279

earth. As long as heaven vouchsafes him health and
strength, he thinks that he shall come to no harm hereafter, and even when the blessed gods bring sorrow
upon him, he bears it as he needs must, and makes the
best of it; for God almighty gives men their daily
minds day by day. I know all about it, for I was a rich
man once, and did much wrong in the stubbornness of
my pride, and in the confidence that my father and my
brothers would support me; therefore let a man fear
God in all things always, and take the good that heaven
may see fit to send him without vainglory. Consider
the infamy of what these suitors are doing; see how
they are wasting the estate, and doing dishonour to the
wife, of one who is certain to return some day, and that,
too, not long hence. Nay, he will be here soon; may
heaven send you home quietly first that you may not
meet with him in the day of his coming, for once he is
here the suitors and he will not part bloodlessly."

151   With these words he made a drink-offering, and when
he had drunk he put the gold cup again into the hands
of Amphinomus, who walked away serious and bowing
his head, for he foreboded evil. But even so he did not
escape destruction, for Minerva had doomed him to fall
by the hand of Telemachus. So he took his seat again
at the place from which he had come.

158   Then Minerva put it into the mind of Penelope to
show herself to the suitors, that she might make them
still more enamoured of her, and win still further
honour from her son and husband. So she feigned a
mocking laugh and said, " Eurynome, I have changed
my mind, and have a fancy to show myself to the suitors
although I detest them. I should like also to give my
son a hint that he had better not have anything more to
do with them. They speak fairly enough but they mean
mischief."

" My dear child," answered Eurynome, " all that you 169 have said is true, go and tell your son about it, but first wash yourself and anoint your face. Do not go about with your cheeks all covered with tears; it is not right that you should grieve so incessantly; for Telemachus, whom you always prayed that you might live to see with a beard, is already grown up."

" I know, Eurynome," replied Penelope, " that you 177 mean well, but do not try and persuade me to wash and to anoint myself, for heaven robbed me of all my beauty on the day my husband sailed; nevertheless, tell Autonoe and Hippodamia that I want them. They must be with me when I am in the cloister; I am not going among the men alone; it would not be proper for me to do so."

On this the old woman [1] went out of the room to bid 185 the maids go to their mistress. In the meantime Minerva bethought her of another matter, and sent Penelope off into a sweet slumber; so she lay down on her couch and her limbs became heavy with sleep. Then the goddess shed grace and beauty over her that all the Achaeans might admire her. She washed her face with the ambrosial loveliness that Venus wears when she goes dancing with the Graces; she made her taller and of a more commanding figure, while as for her complexion it was whiter than sawn ivory. When Minerva had done all this she went away, whereon the maids came in from the women's room and woke Penelope with the sound of their talking.

" What an exquisitely delicious sleep I have been 200 having," said she, as she passed her hands over her face, " in spite of all my misery. I wish Diana would let me die so sweetly now at this very moment, that I

[1] Surely in this scene, again, Eurynome is in reality Euryclea. See note on xx, 4.

might no longer waste in despair for the loss of my dear husband, who possessed every kind of good quality and was the most distinguished man among the Achaeans."

206 With these words she came down from her upper room, not alone but attended by two of her maidens, and when she reached the suitors she stood by one of the bearing-posts supporting the roof of the cloister, holding a veil before her face, and with a staid maid servant on either side of her. As they beheld her the suitors were so overpowered and became so desperately enamoured of her, that each one prayed he might win her for his own bed fellow.

214 " Telemachus," said she, addressing her son, " I fear you are no longer so discreet and well conducted as you used to be. When you were younger you had a greater sense of propriety; now, however, that you are grown up, though a stranger to look at you would take you for the son of a well-to-do father as far as size and good looks go, your conduct is by no means what it should be. What is all this disturbance that has been going on, and how came you to allow a stranger to be so disgracefully ill-treated? What would have happened if he had suffered serious injury while a suppliant in our house? Surely this would have been very discreditable to you."

226 " I am not surprised, my dear mother, at your displeasure," replied Telemachus, " I understand all about it and know when things are not as they should be, which I could not do when I was younger; I cannot, however, behave with perfect propriety at all times. First one and then another of these wicked people here keeps driving me out of my mind, and I have no one to stand by me. After all, however, this fight between Irus and the stranger did not turn out as the suitors meant it to do, for the stranger got the best of it. I wish

Father Jove, Minerva, and Apollo would break the neck of every one of these wooers of yours, some inside the house and some out; and I wish they might all be as limp as Irus is over yonder in the gate of the outer court. See how he nods his head like a drunken man; he has had such a thrashing that he cannot stand on his feet nor get back to his home, wherever that may be, for he has no strength left in him."

Thus did they converse. Eurymachus then came up 243 and said, " Queen Penelope, daughter of Icarius, if all the Achaeans in Iasian Argos could see you at this moment, you would have still more suitors in your house by to-morrow morning, for you are the most admirable woman in the whole world both as regards personal beauty and strength of understanding."

To this Penelope replied, " Eurymachus, heaven 250 robbed me of all my beauty whether of face or figure when the Argives set sail for Troy and my dear husband with them. If he were to return and look after my affairs, I should both be more respected and show a better presence to the world. As it is, I am oppressed with care, and with the afflictions which heaven has seen fit to heap upon me. My husband foresaw it all, and when he was leaving home he took my right wrist in his hand–' Wife,' he said, ' we shall not all of us come safe home from Troy, for the Trojans fight well both with bow and spear. They are excellent also at fighting from chariots, and nothing decides the issue of a fight sooner than this. I know not, therefore, whether heaven will send me back to you, or whether I may not fall over there at Troy. In the meantime do you look after things here. Take care of my father and mother as at present, and even more so during my absence, but when you see our son growing a beard, then marry whom you will, and leave this your present

283

home.' This is what he said and now it is all coming true. A night will come when I shall have to yield myself to a marriage which I detest, for Jove has taken from me all hope of happiness. This further grief, moreover, cuts me to the very heart. You suitors are not wooing me after the custom of my country. When men are courting a woman who they think will be a good wife to them and who is of noble birth, and when they are each trying to win her for himself, they usually bring oxen and sheep to feast the friends of the lady, and they make her magnificent presents, instead of eating up other people's property without paying for it."

281   This was what she said, and Ulysses was glad when he heard her trying to get presents out of the suitors, and flattering them with fair words which he knew she did not mean.

284   Then Antinous said, " Queen Penelope, daughter of Icarius, take as many presents as you please from any one who will give them to you; it is not well to refuse a present; but we will not go about our business nor stir from where we are, till you have married the best man among us whoever he may be."

290   The others applauded what Antinous had said, and each one sent his servant to bring his present. Antinous's man returned with a large and lovely dress most exquisitely embroidered. It had twelve beautifully made brooch pins of pure gold with which to fasten it. Eurymachus immediately brought her a magnificent chain of gold and amber beads that gleamed like sunlight. Eurydamas's two men returned with some earrings fashioned into three brilliant pendants which glistened most beautifully; while king Pisander son of Polyctor gave her a necklace of the rarest workmanship, and every one else brought her a beautiful present of some kind.

Then the queen went back to her room upstairs, and 302
her maids brought the presents after her. Meanwhile
the suitors took to singing and dancing, and stayed till
evening came. They danced and sang till it grew dark;
they then brought in three braziers [1] to give light, and
piled them up with chopped firewood very old and dry,
and they lit torches from them, which the maids held
up turn and turn about. Then Ulysses said:

"Maids, servants of Ulysses who has so long been 313
absent, go to the queen inside the house; sit with her
and amuse her, or spin, and pick wool. I will hold the
light for all these people. They may stay till morning,
but shall not beat me, for I can stand a great deal."

The maids looked at one another and laughed, while 320
pretty Melantho began to gibe at him contemptuously.
She was daughter to Dolius, but had been brought up
by Penelope, who used to give her toys to play with,
and looked after her when she was a child; but in spite
of all this she showed no consideration for the sorrows
of her mistress, and used to misconduct herself with
Eurymachus, with whom she was in love.

"Poor wretch," said she, "are you gone clean out 327
of your mind? Go and sleep in some smithy, or place
of public gossips, instead of chattering here. Are you
not ashamed of opening your mouth before your
betters—so many of them too? Has the wine been
getting into your head, or do you always babble in this
way? You seem to have lost your wits because you
beat the tramp Irus; take care that a better man than he
does not come and cudgel you about the head till he
pack you bleeding out of the house."

---

[1] These, I imagine, must have been in the open part of the
inner courtyard, where the maids also stood, and threw the light
of their torches into the covered cloister that ran all round it.
The smoke would otherwise have been intolerable.

337 " Vixen," replied Ulysses, scowling at her, " I will go and tell Telemachus what you have been saying, and he will have you torn limb from limb."

340 With these words he scared the women, and they went off into the body of the house. They trembled all over, for they thought he would do as he said. But Ulysses took his stand near the burning braziers, holding up torches and looking at the people—brooding the while on things that should surely come to pass.

346 But Minerva would not let the suitors for one moment cease their insolence, for she wanted Ulysses to become even more bitter against them; she therefore set Eurymachus son of Polybus on to gibe at him, which made the others laugh. " Listen to me," said he, " you suitors of Queen Penelope, that I may speak even as I am minded. It is not for nothing that this man has come to the house of Ulysses; I believe the light has not been coming from the torches, but from his own head—for his hair is all gone, every bit of it."

356 Then turning to Ulysses he said, " Stranger, will you work as a servant, if I send you to the wolds and see that you are well paid? Can you build a stone fence, or plant trees? I will have you fed all the year round, and will find you in shoes and clothing. Will you go, then? Not you; for you have got into bad ways, and do not want to work; you had rather fill your belly by going round the country begging."

366 " Eurymachus," answered Ulysses, " if you and I were to work one against the other in early summer when the days are at their longest—give me a good scythe, and take another yourself, and let us see which will fast the longer or mow the stronger, from dawn till dark when the mowing grass is about. Or if you will plough against me, let us each take a yoke of tawny oxen, well-mated and of great strength and endurance:

286

turn me into a four acre field, and see whether you or I
can drive the straighter furrow. If, again, war were to
break out this day, give me a shield, a couple of spears
and a helmet fitting well upon my temples–you would
find me foremost in the fray, and would cease your
gibes about my belly. You are insolent and cruel, and
think yourself a great man because you live in a little
world, and that a bad one. If Ulysses comes to his own
again, the doors of his house are wide, but you will find
them narrow when you try to fly through them."

Eurymachus was furious at all this. He scowled at 387
him and cried, " You wretch, I will soon pay you out
for daring to say such things to me, and in public too.
Has the wine been getting into your head or do you
always babble in this way? You seem to have lost
your wits because you beat the tramp Irus." With this
he caught hold of a footstool, but Ulysses sought
protection at the knees of Amphinomus of Dulichium,
for he was afraid. The stool hit the cupbearer on his
right hand and knocked him down: the man fell with a
cry flat on his back, and his wine-jug fell ringing to the
ground. The suitors in the covered cloister were now in
an uproar, and one would turn towards his neighbour,
saying, " I wish the stranger had gone somewhere else,
bad luck to him, for all the trouble he gives us. We
cannot permit such disturbance about a beggar; if such
ill counsels are to prevail we shall have no more pleasure
at our banquet."

On this Telemachus came forward and said, " Sirs, 405
are you mad? Can you not carry your meat and your
liquor decently? Some evil spirit has possessed you.
I do not wish to drive any of you away, but you have
had your suppers, and the sooner you all go home to
bed the better."

The suitors bit their lips and marvelled at the bold- 410

ness of his speech; but Amphinomus the son of Nisus, who was son to Aretias, said, "Do not let us take offence; it is reasonable, so let us make no answer. Neither let us do violence to the stranger nor to any of Ulysses' servants. Let the cupbearer go round with the drink-offerings, that we may make them and go home to our rest. As for the stranger, let us leave Telemachus to deal with him, for it is to his house that he has come."

₄₂₂ Thus did he speak, and his saying pleased them well, so Mulius of Dulichium, servant to Amphinomus, mixed them a bowl of wine and water and handed it round to each of them man by man, whereon they made their drink-offerings to the blessed gods. Then, when they had made their drink-offerings and had drunk each one as he was minded, they took their several ₄₂₈ ways each of them to his own abode.

ULYSSES WAS LEFT IN THE CLOISTER, pondering on the means whereby with Minerva's help he might be able to kill the suitors. Presently he said to Telemachus, "Telemachus, we must get the armour together and take it down inside. Make some excuse when the suitors ask you why you have removed it. Say that you have taken it to be out of the way of the smoke, inasmuch as it is no longer what it was when Ulysses went away, but has become soiled and begrimed with soot. Add to this more particularly that you are afraid Jove may set them on to quarrel over their wine, and that they may do each other some harm which may disgrace both banquet and wooing, for the sight of arms sometimes tempts people to use them."

Telemachus approved of what his father had said, so 14 he called nurse Euryclea and said, "Nurse, shut the women up in their room, while I take the armour that my father left behind him down into the store room. No one looks after it now my father is gone, and it has got all smirched with soot during my own boyhood. I want to take it down where the smoke cannot reach it."

"I wish, child," answered Euryclea, "that you 21 would take the management of the house into your own hands altogether, and look after all the property yourself. But who is to go with you and light you to the store room? The maids would have done so, but you would not let them."

"The stranger," said Telemachus, "shall show me a 26 light; when people eat my bread they must earn it, no matter where they come from."

29 Euryclea did as she was told, and bolted the women inside their room. Then Ulysses and his son made all haste to take the helmets, shields, and spears inside; and Minerva went before them with a gold lamp in her hand that shed a soft and brilliant radiance, whereon Telemachus said, "Father, my eyes behold a great marvel: the walls, with the rafters, crossbeams, and the supports on which they rest are all aglow as with a flaming fire. Surely there is some god here who has come down from heaven."

41 "Hush," answered Ulysses, "hold your peace and ask no questions, for this is the manner of the gods. Get you to your bed, and leave me here to talk with your mother and the maids. Your mother in her grief will ask me all sorts of questions."

47 On this Telemachus went by torch-light to the other side of the inner court, to the room in which he always slept. There he lay in his bed till morning, while Ulysses was left in the cloister pondering on the means whereby with Minerva's help he might be able to kill the suitors.

53 Then Penelope came down from her room looking like Venus or Diana, and they set her a seat inlaid with scrolls of silver and ivory near the fire in her accustomed place. It had been made by Icmalius and had a foot-stool all in one piece with the seat itself; and it was covered with a thick fleece: on this she now sat, and the maids came from the women's room to join her. They set about removing the tables at which the wicked suitors had been dining, and took away the bread that was left, with the cups from which they had drunk. They emptied the embers out of the braziers, and heaped much wood upon them to give both light and heat; but Melantho began to rail at Ulysses a second time and said, "Stranger, do you mean to plague us by hanging

about the house all night and spying upon the women?
Be off, you wretch, outside, and eat your supper there,
or you shall be driven out with a firebrand."

Ulysses scowled at her and answered, " My good 70
woman, why should you be so angry with me? Is it
because I am not clean, and my clothes are all in rags,
and because I am obliged to go begging about after the
manner of tramps and beggars generally? I too was a
rich man once, and had a fine house of my own; in
those days I gave to many a tramp such as I now am,
no matter who he might be nor what he wanted. I had
any number of servants, and all the other things which
people have who live well and are accounted wealthy,
but it pleased Jove to take all away from me; therefore,
woman, beware lest you too come to lose that pride and
place in which you now wanton above your fellows;
have a care lest you get out of favour with your mistress,
and lest Ulysses should come home, for there is still a
chance that he may do so. Moreover, though he be
dead as you think he is, yet by Apollo's will he has left
a son behind him, Telemachus, who will note anything
done amiss by the maids in the house, for he is now no
longer in his boyhood."

Penelope heard what he was saying and scolded the 89
maid, " Impudent baggage," said she, " I see how
abominably you are behaving, and you shall smart for
it. You knew perfectly well, for I told you myself,
that I was going to see the stranger and ask him about
my husband, for whose sake I am in such continual
sorrow."

Then she said to her head waiting woman Eurynome, 96
" Bring a seat with a fleece upon it, for the stranger to
sit upon while he tells his story, and listens to what I
have to say. I wish to ask him some questions."

Eurynome brought the seat at once and set a fleece 100

upon it, and as soon as Ulysses had sat down Penelope
began by saying, " Stranger, I shall first ask you who
and whence are you? Tell me of your town and
parents."

106   " Madam," answered Ulysses, " who on the face of
the whole earth can dare to chide with you? Your
fame reaches the firmament of heaven itself; you are
like some blameless king, who upholds righteousness,
as the monarch over a great and valiant nation: the
earth yields its wheat and barley, the trees are loaded
with fruit, the ewes bring forth lambs, and the sea
abounds with fish by reason of his virtues, and his
people do good deeds under him. Nevertheless, as I
sit here in your house, ask me some other question and
do not seek to know my race and family, or you will
recall memories that will yet more increase my sorrow.
I am full of heaviness, but I ought not to sit weeping
and wailing in another person's house, nor is it well
to be thus grieving continually. I shall have one of the
servants or even yourself complaining of me, and
saying that my eyes swim with tears because I am heavy
with wine."

123   Then Penelope answered, " Stranger, heaven robbed
me of all beauty, whether of face or figure, when the
Argives set sail for Troy and my dear husband with
them. If he were to return and look after my affairs I
should be both more respected and should show a better
presence to the world. As it is, I am oppressed with
care, and with the afflictions which heaven has seen fit
to heap upon me. The chiefs from all our islands—
Dulichium, Same, and Zacynthus, as also from Ithaca
itself, are wooing me against my will and are wasting
my estate. I can therefore show no attention to
strangers, nor suppliants, nor to people who say that
they are skilled artisans, but am all the time broken-

hearted about Ulysses. They want me to marry again at once, and I have to invent stratagems in order to deceive them. In the first place heaven put it in my mind to set up a great tambour-frame in my room, and to begin working upon an enormous piece of fine needlework. Then I said to them, 'Sweethearts, Ulysses is indeed dead, still, do not press me to marry again immediately; wait—for I would not have my skill in needlework perish unrecorded—till I have finished making a pall for the hero Laertes, to be ready against the time when death shall take him. He is very rich, and the women of the place will talk if he is laid out without a pall.' This was what I said, and they assented; whereon I used to keep working at my great web all day long, but at night I would unpick the stitches again by torch light. I fooled them in this way for three years without their finding it out, but as time wore on and I was now in my fourth year, in the waning of moons, and many days had been accomplished, those good-for-nothing hussies my maids betrayed me to the suitors, who broke in upon me and caught me; they were very angry with me, so I was forced to finish my work whether I would or no. And now I do not see how I can find any further shift for getting out of this marriage. My parents are putting great pressure upon me, and my son chafes at the ravages the suitors are making upon his estate, for he is now old enough to understand all about it and is perfectly able to look after his own affairs, for heaven has blessed him with an excellent disposition. Still, notwithstanding all this, tell me who you are and where you come from—for you must have had father and mother of some sort; you cannot be the son of an oak or of a rock."

Then Ulysses answered, " Madam, wife of Ulysses, 164 since you persist in asking me about my family, I will

293

answer, no matter what it costs me: people must expect
to be pained when they have been exiles as long as I
have, and suffered as much among as many peoples.
Nevertheless, as regards your question I will tell you
all you ask.   There is a fair and fruitful island in mid-
ocean called Crete; it is thickly peopled and there are
ninety cities in it: the people speak many different
languages which overlap one another, for there are
Achaeans, brave Eteocretans, Dorians of three-fold race,
and noble Pelasgi.   There is a great town there, Cnossus,
where Minos reigned who every nine years had a con-
ference with Jove himself.[1]   Minos was father to
Deucalion, whose son I am, for Deucalion had two sons
Idomeneus and myself.   Idomeneus sailed for Troy,
and I, who am the younger, am called Aethon; my
brother, however, was at once the older and the more
valiant of the two; hence it was in Crete that I saw
Ulysses and showed him hospitality, for the winds took
him there as he was on his way to Troy, carrying him
out of his course from cape Malea and leaving him in
Amnisus off the cave of Ilithuia, where the harbours are
difficult to enter and he could hardly find shelter from
the winds that were then raging.   As soon as he got
there he went into the town and asked for Idomeneus,
claiming to be his old and valued friend, but Idomeneus
had already set sail for Troy some ten or twelve days
earlier, so I took him to my own house and showed him
every kind of hospitality, for I had abundance of everything.   Moreover, I fed the men who were with him
with barley meal from the public store, and got sub-
scriptions of wine and oxen for them to sacrifice to their
heart's content.   They stayed with me twelve days,
for there was a gale blowing from the North so strong

---

[1] Translation very uncertain ; *vide* Liddell and Scott, under
ἐννέωρος.

A COIN OF ABOUT 430 B.C.

Now in the British Museum, and classed by the authorities as
belonging to some town in the neighbourhood of Mt. Eryx,
reproduces Ulysses' brooch, with obvious intention, as may
be seen by the accompanying illustration, which, however,
is enlarged to about double the diameter of the coin itself.
The legend IAKIN (abbreviation for IAKINON–*i.e.* of the
Iacenses, or Ionians–for IAKOS means Ionian) indicates that
this town, in the neighbourhood of Mt. Eryx, was reputed to
be of Ionian origin, while the presence of Ulysses' brooch
upon the coin almost compels the conclusion that the
inhabitants of the coining city claimed a connection with the
Odyssey, which they expressed by numismatic allusion to
the passage which suggests itself as more suitable for such
allusion than any other in the whole poem–See *Authoress of
the Odyssey*, pp. 237-242

that one could hardly keep one's feet on land. I suppose
some unfriendly god had raised it for them, but on
the thirteenth day the wind dropped, and they got
away."

Many a plausible tale did Ulysses further tell her, and 203
Penelope wept as she listened, for her heart was melted.
As the snow wastes upon the mountain tops when the
winds from South East and West have breathed upon it
and thawed it till the rivers run bank full with water,
even so did her cheeks overflow with tears for the
husband who was all the time sitting by her side.
Ulysses felt for her and was sorry for her, but he kept
his eyes as hard as horn or iron without letting them
so much as quiver, so cunningly did he restrain his tears.
Then, when she had relieved herself by weeping, she
turned to him again and said: " Now, stranger, I shall
put you to the test and see whether or no you really did
entertain my husband and his men, as you say you did.
Tell me, then, how he was dressed, what kind of a man
he was to look at, and so also with his companions."

" Madam," answered Ulysses, " it is such a long time 220
ago that I can hardly say. Twenty years are come and
gone since he left my home, and went elsewhither; but
I will tell you as well as I can recollect. Ulysses wore
a mantle of purple wool, double lined, and it was
fastened by a gold brooch with two catches for the pin.
On the face of this there was a device that showed a dog
holding a spotted fawn between his fore paws, and
watching it as it lay panting upon the ground. Every
one marvelled at the way in which these things had
been done in gold, the dog looking at the fawn, and
strangling it, while the fawn was struggling convulsively to escape.[1] As for the shirt that he wore next
his skin, it was so soft that it fitted him like the skin

[1] See illustration.

295

of an onion, and glistened in the sunlight to the admiration of all the women who beheld it. Furthermore I say, and lay my saying to your heart, that I do not know whether Ulysses wore these clothes when he left home, or whether one of his companions had given them to him while he was on his voyage; or possibly some one at whose house he was staying made him a present of them, for he was a man of many friends and had few equals among the Achaeans. I myself gave him a sword of bronze and a beautiful purple mantle, double lined, with a shirt that went down to his feet, and I sent him on board his ship with every mark of honour. He had a servant with him, a little older than himself, and I can tell you what he was like; his shoulders were hunched,[1] he was dark, and he had thick curly hair. His name was Eurybates, and Ulysses treated him with greater familiarity than he did any of the others, as being the most like-minded with himself."

249   Penelope was moved still more deeply as she heard the indisputable proofs that Ulysses laid before her; and when she had again found relief in tears she said to him, " Stranger, I was already disposed to pity you, but henceforth you shall be honoured and made welcome in my house. It was I who gave Ulysses the clothes you speak of. I took them out of the store room and folded them up myself, and I gave him also the gold brooch to wear as an ornament. Alas! I shall never welcome him home again. It was by an ill fate that he ever set out for that detested city whose very name I cannot bring myself even to mention."

[1] *Cf.* Il., ii, 184, and 217, 218. An additional and well-marked feature being wanted to convince Penelope, the writer has taken the hunched shoulders of Thersites (who is mentioned immediately after Eurybates in the Iliad) and put them on to Eurybates' back.

Then Ulysses answered, " Madam, wife of Ulysses, 261 do not disfigure yourself further by grieving thus bitterly for your loss, though I can hardly blame you for doing so. A woman who has loved her husband and borne him children, would naturally be grieved at losing him, even though he were a worse man than Ulysses, who they say was like a god. Still, cease your tears and listen to what I can tell you. I will hide nothing from you, and can say with perfect truth that I have lately heard of Ulysses as being alive and on his way home; he is among the Thesprotians, and is bringing back much valuable treasure that he has begged from one and another of them; but his ship and all his crew were lost as they were leaving the Thrinacian island, for Jove and the sun-god were angry with him because his men had slaughtered the sun-god's cattle, and they were all drowned to a man. But Ulysses stuck to the keel of the ship and was drifted on to the land of the Phaeacians, who are near of kin to the immortals, and who treated him as though he had been a god, giving him many presents, and wishing to escort him home safe and sound. In fact Ulysses would have been here long ago, had he not thought better to go from land to land gathering wealth; for there is no man living who is so wily as he is; there is no one can compare with him. Pheidon king of the Thesprotians told me all this, and he swore to me – making drink-offerings in his house as he did so – that the ship was by the water side and the crew found who would take Ulysses to his own country. He sent me off first, for there happened to be a Thesprotian ship sailing for the wheat-growing island of Dulichium, but he showed me all the treasure Ulysses had got together, and he had enough lying in the house of king Pheidon to keep his family for ten generations; but the king said Ulysses had gone to Dodona that he might learn Jove's mind from the high oak tree, and know whether after so long an absence he should return to Ithaca openly or in secret. So you may know he is safe and will be here shortly; he is close at hand and cannot remain away from home much longer; nevertheless I will confirm my words with an oath, and call Jove who is the first and mightiest of all gods to witness, as also that hearth of Ulysses to which I have now come, that all I have spoken shall surely come to pass. Ulysses will return in this self same year; with the end of this moon and the beginning of the next he will be here."

308 " May it be even so," answered Penelope; " if your words come true you shall have such gifts and such good will from me that all who see you shall congratulate you; but I know very well how it will all be. Ulysses will not return, neither will you get your escort hence, for so surely as that Ulysses ever was, there are now no longer any such masters in the house as he was, to receive honourable strangers or to further them on their way home. And now, you maids, wash his feet for him, and make him a bed on a couch with rugs and blankets, that he may be warm and quiet till morning. Then, at day break wash him and anoint him again, that he may sit in the cloister and take his meals with Telemachus. It shall be the worse for any one of these hateful people who is uncivil to him; like it or not, he shall have no more to do in this house. For how, sir, shall you be able to learn whether or no I am superior to others of my sex both in goodness of heart and understanding, if I let you dine in my cloisters squalid and ill clad? Men live but for a little season; if they are hard, and deal hardly, people wish them ill so long as they are alive, and speak contemptuously of them when they are dead, but he that is righteous and deals righteously,

298

the people tell of his praise among all lands, and many
shall call him blessed."

Ulysses answered, " Madam, I have foresworn rugs 335
and blankets from the day that I left the snowy ranges
of Crete to go on shipboard. I will lie as I have lain
on many a sleepless night hitherto. Night after night
have I passed in any rough sleeping place, and waited
for morning. Nor, again, do I like having my feet
washed; I shall not let any of the young hussies about
your house touch my feet; but, if you have any old and
respectable woman who has gone through as much
trouble as I have, I will allow her to wash them."

To this Penelope said, " My dear sir, of all the guests 349
who ever yet came to my house there never was one
who spoke in all things with such admirable propriety
as you do. There happens to be in the house a most
respectable old woman—the same who received my
poor dear husband in her arms the night he was born,
and nursed him in infancy. She is very feeble now, but
she shall wash your feet." " Come here," said she,
" Euryclea, and wash your master's age-mate; I
suppose Ulysses' hands and feet are very much the
same now as his are, for trouble ages all of us dreadfully
fast."

On these words the old woman covered her face with 361
her hands; she began to weep and made lamentation
saying, " My dear child, I cannot think whatever I am
to do with you. I am certain no one was ever more
god-fearing than yourself, and yet Jove hates you.
No one in the whole world ever burned him more
thigh bones, nor gave him finer hecatombs when you
prayed you might come to a green old age yourself and
see your son grow up to take your place after you: yet
see how he has prevented you alone from ever getting
back to your own home. I have no doubt the women

299

in some foreign palace which Ulysses has got to are gibing at him as all these sluts here have been gibing at you. I do not wonder at your not choosing to let them wash you after the manner in which they have insulted you; I will wash your feet myself gladly enough, as Penelope has said that I am to do so; I will wash them both for Penelope's sake and for your own, for you have raised the most lively feelings of compassion in my mind; and let me say this moreover, which pray attend to; we have had all kinds of strangers in distress come here before now, but I make bold to say that no one ever yet came who was so like Ulysses in figure, voice, and feet as you are."

382 "Those who have seen us both," answered Ulysses, "have always said we were wonderfully like each other, and now you have noticed it too."

386 Then the old woman took the cauldron in which she was going to wash his feet, and poured plenty of cold water into it, adding hot till the bath was warm enough. Ulysses sat by the fire, but ere long he turned away from the light, for it occurred to him that when the old woman had hold of his leg she would recognize a certain scar which it bore, whereon the whole truth would come out. And indeed as soon as she began washing her master, she at once knew the scar as one that had been given him by a wild boar when he was hunting on Mount Parnassus with his excellent grandfather Autolycus—who was the most accomplished thief and perjurer in the whole world—and with the sons of Autolycus. Mercury himself had endowed him with this gift, for he used to burn the thigh bones of goats and kids to him, so he took pleasure in his companionship. It happened once that Autolycus had gone to Ithaca and had found the child of his daughter just born. As soon as he had done supper Euryclea set the

infant upon his knees and said, " Autolycus, you muſt
find a name for your grandson; you greatly wished
that you might have one."

" Son-in-law and daughter," replied Autolycus, " call 406
the child thus: I am highly displeased with a large
number of people in one place and another, both men
and women; so name the child ' Ulysses,' or the child
of anger.   When he grows up and comes to visit his
mother's family on Mount Parnassus, where my possessions lie, I will make him a present and will send him
on his way rejoicing."

Ulysses, therefore, went to Parnassus to get the 413
presents from Autolycus, who with his sons shook
hands with him and gave him welcome.   His grand-
mother Amphithea threw her arms about him, and
kissed his head, and both his beautiful eyes, while
Autolycus desired his sons to get dinner ready, and
they did as he told them.   They brought in a five year
old bull, flayed it, made it ready and divided it into
joints; these they then cut carefully up into smaller
pieces and spitted them; they roaſted them sufficiently
and served the portions round.   Thus through the
livelong day to the going down of the sun they feaſted,
and every man had his full share so that all were
satisfied; but when the sun set and it came on dark,
they went to bed and enjoyed the boon of sleep.

When the child of morning, rosy-fingered Dawn, 426
appeared, the sons of Autolycus went out with their
hounds hunting, and Ulysses went too.   They climbed
the wooded slopes of Parnassus and soon reached its
breezy upland valleys; but as the sun was beginning to
beat upon the fields, fresh-risen from the slow ſtill
currents of Oceanus, they came to a mountain dell.
The dogs were in front searching for the tracks of the
beaſt they were chasing, and after them came the sons

of Autolycus, among whom was Ulysses, close behind the dogs, and he had a long spear in his hand. Here was the lair of a huge boar among some thick brushwood, so dense that the wind and rain could not get through it, nor could the sun's rays pierce it, and the ground underneath lay thick with fallen leaves. The boar heard the noise of the men's feet, and the hounds baying on every side as the huntsmen came up to him, so he rushed from his lair, raised the bristles on his neck, and stood at bay with fire flashing from his eyes. Ulysses was the first to raise his spear and try to drive it into the brute, but the boar was too quick for him, and charged him sideways, ripping him above the knee with a gash that tore deep though it did not reach the bone. As for the boar, Ulysses hit him on the right shoulder, and the point of the spear went right through him, so that he fell groaning in the dust until the life went out of him. The sons of Autolycus busied themselves with the carcass of the boar, and bound Ulysses' wound; then, after saying a spell to stop the bleeding, they went home as fast as they could. But when Autolycus and his sons had thoroughly healed Ulysses, they made him some splendid presents, and sent him back to Ithaca with much mutual good will. When he got back, his father and mother were rejoiced to see him, and asked him all about it, and how he had hurt himself to get the scar; so he told them how the boar had ripped him when he was out hunting with Autolycus and his sons on Mount Parnassus.

467   As soon as Euryclea had got the scarred limb in her hands and had well hold of it, she recognized it and dropped the foot at once. The leg fell into the bath, which rang out and was overturned, so that all the water was spilt on the ground; Euryclea's eyes between her joy and her grief filled with tears, and she could not

speak, but she caught Ulysses by the beard and said, "My dear child, I am sure you must be Ulysses himself, only I did not know you till I had actually touched and handled you."

As she spoke she looked towards Penelope, as though 476 wanting to tell her that her dear husband was in the house, but Penelope was unable to look in that direction and observe what was going on, for Minerva had diverted her attention; so Ulysses caught Euryclea by the throat with his right hand and with his left drew her close to him, and said, "Nurse, do you wish to be the ruin of me, you who nursed me at your own breast, now that after twenty years of wandering I am at last come to my own home again? Since it has been borne in upon you by heaven to recognize me, hold your tongue, and do not say a word about it to any one else in the house, for if you do I tell you—and it shall surely be—that if heaven grants me to take the lives of these suitors, I will not spare you, though you are my own nurse, when I am killing the other women."

"My child," answered Euryclea, "what are you 491 talking about? You know very well that nothing can either bend or break me. I will hold my tongue like a stone or a piece of iron; furthermore let me say, and lay my saying to your heart, when heaven has delivered the suitors into your hand, I will give you a list of the women in the house who have been ill-behaved, and of those who are guiltless."

And Ulysses answered, "Nurse, you ought not to 499 speak in that way; I am well able to form my own opinion about one and all of them; hold your tongue and leave everything to heaven."

As he said this Euryclea left the cloister to fetch some 503 more water, for the first had been all spilt; and when she had washed him and anointed him with oil, Ulysses drew his seat nearer to the fire to warm himself, and hid the scar under his rags. Then Penelope began talking to him and said:

509   " Stranger, I should like to speak with you briefly about another matter. It is indeed nearly bed time—for those, at least, who can sleep in spite of sorrow. As for myself, heaven has given me a life of such unmeasurable woe, that even by day when I am attending to my duties and looking after the servants, I am still weeping and lamenting during the whole time; then, when night comes, and we all of us go to bed, I lie awake thinking, and my heart becomes a prey to the most incessant and cruel tortures. As the dun nightingale, daughter of Pandareus, sings in the early spring from her seat in shadiest covert hid, and with many a plaintive trill pours out the tale how by mishap she killed her own child Itylus, son of king Zethus, even so does my mind toss and turn in its uncertainty whether I ought to stay with my son here, and safeguard my substance, my bondsmen, and the greatness of my house, out of regard to public opinion and the memory of my late husband, or whether it is not now time for me to go with the best of these suitors who are wooing me and making me such magnificent presents. As long as my son was still young, and unable to understand, he would not hear of my leaving my husband's house, but now that he is full grown he begs and prays me to do so, being incensed at the way in which the suitors are eating up his property. Listen, then, to a dream that I have had and interpret it for me if you can. I have twenty geese about the house that eat mash out of a trough,[1] and of which I am exceedingly fond. I dreamed that a great eagle came swooping down from a

[1] This is how geese are now fed in Sicily, at any rate in summer, when the grass is all burnt up. I have never seen them grazing.

304

mountain, and dug his curved beak into the neck of each of them till he had killed them all. Presently he soared off into the sky, and left them lying dead about the yard; whereon I wept in my dream till all my maids gathered round me, so piteously was I grieving because the eagle had killed my geese. Then he came back again, and perching on a projecting rafter spoke to me with human voice, and told me to leave off crying. ' Be of good courage,' he said, ' daughter of Icarius; this is no dream, but a vision of good omen that shall surely come to pass. The geese are the suitors, and I am no longer an eagle, but your own husband, who am come back to you, and who will bring these suitors to a disgraceful end.' On this I woke, and when I looked out I saw my geese at the trough eating their mash as usual."

" This dream, Madam," replied Ulysses, " can admit 554 but of one interpretation, for had not Ulysses himself told you how it shall be fulfilled? The death of the suitors is portended, and not one single one of them will escape."

And Penelope answered, " Stranger, dreams are very 559 curious and unaccountable things, and they do not by any means invariably come true. There are two gates through which these unsubstantial fancies proceed; the one is of horn, and the other ivory. Those that come through the gate of ivory are fatuous, but those from the gate of horn mean something to those that see them. I do not think, however, that my own dream came through the gate of horn, though I and my son should be most thankful if it proves to have done so. Furthermore I say—and lay my saying to your heart—the coming dawn will usher in the ill-omened day that is to sever me from the house of Ulysses, for I am about to hold a tournament of axes. My husband used to set up twelve axes in the court, one in front of the other, like the stays upon which a ship is built; he would then go back from them and shoot an arrow through the whole twelve. I shall make the suitors try to do the same thing, and whichever of them can string the bow most easily, and send his arrow through all the twelve axes, him will I follow, and quit this house of my lawful husband, so goodly and so abounding in wealth. But even so, I doubt not that I shall remember it in my dreams."

582 Then Ulysses answered, "Madam, wife of Ulysses, you need not defer your tournament, for Ulysses will return ere ever they can string the bow, handle it how they will, and send their arrows through the iron."

588 To this Penelope said, "As long, sir, as you will sit here and talk to me, I can have no desire to go to bed. Still, people cannot do permanently without sleep, and heaven has appointed us dwellers on earth a time for all things. I will therefore go upstairs and recline upon that couch which I have never ceased to flood with my tears from the day Ulysses set out for the city with a hateful name."

600 She then went upstairs to her own room, not alone, but attended by her maidens, and when there, she lamented her dear husband till Minerva shed sweet 604 sleep over her eyelids.

ULYSSES SLEPT IN THE CLOISTER UPON an undressed bullock's hide, on the top of which he threw several skins of the sheep the suitors had eaten, and Eurynome[1] threw a cloak over him after he had laid himself down. There, then, Ulysses lay wakefully brooding upon the way in which he should kill the suitors; and by and by, the women who had been in the habit of misconducting themselves with them, left the house giggling and laughing with one another. This made Ulysses very angry, and he doubted whether to get up and kill every single one of them then and there, or to let them sleep one more and last time with the suitors. His heart growled within him, and as a bitch with puppies growls and shows her teeth when she sees a stranger, so did his heart growl with anger at the evil deeds that were being done: but he beat his breast and said, " Heart, be still,

[1] Lower down (line 143) Euryclea says it was herself that had thrown the cloak over Ulysses–for the plural should not be taken as implying more than one person. The writer is evidently still fluctuating between Euryclea and Eurynome as the name for the old nurse. She probably originally meant to call her Euryclea, but finding it not immediately easy to make Euryclea scan in xvii, 495, she hastily called her Eurynome, intending either to alter this name later or to change the earlier Euryclea's into Eurynome. She then drifted on to Eurynome as convenience further directed, still nevertheless hankering after Euryclea, till at last she found that the path of least resistance would lie in the direction of making Eurynome and Euryclea two persons. Therefore in xxiii, 289-292, both Eurynome and " the nurse " (who can be none other than Euryclea) come on together. I do not say that this is feminine, but it is not unfeminine.

you had worse than this to bear on the day when the terrible Cyclops ate your brave companions; yet you bore it in silence till your cunning got you safe out of the cave, though you made sure of being killed."

22 Thus he chided with his heart, and checked it into endurance, but he tossed about as one who turns a paunch full of blood and fat in front of a hot fire, doing it first on one side and then on the other, that he may get it cooked as soon as possible, even so did he turn himself about from side to side, thinking all the time how, single handed as he was, he should contrive to kill so large a body of men as the wicked suitors.[1] But by and by Minerva came down from heaven in the likeness of a woman, and hovered over his head saying, " My poor unhappy man, why do you lie awake in this way? This is your house: your wife is safe inside it, and so is your son who is just such a young man as any father may be proud of."

36 " Goddess," answered Ulysses, " all that you have said is true, but I am in some doubt as to how I shall be able to kill these wicked suitors single handed, seeing what a number of them there always are. And there is this further difficulty, which is still more considerable. Supposing that with Jove's and your assistance I succeed in killing them, I must ask you to consider where I am to escape to from their avengers when it is all over."

44 " For shame," replied Minerva, " why, any one else would trust a worse ally than myself, even though that ally were only a mortal and less wise than I am. Am I not a goddess, and have I not protected you throughout in all your troubles? I tell you plainly that even though there were fifty bands of men surrounding us and eager to kill us, you should take all their sheep and

[1] [See pp. xix, xx.]

cattle, and drive them away with you. But go to sleep;
it is a very bad thing to lie awake all night, and you
shall be out of your troubles before long."

As she spoke she shed sleep over his eyes, and then 54
went back to Olympus.

While Ulysses was thus yielding himself to a very 56
deep slumber that eased the burden of his sorrows, his
admirable wife awoke, and sitting up in her bed began
to cry. When she had relieved herself by weeping she
prayed to Diana saying, "Great Goddess Diana,
daughter of Jove, drive an arrow into my heart and
slay me; or let some whirlwind snatch me up and bear
me through paths of darkness till it drop me into the
mouths of overflowing Oceanus, as it did the daughters
of Pandareus. The daughters of Pandareus lost their
father and mother, for the gods killed them, so they
were left orphans. But Venus took care of them, and
fed them on cheese, honey, and sweet wine. Juno
taught them to excel all women in beauty of form and
understanding; Diana gave them an imposing presence,
and Minerva endowed them with every kind of accom-
plishment; but one day when Venus had gone up to
Olympus to see Jove about getting them married (for
well does he know both what shall happen and what not
happen to every one) the storm winds came and spirited
them away to become handmaids to the dread Erinyes.
Even so I wish that the gods who live in heaven would
hide me from mortal sight, or that fair Diana might
strike me, for I would fain go even beneath the sad
earth if I might do so still looking towards Ulysses only,
and without having to yield myself to a worse man than
he was. Besides, no matter how much people may
grieve by day, they can put up with it so long as they
can sleep at night, for when the eyes are closed in
slumber people forget good and ill alike; whereas my

misery haunts me even in my dreams. This very night methought there was one lying by my side who was like Ulysses as he was when he went away with his host, and I rejoiced, for I believed that it was no dream, but the very truth itself."

91   On this the day broke, but Ulysses heard the sound of her weeping, and it puzzled him, for it seemed as though she already knew him and was by his side. Then he gathered up the cloak and the fleeces on which he had lain, and set them on a seat in the cloister, but he took the bullock's hide out into the open. He lifted up his hands to heaven, and prayed, saying, " Father Jove, since you have seen fit to bring me over land and sea to my own home after all the afflictions you have laid upon me, give me a sign out of the mouth of some one or other of those who are now waking within the house, and let me have another sign of some kind from outside."

102   Thus did he pray. Jove heard his prayer and forthwith thundered high up among the clouds from the splendour of Olympus, and Ulysses was glad when he heard it. At the same time within the house, a miller-woman from hard by in the mill room lifted up her voice and gave him another sign. There were twelve miller-women whose business it was to grind wheat and barley which are the staff of life. The others had ground their task and had gone to take their rest, but this one had not yet finished, for she was not so strong as they were, and when she heard the thunder she stopped grinding and gave the sign to her master. " Father Jove," said she, " you who rule over heaven and earth, you have thundered from a clear sky without so much as a cloud in it, and this means something for somebody; grant the prayer, then, of me your poor servant who calls upon you, and let this be the very

last day that the suitors dine in the house of Ulysses.
They have worn me out with the labour of grinding
meal for them, and I hope they may never have another
dinner anywhere at all.''

Ulysses was glad when he heard the omens conveyed 120
to him by the woman's speech, and by the thunder, for
he knew they meant that he should avenge himself on
the suitors.

Then the other maids in the house rose and lit the 122
fire on the hearth; Telemachus also rose and put on
his clothes. He girded his sword about his shoulder,
bound his sandals on his comely feet, and took a
doughty spear with a point of sharpened bronze; then
he went to the threshold of the cloister and said to
Euryclea, " Nurse, did you make the stranger comfortable both as regards bed and board, or did you let him
shift for himself?—for my mother, good woman though
she is, has a way of paying great attention to second-rate
people, and of neglecting others who are in reality
much better men.''

" Do not find fault child," said Euryclea, " when 134
there is no one to find fault with. The stranger sat and
drank his wine as long as he liked: your mother did
ask him if he would take any more bread and he said
he would not. When he wanted to go to bed she told
the servants to make one for him, but he said he was
such a wretched outcast that he would not sleep on a
bed and under blankets; he insisted on having an
undressed bullock's hide and some sheepskins put for
him in the cloister and I threw a cloak over him myself." [1]

Then Telemachus went out of the court to the place 144
where the Achaeans were meeting in assembly; he had
his spear in his hand, and he was not alone, for his two

[1] See note on line 4 of this book.

dogs went with him. But Euryclea called the maids and said, " Come, wake up; set about sweeping the cloisters and sprinkling them with water to lay the dust; put the covers on the seats; wipe down the tables, some of you, with a wet sponge; clean out the mixing-jugs and the cups, and go for water from the fountain at once; the suitors will be here directly; they will be here early, for it is a feast day."

157 Thus did she speak, and they did even as she had said: twenty of them went to the fountain for water, and the others set themselves busily to work about the house. The men who were in attendance on the suitors also came up and began chopping firewood. By and by the women returned from the fountain, and the swineherd came after them with the three best pigs he could pick out. These he let feed about the premises, and then he said good-humouredly to Ulysses, " Stranger, are the suitors treating you any better now, or are they as insolent as ever? "

169 " May heaven," answered Ulysses, " requite to them the wickedness with which they deal high-handedly in another man's house without any sense of shame."

172 Thus did they converse; meanwhile Melanthius the goatherd came up, for he too was bringing in his best goats for the suitors' dinner; and he had two shepherds with him. They tied the goats up under the gatehouse, and then Melanthius began gibing at Ulysses. " Are you still here, stranger," said he, " to pester people by begging about the house? Why can you not go elsewhere? You and I shall not come to an understanding before we have given each other a taste of our fists. You beg without any sense of decency: are there not feasts elsewhere among the Achaeans, as well as here? "

183 Ulysses made no answer, but bowed his head and

312

brooded. Then a third man, Philoetius, joined them, who was bringing in a barren heifer and some goats. These were brought over by the boatmen who are there to take people over when any one comes to them. So Philoetius made his heifer and his goats secure under the gatehouse, and then went up to the swineherd. " Who, Swineherd," said he, " is this stranger that is lately come here? Is he one of your men? What is his family? Where does he come from? Poor fellow, he looks as if he had been some great man, but the gods give sorrow to whom they will—even to kings if it so pleases them."

As he spoke he went up to Ulysses and saluted him 197 with his right hand; "Good day to you, father stranger," said he, " you seem to be very poorly off now, but I hope you will have better times by and by. Father Jove, of all gods you are the most malicious. We are your own children, yet you show us no mercy in all our misery and afflictions. A sweat came over me when I saw this man, and my eyes filled with tears, for he reminds me of Ulysses, who I fear is going about in just such rags as this man's are, if indeed he is still among the living. If he is already dead and in the house of Hades, then, alas! for my good master, who made me his stockman when I was quite young among the Cephallenians, and now his cattle are countless; no one could have done better with them than I have, for they have bred like ears of corn; nevertheless I have to keep bringing them in for others to eat, who take no heed of his son though he is in the house, and fear not the wrath of heaven, but are already eager to divide Ulysses' property among them because he has been away so long. I have often thought—only it would not be right while his son is living—of going off with the cattle to some foreign country; bad as this would be, it is still harder to stay

313

here and be ill-treated about other people's herds. My position is intolerable, and I should long since have run away and put myself under the protection of some other chief, only that I believe my poor master will yet return, and send all these suitors flying out of the house."

226 " Stockman," answered Ulysses, " you seem to be a very well-disposed person, and I can see that you are a man of sense. Therefore I will tell you, and will confirm my words with an oath: by Jove, the chief of all gods, and by that hearth of Ulysses to which I am now come, Ulysses shall return before you leave this place, and if you are so minded you shall see him killing the suitors who are now masters here."

235 " If Jove were to bring this to pass," replied the stockman, " you should see how I would do my very utmost to help him."

238 And in like manner Eumaeus prayed that Ulysses might return home.

240 Thus did they converse. Meanwhile the suitors were hatching a plot to murder Telemachus: but a bird flew near them on their left hand—an eagle with a dove in its talons. On this Amphinomus said, " My friends, this plot of ours to murder Telemachus will not succeed; let us go to dinner instead."

247 The others assented, so they went inside and laid their cloaks on the benches and seats. They sacrificed the sheep, goats, pigs, and the heifer, and when the inward meats were cooked they served them round. They mixed the wine in the mixing-bowls, and the swineherd gave every man his cup, while Philoetius handed round the bread in the bread-baskets, and Melanthius poured them out their wine. Then they laid their hands upon the good things that were before them.

257 Telemachus purposely made Ulysses sit in the part

of the cloister that was paved with stone;[1] he gave him
a shabby-looking seat at a little table to himself, and
had his portion of the inward meats brought to him,
with his wine in a gold cup. " Sit there," said he, " and
drink your wine among the great people. I will put a
stop to the gibes and blows of the suitors, for this is no
public house, but belongs to Ulysses, and has passed
from him to me. Therefore, suitors, keep your hands
and your tongues to yourselves, or there will be mischief."

The suitors bit their lips, and marvelled at the bold- 268
ness of his speech; then Antinous said, " We do not
like such language but we will put up with it, for Telemachus is threatening us in good earnest. If Jove had
let us we should have put a stop to his brave talk ere
now."

Thus spoke Antinous, but Telemachus heeded him 275
not. Meanwhile the heralds were bringing the holy
hecatomb through the city, and the Achaeans gathered
under the shady grove of Apollo.

Then they roasted the outer meat, drew it off the 279
spits, gave every man his portion, and feasted to their
hearts' content; those who waited at table gave Ulysses
exactly the same portion as the others had, for Telemachus had told them to do so.

But Minerva would not let the suitors for one 284
moment drop their insolence, for she wanted Ulysses to
become still more bitter against them. Now there
happened to be among them a ribald fellow, whose
name was Ctesippus, and who came from Same. This
man, confident in his great wealth, was paying court to
the wife of Ulysses, and said to the suitors, " Hear
what I have to say. The stranger has already had as

[1] This, I take it, was immediately in front of the main entrance
from the inner courtyard into the body of the house.

large a portion as any one else; this is well, for it is not right nor reasonable to ill-treat any guest of Telemachus who comes here. I will, however, make him a present on my own account, that he may have something to give to the bath-woman, or to some other of Ulysses' servants."

299   As he spoke he picked up a heifer's foot from the meat-basket in which it lay, and threw it at Ulysses, but Ulysses turned his head a little aside, and avoided it, smiling grimly Sardinian fashion [1] as he did so, and it hit the wall, not him. On this Telemachus spoke fiercely to Ctesippus, " It is a good thing for you," said he, " that the stranger turned his head so that you missed him. If you had hit him I should have run you through with my spear, and your father would have had to see about getting you buried rather than married in this house. So let me have no more unseemly behaviour from any of you, for I am grown up now to the knowledge of good and evil and understand what is going on, instead of being the child that I have been heretofore. I have long seen you killing my sheep and making free with my corn and wine: I have put up with this, for one man is no match for many, but do me no further violence. Still, if you wish to kill me, kill me; I would far rather die than see such disgraceful scenes day after day—guests insulted, and men dragging the women servants about the house in an unseemly way."

320   They all held their peace till at last Agelaus son of Damastor said, " No one should take offence at what has just been said, nor gainsay it, for it is quite reasonable. Leave off, therefore, ill-treating the stranger, or any one else of the servants who are about the house; I would say, however, a friendly word to Telemachus

[1] This is the only allusion to Sardinia in either Iliad or Odyssey.

and his mother, which I trust may commend itself to both. ' As long,' I would say, ' as you had ground for hoping that Ulysses would one day come home, no one could complain of your waiting and suffering[1] the suitors to be in your house. It would have been better that he should have returned, but it is now sufficiently clear that he will never do so; therefore talk all this quietly over with your mother, and tell her to marry the best man, and the one who makes her the most advantageous offer. Thus you will yourself be able to manage your own inheritance, and to eat and drink in peace, while your mother will look after some other man's house, not yours.' "

To this Telemachus answered, " By Jove, Agelaus, 338 and by the sorrows of my unhappy father, who has either perished far from Ithaca, or is wandering in some distant land, I throw no obstacles in the way of my mother's marriage; on the contrary I urge her to choose whomsoever she will, and I will give her numberless gifts into the bargain, but I dare not insist point blank that she shall leave the house against her own wishes. Heaven forbid that I should do this."

Minerva now made the suitors fall to laughing im- 345 moderately, and set their wits wandering; but they were laughing with a forced laughter. Their meat became smeared with blood; their eyes filled with tears, and their hearts were heavy with forebodings. Theoclymenus saw this and said, " Unhappy men, what is it that ails you? There is a shroud of darkness drawn over you from head to foot, your cheeks are wet with tears; the air is alive with wailing voices; the walls and

---

[1] The normal translation of the Greek word would be " holding back," " curbing," " restraining," but I cannot think that the writer meant this - she must have been using the word in its other sense of " having," " holding," " keeping," " maintaining."

roof-beams drip blood; the gate of the cloisters and the court beyond them are full of ghosts trooping down into the night of hell; the sun is blotted out of heaven, and a blighting gloom is over all the land."

358 Thus did he speak, and they all of them laughed heartily. Eurymachus then said, "This stranger who has lately come here has lost his senses. Servants, turn him out into the streets, since he finds it so dark here."

363 But Theoclymenus said, "Eurymachus, you need not send any one with me. I have eyes, ears, and a pair of feet of my own, to say nothing of an understanding mind. I will take these out of the house with me, for I see mischief overhanging you, from which not one of you men who are insulting people and plotting ill deeds in the house of Ulysses will be able to escape."

371 He left the house as he spoke, and went back to Piraeus who gave him welcome, but the suitors kept looking at one another and provoking Telemachus by laughing at the strangers. One insolent fellow said to him, "Telemachus, you are not happy in your guests; first you have this importunate tramp, who comes begging bread and wine and has no skill for work or for hard fighting, but is perfectly useless, and now here is another fellow who is setting himself up as a prophet. Let me persuade you, for it will be much better, to put them on board ship and send them off to the Sicels to sell for what they will bring."

384 Telemachus gave him no heed, but sate silently watching his father, expecting every moment that he would begin his attack upon the suitors.

387 Meanwhile the daughter of Icarius, wise Penelope, had had a rich seat placed for her facing the court and cloisters, so that she could hear what every one was saying. The dinner indeed had been prepared amid much merriment; it had been both good and abundant,

for they had sacrificed many victims; but the supper was yet to come, and nothing can be conceived more gruesome than the meal which a goddess and a brave man were soon to lay before them—for they had brought their doom upon themselves. 394

MINERVA NOW PUT IT IN PENELOPE'S
mind to make the suitors try their skill with
the bow and with the iron axes, in contest
among themselves, as a means of bringing
about their destruction. She went upstairs and got the
store room key, which was made of bronze and had a
handle of ivory; she then went with her maidens into
the store room at the end of the house, where her
husband's treasures of gold, bronze, and wrought iron
were kept, and where was also his bow, and the quiver
full of deadly arrows that had been given him by a
friend whom he had met in Lacedaemon—Iphitus the
son of Eurytus. The two fell in with one another in
Messene at the house of Ortilochus, where Ulysses
was staying in order to recover a debt that was owing
from the whole people; for the Messenians had carried
off three hundred sheep from Ithaca, and had sailed
away with them and with their shepherds. In quest
of these Ulysses took a long journey while still quite
young, for his father and the other chieftains sent him
on a mission to recover them. Iphitus had gone there
also to try and get back twelve brood mares that he had
lost, and the mule foals that were running with them.
These mares were the death of him in the end, for when
he went to the house of Jove's son, mighty Hercules,
who performed such prodigies of valour, Hercules to
his shame killed him, though he was his guest, for he
feared not heaven's vengeance, nor yet respected his
own table which he had set before Iphitus, but killed
him in spite of everything, and kept the mares himself.
It was when claiming these that Iphitus met Ulysses,
and gave him the bow which mighty Eurytus had been
used to carry, and which on his death had been left by

him to his son. Ulysses gave him in return a sword and a spear, and this was the beginning of a fast friendship, although they never visited at one another's houses, for Jove's son Hercules killed Iphitus ere they could do so. This bow, then, given him by Iphitus, had not been taken with him by Ulysses when he sailed for Troy; he had used it so long as he had been at home, but had left it behind as having been a keepsake from a valued friend.

Penelope presently reached the oak threshold of the 42 store room; the carpenter had planed this duly, and had drawn a line on it so as to get it quite straight; he had then set the door posts into it and hung the doors. She loosed the strap from the handle of the door, put in the key, and drove it straight home to shoot back the bolts that held the doors; [1] these flew open with a noise like a bull bellowing in a meadow, and Penelope stepped upon the raised platform, where the chests stood in which the fair linen and clothes were laid by along with fragrant herbs: reaching thence, she took down the bow with its bow case from the peg on which it hung. She sat down with it on her knees, weeping bitterly as she took the bow out of its case, and when her tears had relieved her, she went to the cloister where the suitors were, carrying the bow and the quiver, with the many deadly arrows that were inside it. Along with her came her maidens, bearing a chest that contained much iron and bronze which her husband had won as prizes. When she reached the suitors, she stood by one of the bearing-posts supporting the roof of the cloister, holding a veil before her face, and with a maid on either side of her. Then she said:

"Listen to me you suitors, who persist in abusing the 68

[1] I have vainly tried to realize the construction of the fastening here described.

hospitality of this house because its owner has been long absent, and without other pretext than that you want to marry me; this, then, being the prize that you are contending for, I will bring out the mighty bow of Ulysses, and whomsoever of you shall string it most easily and send his arrow through each one of twelve axes, him will I follow and quit this house of my lawful husband, so goodly, and so abounding in wealth. But even so I doubt not that I shall remember it in my dreams."

80 As she spoke, she told Eumaeus to set the bow and the pieces of iron before the suitors, and Eumaeus wept as he took them to do as she had bidden him. Hard by, the stockman wept also when he saw his master's bow, but Antinous scolded them. "You country louts," said he, " silly simpletons; why should you add to the sorrows of your mistress by crying in this way? She has enough to grieve her in the loss of her husband; sit still, therefore, and eat your dinners in silence, or go outside if you want to cry, and leave the bow behind you. We suitors shall have to contend for it with might and main, for we shall find it no light matter to string such a bow as this is. There is not a man of us all who is such another as Ulysses; for I have seen him and remember him, though I was then only a child."

96 This was what he said, but all the time he was expecting to be able to string the bow and shoot through the iron, whereas in fact he was to be the first that should taste of the arrows from the hands of Ulysses, whom he was dishonouring in his own house—egging the others on to do so also.

101 Then Telemachus spoke. " Great heavens! " he exclaimed, " Jove must have robbed me of my senses. Here is my dear and excellent mother saying she will quit this house and marry again, yet I am laughing and

enjoying myself as though there were nothing happening. But, suitors, as the conteſt has been agreed upon,
let it go forward. It is for a woman whose peer is not
to be found in Pylos, Argos, or Mycene, nor yet in
Ithaca nor on the mainland. You know this as well as
I do; what need have I to speak in praise of my mother?
Come on, then, make no excuses for delay, but let us see
whether you can ſtring the bow or no. I too will make
trial of it, for if I can ſtring it and shoot through the
iron, I shall not suffer my mother to quit this house with
a ſtranger, not if I can win the prizes which my father
won before me."

As he spoke he sprang from his seat, threw his 118
crimson cloak from him, and took his sword from his
shoulder. Firſt he set the axes in a row, in a long groove
which he had dug for them, and had made ſtraight by
line.[1] Then he ſtamped the earth tight round them, and
everyone was surprised when they saw him set them up
so orderly, though he had never seen anything of the
kind before. This done, he went on to the pavement
to make trial of the bow; thrice did he tug at it, trying
with all his might to draw the ſtring, and thrice he had
to leave off, though he had hoped to ſtring the bow and
shoot through the iron. He was trying for the fourth
time, and would have ſtrung it had not Ulysses made a
sign to check him in spite of all his eagerness. So he said:

" Alas! I shall either be always feeble and of no 131
prowess, or I am too young, and have not yet reached
my full ſtrength so as to be able to hold my own if any
one attacks me. You others, therefore, who are
ſtronger than I, make trial of the bow and get this
conteſt settled."

---

[1] See plan of Ulysses' house in the appendix. It is evident
that the open part of the court had no flooring, but the natural
soil.

136   On this he put the bow down, letting it lean against the door [that led into the house] with the arrow standing against the top of the bow. Then he sat down on the seat from which he had risen, and Antinous said:

141   . " Come on each of you in his turn, going towards the right from the place at which the cupbearer begins when he is handing round the wine."

143   The rest agreed, and Leiodes son of Oenops was the first to rise. He was sacrificial priest to the suitors, and sat in the corner near the mixing-bowl.[1] He was the only man who hated their evil deeds and was indignant with the others. He was now the first to take the bow and arrow, so he went on to the pavement to make his trial, but he could not string the bow, for his hands were weak and unused to hard work, they therefore soon grew tired, and he said to the suitors, " My friends, I cannot string it; let another have it; this bow shall take the life and soul out of many a chief among us, for it is better to die than to live after having missed the prize that we have so long striven for, and which has brought us so long together. Some one of us is even now hoping and praying that he may marry Penelope, but when he has seen this bow and tried it, let him woo and make bridal offerings to some other woman, and let Penelope marry whoever makes her the best offer and whose lot it is to win her."

163   On this he put the bow down, letting it lean against the door,[1] with the arrow standing against the tip of the bow. Then he took his seat again on the seat from which he had risen; and Antinous rebuked him saying:

167   " Leiodes, what are you talking about? Your words are monstrous and intolerable; it makes me angry to listen to you. Shall, then, this bow take the life of

---

[1] See plan of Ulysses' house, and note on xxii, 341.
[2] *I.e.*, the door that led into the body of the house.

many a chief among us, merely because you cannot bend it yourself? True, you were not born to be an archer, but there are others who will soon string it."

Then he said to Melanthius the goatherd, " Look 175 sharp, light a fire in the court, and set a seat hard by with a sheep skin on it; bring us also a large ball of lard, from what they have in the house. Let us warm the bow and grease it–we will then make trial of it again, and bring the contest to an end."

Melanthius lit the fire, and set a seat covered with 181 sheep skins beside it. He also brought a great ball of lard from what they had in the house, and the suitors warmed the bow and again made trial of it, but they were none of them nearly strong enough to string it. Nevertheless there still remained Antinous and Eury-machus, who were the ringleaders among the suitors and much the foremost among them all.

Then the swineherd and the stockman left the clois- 188 ters together, and Ulysses followed them. When they had got outside the gates and the outer yard, Ulysses said to them quietly:

" Stockman, and you swineherd, I have something in 193 my mind which I am in doubt whether to say or no; but I think I will say it. What manner of men would you be to stand by Ulysses, if some god should bring him back here all of a sudden? Say which you are disposed to do–to side with the suitors, or with Ulysses? "

" Father Jove," answered the stockman, " would 199 indeed that you might so ordain it. If some god were but to bring Ulysses back, you should see with what might and main I would fight for him."

In like words Eumaeus prayed to all the gods that 203 Ulysses might return; when, therefore, he saw for certain what mind they were of, Ulysses said, " It is I,

Ulysses, who am here. I have suffered much, but at laſt, in the twentieth year, I am come back to my own country. I find that you two alone of all my servants are glad that I should do so, for I have not heard any of the others praying for my return. To you two, therefore, will I unfold the truth as it shall be. If heaven shall deliver the suitors into my hands, I will find wives for both of you, will give you house and holding close to my own, and you shall be to me as though you were brothers and friends of Telemachus. I will now give you convincing proofs that you may know me and be assured. See, here is the scar from the boar's tooth that ripped me when I was out hunting on Mount Parnassus with the sons of Autolycus."

221 As he spoke he drew his rags aside from the great scar, and when they had examined it thoroughly, they both of them wept about Ulysses, threw their arms round him, and kissed his head and shoulders, while Ulysses kissed their hands and faces in return. The sun would have gone down upon their mourning if Ulysses had not checked them and said:

228 " Case your weeping, leſt some one should come outside and see us, and tell those who are within. When you go in, do so separately, not both together; I will go firſt, and do you follow afterwards; let this moreover be the token between us; the suitors will all of them try to prevent me from getting hold of the bow and quiver; do you, therefore, Eumaeus, place it in my hands when you are carrying it about, and tell the women to close the doors of their apartment. If they hear any groaning or uproar as of men fighting about the house, they muſt not come out; they muſt keep quiet, and ſtay where they are at their work. And I charge you, Philoetius, to make faſt the doors of the outer court, and to bind them securely at once."

242 When he had thus spoken, he went back to the house

and took the seat that he had left. Presently, his two
servants followed him inside.

At this moment the bow was in the hands of Eury- 245
machus, who was warming it by the fire, but even so he
could not string it, and he was greatly grieved. He
heaved a deep sigh and said, " I grieve for myself and
for us all; I grieve that I shall have to forgo the marriage,
but I do not care nearly so much about this, for there
are plenty of other women in Ithaca and elsewhere;
what I feel most is the fact of our being so inferior to
Ulysses in strength that we cannot string his bow. This
will disgrace us in the eyes of those who are yet
unborn."

" It shall not be so, Eurymachus," said Antinous, 256
" and you know it yourself. To-day is the feast of
Apollo throughout all the land; who can string a bow
on such a day as this? Put it on one side—as for the
axes thay can stay where they are, for no one is likely
to come to the house and take them away: let the cupbearer go round with his cups, that we may make our
drink-offerings and drop this matter of the bow; we
will tell Melanthius to bring us in some goats to-morrow
—the best he has; we can then offer thigh bones to
Apollo the mighty archer, and again make trial of the
bow, so as to bring the contest to an end."

The rest approved his words, and thereon men 269
servants poured water over the hands of the guests,
while pages filled the mixing-bowls with wine and water
and handed it round after giving every man his drink-
offering. Then, when they had made their offerings
and had drunk each as much as he desired, Ulysses
craftily said:

" Suitors of the illustrious queen, listen that I may 275
speak even as I am minded. I appeal more especially to
Eurymachus, and to Antinous who has just spoken
with so much reason. Cease shooting for the present

and leave the matter to the gods, but in the morning let heaven give victory to whom it will. For the moment, however, give me the bow that I may prove the power of my hands among you all, and see whether I still have as much strength as I used to have, or whether travel and neglect have made an end of it."

285   This made them all very angry, for they feared he might string the bow; Antinous therefore rebuked him fiercely saying, "Wretched creature, you have not so much as a grain of sense in your whole body; you ought to think yourself lucky in being allowed to dine unharmed among your betters, without having any smaller portion served you than we others have had, and in being allowed to hear our conversation. No other beggar or stranger has been allowed to hear what we say among ourselves; the wine must have been doing you a mischief, as it does with all those who drink immoderately. It was wine that inflamed the Centaur Eurytion when he was staying with Peirithous among the Lapithae. When the wine had got into his head, he went mad and did ill deeds about the house of Peirithous; this angered the heroes who were there assembled, so they rushed at him and cut off his ears and nostrils; then they dragged him through the doorway out of the house, so he went away crazed, and bore the burden of his crime, bereft of understanding. Henceforth, there-fore, there was war between mankind and the centaurs, but he brought it upon himself through his own drunkenness. In like manner I can tell you that it will go hardly with you if you string the bow: you will find no mercy from any one here, for we shall at once ship you off to king Echetus, who kills every one that comes near him: you will never get away alive, so drink and keep quiet without getting into a quarrel with men younger than yourself."

328

Penelope then spoke to him. " Antinous," said she, 311
" it is not right that you should ill-treat any guest of
Telemachus who comes to this house. If the stranger
should prove strong enough to string the mighty bow
of Ulysses, can you suppose that he would take me home
with him and make me his wife? Even the man himself
can have no such idea in his mind: none of you need
let that disturb his feasting; it would be out of all
reason."

" Queen Penelope," answered Eurymachus, " we do 320
not suppose that this man will take you away with him;
it is impossible; but we are afraid lest some of the
baser sort, men or women among the Achaeans, should
go gossiping about and say, ' These suitors are a feeble
folk; they are paying court to the wife of a brave man
whose bow not one of them was able to string, and yet
a beggarly tramp who came to the house strung it at
once and sent an arrow through the iron.' This is what
will be said, and it will be a scandal against us."

" Eurymachus," Penelope answered, " people who 330
persist in eating up the estate of a great chieftain and
dishonouring his house must not expect others to
speak well of them. Why then should you mind if men
talk as you think they will? This stranger is strong
and well-built, he says moreover that he is of noble
birth. Give him the bow, and let us see whether he can
string it or no. I say—and it shall surely be—that if
Apollo vouchsafes him the glory of stringing it, I will
give him a cloak and shirt of good wear, with a javelin
to keep off dogs and robbers, and a sharp sword. I will
also give him sandals, and will see him sent safely
wherever he wants to go."

Then Telemachus said, " Mother, I am the only man 343
either in Ithaca or in the islands that are over against
Elis who has the right to let any one have the bow or to

refuse it. No one shall force me one way or the other, not even though I choose to make the stranger a present of the bow outright, and let him take it away with him. Go, then, within the house and busy yourself with your daily duties, your loom, your distaff, and the ordering of your servants. This bow is a man's matter, and mine above all others, for it is I who am master here."

354 She went wondering back into the house, and laid her son's saying in her heart. Then going upstairs with her handmaids into her room, she mourned her dear husband till Minerva sent sweet sleep over her eyelids.

359 The swineherd now took up the bow and was for taking it to Ulysses, but the suitors clamoured at him from all parts of the cloisters, and one of them said, "You idiot, where are you taking the bow to? Are you out of your wits? If Apollo and the other gods will grant our prayer, your own boarhounds shall get you into some quiet little place, and worry you to death."

366 Eumaeus was frightened at the outcry they all raised, so he put the bow down then and there, but Telemachus shouted out at him from the other side of the cloisters, and threatened him saying, "Father Eumaeus, bring the bow on in spite of them, or young as I am I will pelt you with stones back to the country, for I am the better man of the two. I wish I was as much stronger than all the other suitors in the house as I am than you, I would soon send some of them off sick and sorry, for they mean mischief."

376 Thus did he speak, and they all of them laughed heartily, which put them in a better humour with Telemachus; so Eumaeus brought the bow on and placed it in the hands of Ulysses. When he had done this, he called Euryclea apart and said to her, "Euryclea, Telemachus says you are to close the doors of the

women's apartments. If they hear any groaning or
uproar as of men fighting about the house, they are not
to come out, but are to keep quiet and stay where they
are at their work."

Euryclea did as she was told and closed the doors of ₃₈₆
the women's apartments.

Meanwhile Philoetius slipped quietly out and made ₃₈₈
fast the gates of the outer court. There was a ship's
cable of byblus fibre lying in the gatehouse, so he made
the gates fast with it and then came in again, resuming
the seat that he had left, and keeping an eye on Ulysses,
who had now got the bow in his hands, and was turning
it every way about, and proving it all over to see whether
the worms had been eating into its two horns during
his absence. Then would one turn towards his neighbour saying, " This is some tricky old bow-fancier;
either he has got one like it at home, or he wants to
make one, in such workmanlike style does the old
vagabond handle it."

Another said, " I hope he may be no more successful ₄₀₁
in other things than he is likely to be in stringing this
bow."

But Ulysses, when he had taken it up and examined it ₄₀₄
all over, strung it as easily as a skilled bard strings a new
peg of his lyre and makes the twisted gut fast at both
ends. Then he took it in his right hand to prove the
string, and it sang sweetly under his touch like the
twittering of a swallow. The suitors were dismayed,
and turned colour as they heard it; at that moment,
moreover, Jove thundered loudly as a sign, and the
heart of Ulysses rejoiced as he heard the omen that the
son of scheming Saturn had sent him.

He took an arrow that was lying upon the table [1]—for ₄₁₆

[1] This was, no doubt, the little table that was set for Ulysses,
Od., xx, 259.

those which the Achaeans were so shortly about to taste were all inside the quiver—he laid it on the centre-piece of the bow, and drew the notch of the arrow and the string toward him, still seated on his seat. When he had taken aim he let fly, and his arrow pierced every one of the handle-holes of the axes from the first onwards till it had gone right through them,[1] and into the outer courtyard. Then he said to Telemachus:

425 "Your guest has not disgraced you, Telemachus. I did not miss what I aimed at, and I was not long in stringing my bow. I am still strong, and not as the suitors twit me with being. Now, however, it is time for the Achaeans to prepare supper while there is still daylight, and then otherwise to disport themselves with song and dance which are the crowning ornaments of a banquet."

431 As he spoke he made a sign with his eyebrows, and Telemachus girded on his sword, grasped his spear,
434 and stood armed beside his father's seat.

[1] Surely the difficulty of this passage has been overrated. I suppose the iron part of the axe to have been wedged into the handle, or bound securely to it—the handle being half buried in the ground. The axe would be placed edgeways towards the archer, and he would have to shoot his arrow through the hole into which the handle was fitted when the axe was in use. Twelve axes were placed in a row all at the same height, all exactly in front of one another, all edgeways to Ulysses whose arrow passed through all the holes from the first onward. I cannot see how the Greek can bear any other interpretation, the words being,

πελέκεων δ' οὐκ ἤμβροτε πάντων
πρώτης στειλειῆς —

"He did not miss a single hole from the first onwards," στειλειή according to Liddell and Scott being "the hole for the handle of an axe, etc.," while στειλειόν (Od., ν, 236) is, according to the same authorities, the handle itself. The feat is absurdly impossible, but our authoress sometimes has a soul above impossibilities.

THEN ULYSSES TORE OFF HIS RAGS, AND
sprang on to the broad pavement with his bow
and his quiver full of arrows. He shed the arrows
on to the ground at his feet and said, " The mighty
contest is at an end. I will now see whether Apollo will
vouchsafe it to me to hit another mark which no man
has yet hit."

On this he aimed a deadly arrow at Antinous, who 8
was about to take up a two-handled gold cup to drink
his wine and already had it in his hands. He had no
thought of death—who amongst all the revellers would
think that one man, however brave, would stand alone
among so many and kill him? The arrow struck
Antinous in the throat, and the point went clean through
his neck, so that he fell over and the cup dropped
from his hand, while a thick stream of blood gushed
from his nostrils. He kicked the table from him and
upset the things on it, so that the bread and roasted
meats were all soiled as they fell over on to the ground.[1]
The suitors were in an uproar when they saw that a man
had been hit; they sprang in dismay one and all of them
from their seats and looked everywhere towards the
walls, but there was neither shield nor spear, and they
rebuked Ulysses very angrily. " Stranger," said they,
" you shall pay for shooting people in this way: you
shall see no other contest; you are a doomed man; he
whom you have slain was the foremost youth in Ithaca,
and the vultures shall devour you for having killed him."

Thus they spoke, for they thought that he had killed 31
Antinous by mistake, and did not perceive that death

[1] The reader will note how the spoiling of good food distresses
the writer even in such a supreme moment as this.

was hanging over the head of every one of them. But
Ulysses glared at them and said:

35 "Dogs, did you think that I should not come back
from Troy? You have wasted my substance,[1] have
forced my women servants to lie with you, and have
wooed my wife while I was still living. You have
feared neither God nor man, and now you shall die."

42 They turned pale with fear as he spoke, and every
man looked round about to see whither he might fly for
safety, but Eurymachus alone spoke.

44 "If you are Ulysses," said he, "then what you have
said is just. We have done much wrong on your lands
and in your house. But Antinous who was the head
and front of the offending lies low already. It was all
his doing. It was not that he wanted to marry Penelope;
he did not so much care about that; what he wanted
was something quite different, and Jove has not vouchsafed it to him; he wanted to kill your son and to be
chief man in Ithaca. Now, therefore, that he has met
the death which was his due, spare the lives of your
people. We will make everything good among ourselves, and pay you in full for all that we have eaten and
drunk. Each one of us shall pay you a fine worth
twenty oxen, and we will keep on giving you gold and
bronze till your heart is softened. Until we have done
this no one can complain of your being enraged against
us."

60 Ulysses again glared at him and said, "Though you
should give me all that you have in the world both now
and all that you ever shall have, I will not stay my hand
till I have paid all of you in full. You must fight, or fly
for your lives; and fly, not a man of you shall."

68 Their hearts sank as they heard him, but Eurymachus again spoke saying:

[1] Here we have it again. Waste of substance comes first.

334

" My friends, this man will give us no quarter. He 70
will stand where he is and shoot us down till he has
killed every man among us. Let us then show fight;
draw your swords, and hold up the tables to shield you
from his arrows. Let us have at him with a rush, to
drive him from the pavement and doorway: we can
then get through into the town, and raise such an
alarm as shall soon stay his shooting."

As he spoke he drew his keen blade of bronze, 79
sharpened on both sides, and with a loud cry sprang
towards Ulysses, but Ulysses instantly shot an arrow
into his breast that caught him by the nipple and fixed
itself in his liver. He dropped his sword and fell
doubled up over his table. The cup and all the meats
went over on to the ground as he smote the earth with
his forehead in the agonies of death, and he kicked the
stool with his feet until his eyes were closed in darkness.

Then Amphinomus drew his sword and made 89
straight at Ulysses to try and get him away from the
door; but Telemachus was too quick for him, and
struck him from behind; the spear caught him between
the shoulders and went right through his chest, so that
he fell heavily to the ground and struck the earth with
his forehead. Then Telemachus sprang away from him,
leaving his spear still in the body, for he feared that if he
stayed to draw it out, some one of the Achaeans might
come up and hack at him with his sword, or knock him
down, so he set off at a run, and immediately was at his
father's side. Then he said:

" Father, let me bring you a shield, two spears, and 101
a brass helmet for your temples. I will arm myself
as well, and will bring other armour for the swineherd
and the stockman, for we had better be armed."

" Run and fetch them," answered Ulysses, " while 105

my arrows hold out, or when I am alone they may get me away from the door."

108   Telemachus did as his father said, and went off to the store room where the armour was kept. He chose four shields, eight spears, and four brass helmets with horse-hair plumes. He brought them with all speed to his father, and armed himself first, while the stockman and the swineherd also put on their armour, and took their places near Ulysses. Meanwhile Ulysses, as long as his arrows lasted, had been shooting the suitors one by one, and they fell thick on one another: when his arrows gave out, he set the bow to stand against the end wall of the house by the door post, and hung a shield four hides thick about his shoulders; on his comely head he set his helmet, well wrought with a crest of horse-hair that nodded menacingly above it,[1] and he grasped two redoubtable bronze-shod spears.

126   Now there was a trap door[2] on the wall, while at one end of the pavement[3] there was an exit leading to a narrow passage, and this exit was closed by a well-made door. Ulysses told Philoetius to stand by this door and guard it, for only one person could attack it at a time. But Agelaus shouted out, "Cannot some one go up to the trap door and tell the people what is going on? Help would come at once, and we should soon make an end of this man and his shooting."

135   "This may not be, Agelaus," answered Melanthius, "the mouth of the narrow passage is dangerously near

---

[1] *Cf.* Il., iii, 337 and three other places. It is strange that the author of the Iliad should find a little horse-hair so alarming. Possibly enough he was merely borrowing a common form line from some earlier poet—or poetess—for this is a woman's line rather than a man's.

[2] Or perhaps simply "window." See plan in the appendix.

[3] *I.e.*, the pavement on which Ulysses was standing.

the entrance to the outer court. One brave man could prevent any number from getting in. But I know what I will do, I will bring you arms from the store room, for I am sure it is there that Ulysses and his son have put them."

On this the goatherd Melanthius went by back 142 passages to the store room of Ulysses' house. There he chose twelve shields, with as many helmets and spears, and brought them back as fast as he could to give them to the suitors.[1] Ulysses' heart began to fail him when he saw the suitors putting on their armour and brandish-

---

[1] The interpretation of lines 126-143 is most dubious, and at best we are in a region of melodrama: *cf.*, however, i, 425, etc., from which it appears that there was a tower in the outer court, and that Telemachus used to sleep in it. The ὀρσοθύρα I take to be a door, or trap door, leading on to the roof above Telemachus's bedroom, which we are told was in a place that could be seen from all round – or it might be simply a window in Telemachus's room looking out into the street. From the top of the tower the outer world was to be told what was going on, but people could not get in by the ὀρσοθύρα: they would have to come in by the main entrance, and Melanthius explains that the mouth of the narrow passage (which was in the hands of Ulysses and his friends) commanded the only entrance by which help could come, so that there would be nothing gained by raising an alarm.

As for the ῥῶγες of line 143, no commentator ancient or modern has been able to say what was intended – but whatever they were, Melanthius could never carry twelve shields, twelve helmets, and twelve spears. Moreover, where he could go the others could go also. If a dozen suitors had followed Melanthius into the house, they could have attacked Ulysses in the rear, in which case, unless Minerva had intervened promptly, the Odyssey would have had a different ending. But throughout the scene we are in a region of extravagance rather than of true fiction – it cannot be taken seriously by any but the very serious, until we come to the episode of Phemius and Medon, where the writer begins to be at home again.

ing their spears. He saw the greatness of the danger, and said to Telemachus, " Some one of the women inside is helping the suitors againſt us, or it may be Melanthius."

153 Telemachus answered, " The fault, father, is mine, and mine only; I left the ſtore room door open, and they have kept a sharper look out than I have. Go, Eumaeus, put the door to, and see whether it is one of the women who is doing this, or whether, as I suspeƈt, it is Melanthius the son of Dolius."

160 Thus did they converse. Meanwhile Melanthius was again going to the ſtore room to fetch more armour, but the swineherd saw him and said to Ulysses who was beside him, " Ulysses, noble son of Laertes, it is that scoundrel Melanthius, juſt as we suspeƈted, who is going to the ſtore room. Say, shall I kill him, if I can get the better of him, or shall I bring him here that you may take your own revenge for all the many wrongs that he has done in your house? "

170 Ulysses answered, " Telemachus and I will hold these suitors in check, no matter what they do; go back both of you and bind Melanthius' hands and feet behind him. Throw him into the ſtore room and make the door faſt behind you; then faſten a noose about his body, and ſtring him close up to the rafters from a high bearing-poſt,[1] that he may linger on in an agony."

178 Thus did he speak, and they did even as he had said; they went to the ſtore room, which they entered before Melanthius saw them, for he was busy searching for arms in the innermoſt part of the room, so the two took their ſtand on either side of the door and waited. By and by Melanthius came out with a helmet in one hand, and an old dry-rotted shield in the other, which

---

[1] I presume it was intended that there should be a hook driven into the bearing-poſt.

338

had been borne by Laertes when he was young, but which had been long since thrown aside, and the straps had become unsewn; on this the two seized him, dragged him back by the hair, and threw him struggling to the ground. They bent his hands and feet well behind his back, and bound them tight with a painful bond as Ulysses had told them; then they fastened a noose about his body and strung him up from a high pillar till he was close up to the rafters, and over him did you then vaunt, O swineherd Eumaeus, saying, " Melanthius, you will pass the night on a soft bed as you deserve. You will know very well when morning comes from the streams of Oceanus, and it is time for you to be driving in your goats for the suitors to feast on."

There, then, they left him in very cruel bondage, and 200 having put on their armour they closed the door behind them and went back to take their places by the side of Ulysses; whereon the four men stood in the cloister, fierce and full of fury; nevertheless, those who were in the body of the court were still both brave and many. Then Jove's daughter Minerva came up to them, having assumed the voice and form of Mentor. Ulysses was glad when he saw her and said, " Mentor, lend me your help, and forget not your old comrade, nor the many good turns he has done you. Besides, you are my age-mate."

But all the time he felt sure it was Minerva, and the 210 suitors from the other side raised an uproar when they saw her. Agelaus was the first to reproach her. " Mentor," he cried, " do not let Ulysses beguile you into siding with him and fighting the suitors. This is what we will do: when we have killed these people, father and son, we will kill you too. You shall pay for it with your head, and when we have killed you, we will take all you have, in doors or out, and bring it into hotch-pot with Ulysses' property; we will not let your sons live in your house, nor your daughters, nor shall your widow continue to live in the city of Ithaca."

224   This made Minerva still more furious, so she scolded Ulysses very angrily.[1] "Ulysses," said she, "your strength and prowess are no longer what they were when you fought for nine long years among the Trojans about the noble lady Helen. You killed many a man in those days, and it was through your stratagem that Priam's city was taken. How comes it that you are so lamentably less valiant now that you are on your own ground, face to face with the suitors in your own house? Come on, my good fellow, stand by my side and see how Mentor, son of Alcimus shall fight your foes and requite your kindnesses conferred upon him."

236   But she would not give him full victory as yet, for she wished still further to prove his own prowess and that of his brave son, so she flew up to one of the rafters in the roof of the cloister and sat upon it in the form of a swallow.

241   Meanwhile Agelaus son of Damastor, Eurynomus, Amphimedon, Demoptolemus, Pisander, and Polybus son of Polyctor bore the brunt of the fight upon the suitors' side; of all those who were still fighting for their lives they were by far the most valiant, for the others had already fallen under the arrows of Ulysses. Agelaus shouted to them and said, "My friends, he will soon have to leave off, for Mentor has gone away after having done nothing for him but brag. They are standing at the doors unsupported. Do not aim at him all at once, but six of you throw your spears first, and see if you cannot cover yourselves with glory by killing him. When he has fallen we need not be uneasy about the others."

---

[1] What for?

They threw their spears as he bade them, but Minerva 255 made them all of no effect. One hit the door post; another went against the door; the pointed shaft of another struck the wall; and as soon as they had avoided all the spears of the suitors Ulysses said to his own men, " My friends, I should say we too had better let drive into the middle of them, or they will crown all the harm they have done us by killing us outright."

They therefore aimed straight in front of them and 265 threw their spears.   Ulysses killed Demoptolemus, Telemachus Euryades, Eumaeus Elatus, while the stockman killed Pisander.   These all bit the dust, and as the others drew back into a corner Ulysses and his men rushed forward and regained their spears by drawing them from the bodies of the dead.

The suitors now aimed a second time, but again 272 Minerva made their weapons for the most part without effect.   One hit a bearing-post of the cloister; another went against the door; while the pointed shaft of another struck the wall.   Still, Amphimedon just took a piece of the top skin from off Telemachus's wrist, and Ctesippus managed to graze Eumaeus's shoulder above his shield; but the spear went on and fell to the ground. Then Ulysses and his men let drive into the crowd of suitors.   Ulysses hit Eurydamas, Telemachus Amphimedon, and Eumaeus Polybus.   After this the stockman hit Ctesippus in the breast, and taunted him saying, " Foul-mouthed son of Polytherses, do not be so foolish as to talk wickedly another time, but let heaven direct your speech, for the gods are far stronger than men.   I make you a present of this advice to repay you for the foot which you gave Ulysses when he was begging about in his own house."

Thus spoke the stockman, and Ulysses struck the son 292 of Damastor with a spear in close fight, while Telemachus hit Leocritus son of Evenor in the belly, and the dart went clean through him, so that he fell forward full on his face upon the ground. Then Minerva from her seat on the rafter held up her deadly aegis, and the hearts of the suitors quailed. They fled to the other end of the court like a herd of cattle maddened by the gadfly in early summer when the days are at their longest. As eagle-beaked, crook-taloned vultures from the mountains swoop down on the smaller birds that cower in flocks upon the ground, and kill them, for they cannot either fight or fly, and lookers on enjoy the sport—even so did Ulysses and his men fall upon the suitors and smite them on every side. They made a horrible groaning as their brains were being battered in, and the ground seethed with their blood.

310 Leiodes then caught the knees of Ulysses and said, "Ulysses I beseech you have mercy upon me and spare me. I never wronged any of the women in your house either in word or deed, and I tried to stop the others. I saw them, but they would not listen, and now they are paying for their folly. I was their sacrificing priest; if you kill me, I shall die without having done anything to deserve it, and shall have got no thanks for all the good that I did."

320 Ulysses looked sternly at him and answered, "If you were their sacrificing priest, you must have prayed many a time that it might be long before I got home again, and that you might marry my wife and have children by her. Therefore you shall die."

326 With these words he picked up the sword that Agelaus had dropped when he was being killed, and which was lying upon the ground. Then he struck Leiodes on the back of his neck, so that his head fell rolling in the dust while he was yet speaking.

330 The minstrel Phemius son of Terpes—he who had

been forced by the suitors to sing to them—now tried
to save his life. He was standing near towards the trap
door,[1] and held his lyre in his hand. He did not know
whether to fly out of the cloister and sit down by the
altar of Jove that was in the outer court, and on which
both Laertes and Ulysses had offered up the thigh bones
of many an ox, or whether to go straight up to Ulysses
and embrace his knees, but in the end he deemed it best
to embrace Ulysses' knees. So he laid his lyre on the
ground between the mixing-bowl[2] and the silver-
studded seat; then going up to Ulysses he caught hold
of his knees and said, " Ulysses, I beseech you have
mercy on me and spare me. You will be sorry for it
afterwards if you kill a bard who can sing both for gods
and men as I can. I make all my lays myself, and heaven
visits me with every kind of inspiration. I would sing
to you as though you were a god, do not therefore be
in such a hurry to cut my head off. Your own son
Telemachus will tell you that I did not want to frequent
your house and sing to the suitors after their meals,
but they were too many and too strong for me, so they
made me."

Telemachus heard him, and at once went up to his 354
father. " Hold! " he cried, " the man is guiltless, do
him no hurt; and we will spare Medon too, who was
always good to me when I was a boy, unless Philoetius
or Eumaeus has already killed him, or he has fallen in
your way when you were raging about the court."

Medon caught these words of Telemachus, for he 361
was crouching under a seat beneath which he had
hidden by covering himself up with a freshly flayed

---

[1] Gr. ἄγχι παρ' ὀρσοθύρην. This is not ἄγχι τῆς ὀρσοθύρης.

[2] From lines 333 and 341 of this book, and lines 145 and 146
of bk. xxi we can locate the approach to the ὀρσοθύρα with some
certainty.

heifer's hide, so he threw off the hide, went up to Telemachus, and laid hold of his knees.

367 "Here I am, my dear sir," said he, "Stay your hand therefore, and tell your father, or he will kill me in his rage against the suitors for having wasted his substance and been so foolishly disrespectful to yourself."

371 Ulysses smiled at him and answered, "Fear not; Telemachus has saved your life, that you may know in future, and tell other people, how greatly better good deeds prosper than evil ones. Go, therefore, outside the cloisters into the outer court, and be out of the way of the slaughter—you and the bard—while I finish my work here inside."

378 The pair went into the outer court as fast as they could, and sat down by Jove's great altar, looking fearfully round, and still expecting that they would be killed. Then Ulysses searched the whole court carefully over, to see if anyone had managed to hide himself and was still living, but he found them all lying in the dust and weltering in their blood. They were like fishes which fishermen have netted out of the sea, and thrown upon the beach to lie gasping for water till the heat of the sun makes an end of them. Even so were the suitors lying all huddled up one against the other.

390 Then Ulysses said to Telemachus, "Call nurse Euryclea; I have something to say to her."

393 Telemachus went and knocked at the door of the women's room. "Make haste," said he, "you old woman who have been set over all the other women in the house. Come outside; my father wishes to speak to you."

398 When Euryclea heard this she unfastened the door of the women's room and came out, following Telemachus. She found Ulysses among the corpses bespattered with blood and filth like a lion that has

just been devouring an ox, and his breast and both his cheeks are all bloody, so that he is a fearful sight; even so was Ulysses besmirched from head to foot with gore. When she saw all the corpses and such a quantity of blood, she was beginning to cry out for joy, for she saw that a great deed had been done; but Ulysses checked her, " Old woman," said he, " rejoice in silence; restrain yourself, and do not make any noise about it; it is an unholy thing to vaunt over dead men. Heaven's doom and their own evil deeds have brought these men to destruction, for they respected no man in the whole world, neither rich nor poor, who came near them, and they have come to a bad end as a punishment for their wickedness and folly. Now, however, tell me which of the women in the house have misconducted themselves, and who are innocent." [1]

" I will tell you the truth, my son," answered 419 Euryclea. " There are fifty women in the house whom we teach to do things, such as carding wool, and all kinds of household work. Of these, twelve in all [2] have misbehaved, and have been wanting in respect to me, and also to Penelope. They showed no disrespect to Telemachus, for he has only lately grown up, and his mother never permitted him to give orders to the female servants; but let me go upstairs and tell your wife all that has happened, for some god has been sending her to sleep."

" Do not wake her yet," answered Ulysses, " but tell 430 the women who have misconducted themselves to come to me."

Euryclea left the cloister to tell the women, and make 433

---

[1] But in xix, 500-502, Ulysses scolded Euryclea for offering information on this very point, and declared himself quite able to settle it for himself.

[2] There were a hundred and eight suitors.

them come to Ulysses; in the meantime he called Telemachus, the Stockman, and the swineherd. "Begin," said he, "to remove the dead, and make the women help you. Then, get sponges and clean water to swill down the tables and seats. When you have thoroughly cleansed the whole cloisters, take the women into the space between the domed room and the wall of the outer court, and run them through with your swords till they are quite dead, and have forgotten all about love and the way in which they used to lie in secret with the suitors."

446 On this the women came down in a body, weeping and wailing bitterly. First they carried the dead bodies out, and propped them up against one another in the gatehouse. Ulysses ordered them about and made them do their work quickly, so they had to carry the bodies out. When they had done this, they cleaned all the tables and seats with sponges and water, while Telemachus and the two others shovelled up the blood and dirt from the ground, and the women carried it all away and put it out of doors. Then when they had made the whole place quite clean and orderly, they took the women out and hemmed them in the narrow space between the wall of the domed room and that of the yard, so that they could not get away: and Telemachus said to the other two, "I shall not let these women die a clean death, for they were insolent to me and my mother, and used to sleep with the suitors."

465 So saying he made a ship's cable fast to one of the bearing-posts that supported the roof of the domed room, and secured it all around the building, at a good height, lest any of the women's feet should touch the ground; and as thrushes or doves beat against a net that has been set for them in a thicket just as they were getting to their nest, and a terrible fate awaits them, even

346

so did the women have to put their heads in nooses one
after the other and die most miserably.[1]   Their feet
moved convulsively for a while, but not for very long.

As for Melanthius, they took him through the cloister 474
into the inner court.   There they cut off his nose and
his ears; they drew out his vitals and gave them to the
dogs raw, and then in their fury they cut off his hands
and his feet.

When they had done this they washed their hands 478
and feet and went back into the house, for all was now
over; and Ulysses said to the dear old nurse Euryclea,

[1] Lord Grimthorpe, whose understanding does not lend itself
to easy imposition, has been good enough to write to me about
my conviction that the Odyssey was written by a woman, and
to send me some remarks upon the gross absurdity of the inci-
dent here recorded.   It is plain that all the authoress cared about
was that the women should be hanged : as for attempting to
realize, or to make her readers realize, how the hanging was done,
this was of no consequence.   The reader must take her word for
it and ask no questions.   Lord Grimthorpe wrote :

" I had better send you my ideas about Nausicaa's hanging
of the maids (not ' maidens,' of whom Froude wrote so well in his
Science of History) before I forget it all.   Luckily for me Liddell
and Scott have specially translated most of the doubtful words,
referring to this very place.

" *A ship's cable*.   I don't know how big a ship she meant,
but it must have been a very small one indeed if its ' cable '
could be used to tie tightly round a woman's neck, and still
more round a dozen of them ' in a row,' besides being strong
enough to hold them and pull them all up.

" A dozen average women would need the weight and strength
of more than a dozen strong heavy men even over the best pulley
hung to the roof over them; and the idea of pulling them up by
a rope going anyhow round a pillar (κίονοc) is absurdly impossible ; and how a dozen of them could be hung dangling
round one post is a problem which a senior wrangler would be
puzzled to answer. . . . She had better have let Telemachus
use his sword as he had intended till she changed his mind for
him."

" Bring me sulphur, which cleanses all pollution, and fetch fire also that I may burn it, and purify the cloisters. Go, moreover, and tell Penelope to come here with her attendants, and also all the maid servants that are in the house."

485 " All that you have said is true," answered Euryclea, " but let me bring you some clean clothes – a shirt and cloak. Do not keep these rags on your back any longer. It is not right."

490 " First light me a fire," replied Ulysses.

492 She brought the fire and sulphur, as he had bidden her, and Ulysses thoroughly purified the cloisters and both the inner and outer courts. Then she went inside to call the women and tell them what had happened; whereon they came from their apartment with torches in their hands, and pressed round Ulysses to embrace him, kissing his head and shoulders and taking hold of his hands. It made him feel as if he should like to

501 weep, for he remembered every one of them.[1]

---

[1] Then they had all been in Ulysses' service over twenty years ; perhaps the twelve guilty ones had been engaged more recently.

EURYCLEA NOW WENT UPSTAIRS LAUGH-
ing to tell her mistress that her dear husband had
come home. Her aged knees became young again
and her feet were nimble for joy as she went up to
her mistress and bent over her head to speak to her.
"Wake up Penelope, my dear child," she exclaimed,
"and see with your own eyes something that you have
been wanting this long time past. Ulysses has at last
indeed come home again, and has killed the suitors
who were giving so much trouble in his house, eating
up his estate and ill-treating his son."

"My good nurse," answered Penelope, "you must 10
be mad. The gods sometimes send some very sensible
people out of their minds, and make foolish people
become sensible. This is what they must have been
doing to you; for you always used to be a reasonable
person. Why should you thus mock me when I have
trouble enough already–talking such nonsense, and
waking me up out of a sweet sleep that had taken
possession of my eyes and closed them? I have never
slept so soundly from the day my poor husband went
to that city with the ill-omened name. Go back again
into the women's room; if it had been any one else,
who had woke me up to bring me such absurd news
I should have sent her away with a severe scolding.
As it is, your age shall protect you."

"My dear child," answered Euryclea, "I am not 25
mocking you. It is quite true as I tell you that Ulysses
is come home again. He was the stranger whom they
all kept on treating so badly in the cloister. Telemachus knew all the time that he was come back, but
kept his father's secret that he might have his revenge
on all these wicked people."

32   Then Penelope sprang up from her couch, threw her arms round Euryclea, and wept for joy. " But my dear nurse," said she, " explain this to me; if he has really come home as you say, how did he manage to overcome the wicked suitors single handed, seeing what a number of them there always were? "

39   " I was not there," answered Euryclea, " and do not know; I only heard them groaning while they were being killed. We sat crouching and huddled up in a corner of the women's room with the doors closed, till your son came to fetch me because his father sent him. Then I found Ulysses ſtanding over the corpses that were lying on the ground all round him, one on top of the other. You would have enjoyed it if you could have seen him ſtanding there all bespattered with blood and filth, and looking juſt like a lion. But the corpses are now all piled up in the gatehouse that is in the outer court, and Ulysses has lit a great fire to purify the house with sulphur. He has sent me to call you, so come with me that you may both be happy together after all; for now at laſt the desire of your heart has been fulfilled; your husband is come home to find both wife and son alive and well, and to take his revenge in his own house on the suitors who behaved so badly to him."

58   " My dear nurse," said Penelope, " do not exult too confidently over all this. You know how delighted every one would be to see Ulysses come home—more particularly myself, and the son who has been born to both of us; but what you tell me cannot be really true. It is some god who is angry with the suitors for their great wickedness, and has made an end of them; for they respeſted no man in the whole world, neither rich nor poor, who came near them, and they have come to a bad end in consequence of their iniquity. Ulysses is dead far away from the Achaean land; he will never return home again."

Then nurse Euryclea said, " My child, what are you 69 talking about? but you were always hard of belief, and have made up your mind that your husband is never coming, although he is in the house and by his own fire side at this very moment. Besides I can give you another proof; when I was washing him I perceived the scar which the wild boar gave him, and I wanted to tell you about it, but in his wisdom he would not let me, and clapped his hands over my mouth; so come with me and I will make this bargain with you—if I am deceiving you, you may have me killed by the most cruel death you can think of."

" My dear nurse," said Penelope, " however wise you 80 may be you can hardly fathom the counsels of the gods. Nevertheless, we will go in search of my son, that I may see the corpses of the suitors, and the man who has killed them."

On this she came down from her upper room, and 85 while doing so she considered whether she should keep at a distance from her husband and question him, or whether she should at once go up to him and embrace him. When, however, she had crossed the stone floor of the cloister, she sat down opposite Ulysses by the fire, against the wall at right angles [1] [to that by which she had entered], while Ulysses sat near one of the bearing-posts, looking upon the ground, and waiting to see what his brave wife would say to him when she saw him. For a long time she sat silent and as one lost in amazement. At one moment she looked him full in the face, but then again directly, she was misled by his shabby clothes and failed to recognize him,[2] till Telemachus began to reproach her and said:

[1] Translation very doubtful – *cf*. Il., xxiv, 598.
[2] But why could she not at once ask to see the scar, of which Euryclea had told her, or why could not Ulysses have shown it to her ?

97 " Mother – but you are so hard that I cannot call you by such a name – why do you keep away from my father in this way? Why do you not sit by his side and begin talking to him and asking him questions? No other woman could bear to keep away from her husband when he had come back to her after twenty years of absence, and after having gone through so much; but your heart always was as hard as a stone."

104 Penelope answered, " My son, I am so lost in astonishment that I can find no words in which either to ask questions or to answer them. I cannot even look him straight in the face. Still, if he really is Ulysses come back to his own home again, we shall get to understand one another better by and by, for there are tokens with which we two are alone acquainted, and which are hidden from all others."

111 Ulysses smiled at this, and said to Telemachus, " Let your mother put me to any proof she likes; she will make up her mind about it presently. She rejects me for the moment and believes me to be somebody else, because I am covered with dirt and have such bad clothes on; let us, however, consider what we had better do next. When one man has killed another, even though he was not one who would leave many friends to take up his quarrel, the man who has killed him must still say good bye to his friends and fly the country; whereas we have been killing the stay of a whole town, and all the picked youth of Ithaca. I would have you consider this matter."

123 " Look to it yourself, father," answered Telemachus, " for they say you are the wisest counsellor in the world, and that there is no other mortal man who can compare with you. We will follow you with right good will, nor shall you find us fail you in so far as our strength holds out."

"I will say what I think will be best," answered 129 Ulysses. "First wash and put your shirts on; tell the maids also to go to their own room and dress; Phemius shall then strike up a dance tune on his lyre, so that if people outside hear, or any of the neighbours, or some one going along the street happens to notice it, they may think there is a wedding in the house, and no rumours about the death of the suitors will get about in the town, before we can escape to the woods upon my own land. Once there, we will settle which of the courses heaven vouchsafes us shall seem wisest."

Thus did he speak, and they did even as he had said. 141 First they washed and put their shirts on, while the women got ready. Then Phemius took his lyre and set them all longing for sweet song and stately dance. The house re-echoed with the sound of men and women dancing, and the people outside said, "I suppose the queen has been getting married at last. She ought to be ashamed of herself for not continuing to protect her husband's property until he comes home."[1]

This was what they said, but they did not know what 152 it was that had been happening. The upper servant Eurynome washed and anointed Ulysses in his own house and gave him a shirt and cloak, while Minerva made him look taller and stronger than before; she also made the hair grow thick on the top of his head, and flow down in curls like hyacinth blossoms; she glorified him about the head and shoulders just as a skilful workman who has studied art of all kinds under Vulcan or Minerva—and his work is full of beauty—enriches a piece of silver plate by gilding it. He came from the bath looking like one of the immortals, and sat down opposite his wife on the seat he had left. "My dear,"

[1] The people of Ithaca seem to have been as fond of carping as the Phaeacians were in vi, 273, etc.

said he, " heaven has endowed you with a heart more unyielding than woman ever yet had. No other woman could bear to keep away from her husband when he had come back to her after twenty years of absence, and after having gone through so much. But come, nurse, get a bed ready for me; I will sleep alone, for this woman has a heart as hard as iron."

173 " My dear," answered Penelope, " I have no wish to set myself up, nor to depreciate you; but I am not struck by your appearance, for I very well remember what kind of a man you were when you set sail from Ithaca. Nevertheless, Euryclea, take his bed outside the bed chamber that he himself built. Bring the bed outside this room, and put bedding upon it with fleeces, good coverlets, and blankets."

181 She said this to try him, but Ulysses was very angry and said, " Wife, I am much displeased at what you have just been saying. Who has been taking my bed from the place in which I left it? He must have found it a hard task, no matter how skilled a workman he was, unless some god came and helped him to shift it. There ·- no man living, however strong and in his prime, who could move it from its place, for it is a marvellous curiosity which I made with my very own hands. There was a young olive growing within the precincts of the house, in full vigour, and about as thick as a bearing-post. I built my room round this with strong walls of stone and a roof to cover them, and I made the doors strong and well-fitting. Then I cut off the top boughs of the olive tree and left the stump standing. This I dressed roughly from the root upwards and then worked with carpenter's tools well and skilfully, straightening my work by drawing a line on the wood, and making it into a bed-prop. I then bored a hole down the middle, and made it the centre-post of my

bed, at which I worked till I had finished it, inlaying it
with gold and silver; after this I stretched a hide of
crimson leather from one side of it to the other. So
you see I know all about it, and I desire to learn
whether it is still there, or whether any one has been
removing it by cutting down the olive tree at its roots."

When she heard the sure proofs Ulysses now gave 205
her, she fairly broke down. She flew weeping to his
side, flung her arms about his neck, and kissed him.
" Do not be angry with me Ulysses," she cried, " you,
who are the wisest of mankind. We have suffered,
both of us. Heaven has denied us the happiness of
spending our youth, and of growing old, together; do
not then be aggrieved or take it amiss that I did not
embrace you thus as soon as I saw you. I have been
shuddering all the time through fear that someone might
come here and deceive me with a lying story; for there
are many very wicked people going about. Jove's
daughter Helen would never have yielded herself to
a man from a foreign country, if she had known that the
sons of Achaeans would come after her and bring her
back. Heaven put it in her heart to do wrong, and she
gave no thought to that sin, which has been the source
of all our sorrows. Now, however, that you have
convinced me by showing that you know all about our
bed (which no human being has ever seen but you and
I and a single maid servant, the daughter of Actor, who
was given me by my father on my marriage, and who
keeps the doors of our room) hard of belief though I
have been I can mistrust no longer."

Then Ulysses in his turn melted, and wept as he 231
clasped his dear and faithful wife to his bosom. As the
sight of land is welcome to men who are swimming
towards the shore, when Neptune has wrecked their
ship with the fury of his winds and waves—a few alone

355

reach the land, and these, covered with brine, are thankful when they find themselves on firm ground and out of danger—even so was her husband welcome to her as she looked upon him, and she could not tear her two fair arms from about his neck. Indeed they would have gone on indulging their sorrow till rosy-fingered morn appeared, had not Minerva determined otherwise, and held night back in the far west, while she would not suffer Dawn to leave Oceanus, nor to yoke the two steeds Lampus and Phaethon that bear her onward to break the day upon mankind.

246 At last, however, Ulysses said, " Wife, we have not yet reached the end of our troubles. I have an unknown amount of toil still to undergo. It is long and difficult, but I must go through with it, for thus the shade of Teiresias prophesied concerning me, on the day when I went down into Hades to ask about my return and that of my companions. But now let us go to bed, that we may lie down and enjoy the blessed boon of sleep."

256 " You shall go to bed as soon as you please," replied Penelope, " now that the gods have sent you home to your own good house and to your country. But as heaven has put it in your mind to speak of it, tell me about the task that lies before you. I shall have to hear about it later, so it is better that I should be told at once."

263 " My dear," answered Ulysses, " why should you press me to tell you? Still, I will not conceal it from you, though you will not like it. I do not like it myself, for Teiresias bade me travel far and wide, carrying an oar, till I came to a country where the people have never heard of the sea, and do not even mix salt with their food. They know nothing about ships, nor oars that are as the wings of a ship. He gave me this certain token which I will not hide from you. He said that a

356

wayfarer should meet me and ask me whether it was a winnowing shovel that I had on my shoulder. On this, I was to fix my oar in the ground and sacrifice a ram, a bull, and a boar to Neptune; after which I was to go home and offer hecatombs to all the gods in heaven, one after the other. As for myself, he said that death should come to me from the sea, and that my life should ebb away very gently when I was full of years and peace of mind, and my people should bless me. All this, he said, should surely come to pass."

And Penelope said, " If the gods are going to vouch- 286 safe you a happier time in your old age, you may hope then to have some respite from misfortune."

Thus did they converse. Meanwhile Eurynome and 288 the nurse took torches and made the bed ready with soft coverlets; as soon as they had laid them, the nurse went back into the house to go to her rest, leaving the bed chamber woman Eurynome[1] to show Ulysses and Penelope to bed by torch light. When she had conducted them to their room she went back, and they then came joyfully to the rites of their own old bed. Telemachus, Philoetius, and the swineherd now left off dancing, and made the women leave off also. They then laid themselves down to sleep in the cloisters.

When Ulysses and Penelope had had their fill of love 300 they fell talking with one another. She told him how much she had had to bear in seeing the house filled with a crowd of wicked suitors who had killed so many sheep and oxen on her account, and had drunk so many casks of wine. Ulysses in his turn told her what he had

---

[1] See note on Od., xx, 4. Ulysses' bedroom does not appear to have been upstairs, nor yet quite within the house. Is it possible that it was " the domed room " round the outside of which the erring maids were, for aught we have heard to the contrary, still hanging ?

suffered, and how much trouble he had himself given
to other people. He told her everything, and she was
so delighted to listen that she never went to sleep till he
had ended his whole story.

310   He began with his victory over the Cicons, and how
he thence reached the fertile land of the Lotus-eaters.
He told her all about the Cyclops and how he had
punished him for having so ruthlessly eaten his brave
comrades; how he then went on to Aeolus, who
received him hospitably and furthered him on his way,
but even so he was not to reach home, for to his great
grief a hurricane carried him out to sea again; how he
went on to the Laestrygonian city Telepylos, where the
people destroyed all his ships with their crews, save
himself and his own ship only. Then he told of cunning
Circe and her craft, and how he sailed to the chill house
of Hades, to consult the ghost of the Theban prophet
Teiresias, and how he saw his old comrades in arms, and
his mother who bore him and brought him up when
he was a child; how he then heard the wondrous singing of the Sirens, and went on to the wandering rocks
and terrible Charybdis and to Scylla, whom no man
had ever yet passed in safety; how his men then ate
the cattle of the sun-god, and how Jove therefore struck
the ship with his thunderbolts, so that all his men
perished together, himself alone being left alive; how
at last he reached the Ogygian island and the nymph
Calypso, who kept him there in a cave, and fed him, and
wanted him to marry her, in which case she intended
making him immortal so that he should never grow old,
but she could not persuade him to let her do so; and
how after much suffering he had found his way to the
Phaeacians, who had treated him as though he had been
a god, and sent him back in a ship to his own country
after having given him gold, bronze, and raiment in
great abundance. This was the last thing about which

he told her, for here a deep sleep took hold upon him and eased the burden of his sorrows.

Then Minerva bethought her of another matter. 344 When she deemed that Ulysses had had enough both of his wife and of repose, she bade gold-enthroned Dawn rise out of Oceanus that she might shed light upon mankind. On this, Ulysses rose from his comfortable bed and said to Penelope, " Wife, we have both of us had our full share of troubles, you, here, in lamenting my absence, and I in being prevented from getting home though I was longing all the time to do so. Now, however, that we have at last come together, take care of the property that is in the house. As for the sheep and goats which the wicked suitors have eaten, I will take many myself by force from other people, and will compel the Achaeans to make good the rest till they shall have filled all my yards. I am now going to the wooded lands out in the country to see my father who has so long been grieved on my account, and to yourself I will give these instructions, though you have little need of them. At sunrise it will at once get abroad that I have been killing the suitors; go upstairs, therefore,[1] and stay there with your women. See nobody and ask no questions." [2]

As he spoke he girded on his armour. Then he 366 roused Telemachus, Philoetius, and Eumaeus, and told them all to put on their armour also. This they did, and armed themselves. When they had done so, they opened the gates and sallied forth, Ulysses leading the way. It was now daylight, but Minerva nevertheless concealed them in darkness and led them quickly out of the town.

372

[1] Ulysses' bedroom in the mind of the writer is here, too, apparently downstairs.

[2] Penelope having been now sufficiently whitewashed, disappears from the poem.

THEN MERCURY OF CYLLENE SUMMONED
the ghosts of the suitors, and in his hand he held
the fair golden wand with which he seals men's
eyes in sleep or wakes them just as he pleases;
with this he roused the ghosts and led them, while they
followed whining and gibbering behind him. As bats
fly squealing in the hollow of some great cave, when
one of them has fallen out of the cluster in which they
hang, even so did the ghosts whine and squeal as Mercury
the healer of sorrow led them down into the dark abode
of death. When they had passed the waters of Oceanus
and the rock Leucas, they came to the gates of the sun
and the land of dreams, whereon they reached the
meadow of asphodel where dwell the souls and shadows
of them that can labour no more.

15 Here they found the ghost of Achilles son of Peleus,
with those of Patroclus, Antilochus, and Ajax, who
was the finest and handsomest man of all the Danaans
after the son of Peleus himself.

19 They gathered round the ghost of the son of Peleus,
and the ghost of Agamemnon joined them, sorrowing
bitterly. Round him were gathered also the ghosts of
those who had perished with him in the house of
Aegisthus; and the ghost of Achilles spoke first.

24 "Son of Atreus," it said, " we used to say that Jove
had loved you better from first to last than any other
hero, for you were captain over many and brave men,
when we were all fighting together before Troy; yet
the hand of death, which no mortal can escape, was laid
upon you all too early. Better for you had you fallen
at Troy in the hey-day of your renown, for the Achaeans
would have built a mound over your ashes, and your

360

son would have been heir to your good name, whereas
it has now been your lot to come to a most miserable
end."

"Happy son of Peleus," answered the ghost of 35
Agamemnon, "for having died at Troy far from Argos,
while the bravest of the Trojans and the Achaeans fell
round you fighting for your body. There you lay in
the whirling clouds of dust, all huge and hugely, heed-
less now of your chivalry. We fought the whole of the
livelong day, nor should we ever have left off if Jove
had not sent a hurricane to stay us. Then, when we had
borne you to the ships out of the fray, we laid you on
your bed and cleansed your fair skin with warm water
and with ointments. The Danaans tore their hair and
wept bitterly round about you. Your mother, when
she heard, came with her immortal nymphs from out of
the sea, and the sound of a great wailing went forth
over the waters so that the Achaeans quaked for fear.
They would have fled panic-stricken to their ships had
not wise old Nestor whose counsel was ever truest
checked them saying, 'Hold, Argives, fly not sons of
the Achaeans, this is his mother coming from the sea
with her immortal nymphs to view the body of her son.'

"Thus he spoke, and the Achaeans feared no more. 57
The daughters of the old man of the sea stood round you
weeping bitterly, and clothed you in immortal raiment.
The nine muses also came and lifted up their sweet
voices in lament–calling and answering one another;
there was not an Argive but wept for pity of the dirge
they chaunted. Days and nights seven and ten we
mourned you, mortals and immortals, but on the
eighteenth day we gave you to the flames, and many a
fat sheep with many an ox did we slay in sacrifice
around you. You were burnt in raiment of the gods,
with rich resins and with honey, while heroes, horse and

361

foot, clashed their armour round the pile as you were
burning, with the tramp as of a great multitude. But
when the flames of heaven had done their work, we
gathered your white bones at daybreak and laid them in
ointments and in pure wine. Your mother brought us
a golden vase to hold them—gift of Bacchus, and work
of Vulcan himself; in this we mingled your bleached
bones with those of Patroclus who had gone before you,
and separate we enclosed also those of Antilochus, who
had been closer to you than any other of your comrades
now that Patroclus was no more.

80 "Over these the host of the Argives built a noble
tomb, on a point jutting out over the open Hellespont,
that it might be seen from far out upon the sea by those
now living and by them that shall be born hereafter.
Your mother begged prizes from the gods, and offered
them to be contended for by the noblest of the Achaeans.
You must have been present at the funeral of many a
hero, when the young men gird themselves and make
ready to contend for prizes on the death of some great
chieftain, but you never saw such prizes as silver-footed
Thetis offered in your honour; for the gods loved you
well. Thus even in death your fame, Achilles, has not
been lost, and your name lives evermore among all
mankind. But as for me, what solace had I when the
days of my fighting were done? For Jove willed my
destruction on my return, by the hands of Aegisthus
and those of my wicked wife."

98 Thus did they converse, and presently Mercury came
up to them with the ghosts of the suitors who had been
killed by Ulysses. The ghosts of Agamemnon and
Achilles were astonished at seeing them, and went up
to them at once. The ghost of Agamemnon recognized
Amphimedon son of Melaneus, who lived in Ithaca and
had been his host, so it began to talk to him.

" Amphimedon," it said, " what has happened to all 106
you fine young men–all of an age too–that you are
come down here under the ground?   One could pick
no finer body of men from any city.   Did Neptune
raise his winds and waves against you when you were at
sea, or did your enemies make an end of you on the
mainland when you were cattle-lifting or sheep-stealing,
or while fighting in defence of their wives and city?
Answer my question, for I have been your guest.   Do
you not remember how I came to your house with
Menelaus, to persuade Ulysses to join us with his ships
against Troy?   It was a whole month ere we could
resume our voyage, for we had hard work to persuade
Ulysses to come with us."

And the ghost of Amphimedon answered, " Aga- 120
memnon, son of Atreus, king of men, I remember
everything that you have said, and will tell you fully
and accurately about the way in which our end was
brought about.   Ulysses had been long gone, and we
were courting his wife, who did not say point blank
that she would not marry, nor yet bring matters to an
end, for she meant to compass our destruction: this,
then, was the trick she played us.   She set up a great
tambour frame in her room and began to work on an
enormous piece of fine needlework.   ' Sweethearts,'
said she, ' Ulysses is indeed dead, still, do not press me
to marry again immediately; wait–for I would not
have my skill in needlework perish unrecorded–till I
have completed a pall for the hero Laertes, against the
time when death shall take him.   He is very rich, and
the women of the place will talk if he is laid out without
a pall.'   This is what she said, and we assented; whereupon we could see her working upon her great web
all day long, but at night she would unpick the stitches
again by torchlight.   She fooled us in this way for three

years without our finding it out, but as time wore on and she was now in her fourth year, in the waning of moons and many days had been accomplished, one of her maids who knew what she was doing told us, and we caught her in the act of undoing her work, so she had to finish it whether she would or no; and when she showed us the robe she had made, after she had had it washed,[1] its splendour was as that of the sun or moon.

149   " Then some malicious god conveyed Ulysses to the upland farm where his swineherd lives. Thither presently came also his son, returning from a voyage to Pylos, and the two came to the town when they had hatched their plot for our destruction. Telemachus came first, and then after him, accompanied by the swineherd, came Ulysses, clad in rags and leaning on a staff as though he were some miserable old beggar. He came so unexpectedly that none of us knew him, not even the older ones among us, and we reviled him and threw things at him. He endured both being struck and insulted without a word, though he was in his own house; but when the will of Aegis-bearing Jove inspired him, he and Telemachus took the armour and hid it in an inner chamber, bolting the doors behind them. Then he cunningly made his wife offer his bow and a quantity of iron to be contended for by us ill-fated suitors; and this was the beginning of our end, for not one of us could string the bow–nor nearly do so. When it was about to reach the hands of Ulysses,

[1] So practised a washerwoman as our authoress doubtless knew that by this time the web must have become such a wreck that it would have gone to pieces in the wash.

A lady points out to me, just as these sheets are leaving my hands, that no really good needlewoman–no one, indeed, whose work or character was worth consideration–could have endured, no matter for what reason, the unpicking of her day's work, day after day for between three and four years.

we all of us shouted out that it should not be given him, no matter what he might say, but Telemachus insisted on his having it. When he had got it in his hands he strung it with ease and sent his arrow through the iron. Then he stood on the floor of the cloister and poured his arrows on the ground, glaring fiercely about him. First he killed Antinous, and then, aiming straight before him, he let fly his deadly darts and they fell thick on one another. It was plain that some one of the gods was helping them, for they fell upon us with might and main throughout the cloisters, and there was a hideous sound of groaning as our brains were being battered in, and the ground seethed with our blood. This, Agamemnon, is how we came by our end, and our bodies are lying still uncared for in the house of Ulysses, for our friends at home do not yet know what has happened, so that they cannot lay us out and wash the black blood from our wounds, making moan over us according to the offices due to the departed."

" Happy Ulysses, son of Laertes," replied the ghost 191 of Agamemnon, " you are indeed blessed in the possession of a wife endowed with such rare excellence of understanding, and so faithful to her wedded lord as Penelope the daughter of Icarius. The fame, therefore, of her virtue shall never die, and the immortals shall compose a song that shall be welcome to all mankind in honour of the constancy of Penelope. How far otherwise was the wickedness of the daughter of Tyndareus who killed her lawful husband; her song shall be hateful among men, for she has brought disgrace on all womankind even on the good ones."

Thus did they converse in the house of Hades deep 203 down within the bowels of the earth. Meanwhile Ulysses and the others passed out of the town and soon reached the fair and well-tilled farm of Laertes, which he had reclaimed with infinite labour. Here was his house, with a lean-to running all round it, where the slaves who worked for him slept and sat and ate, while inside the house there was an old Sicel woman, who looked after him in this his country-farm. When Ulysses got there, he said to his son and to the other two:

214 "Go to the house, and kill the beſt pig that you can find for dinner. Meanwhile I want to see whether my father will know me, or fail to recognize me after so long an absence."

219 He then took off his armour and gave it to Eumaeus and Philoetius, who went ſtraight on to the house, while he turned off into the vineyard to make trial of his father. As he went down into the great orchard, he did not see Dolius, nor any of his sons nor of the other bondsmen, for they were all gathering thorns to make a fence for the vineyard, at the place where the old man had told them; he therefore found his father alone, hoeing a vine. He had on a dirty old shirt, patched and very shabby; his legs were bound round with thongs of oxhide to save him from the brambles, and he also wore sleeves of leather; he had a goat skin cap on his head, and was looking very woe-begone. When Ulysses saw him so worn, so old and full of sorrow, he ſtood ſtill under a tall pear tree and began to weep. He doubted whether to embrace him, kiss him, and tell him all about his having come home, or whether he should firſt queſtion him and see what he would say. In the end he deemed it beſt to be crafty with him, so in this mind he went up to his father, who was bending down and digging about a plant.

244 "I see, sir," said Ulysses, "that you are an excellent gardener—what pains you take with it, to be sure. There is not a single plant, not a fig tree, vine, olive,

pear, nor flower bed, but bears the trace of your attention. I trust, however, that you will not be offended
if I say that you take better care of your garden than of
yourself. You are old, unsavoury, and very meanly
clad. It cannot be because you are idle that your
master takes such poor care of you, indeed your face
and figure have nothing of the slave about them, and
proclaim you of noble birth. I should have said that
you were one of those who should wash well, eat well,
and lie soft at night as old men have a right to do; but
tell me, and tell me true, whose bondman are you, and
in whose garden are you working? Tell me also about
another matter. Is this place that I have come to really
Ithaca? I met a man just now who said so, but he was
a dull fellow, and had not the patience to hear my story
out when I was asking him about an old friend of mine,
whether he was still living, or was already dead and in
the house of Hades. Believe me when I tell you that
this man came to my house once when I was in my own
country and never yet did any stranger come to me
whom I liked better. He said that his family came from
Ithaca and that his father was Laertes, son of Arceisius.
I received him hospitably, making him welcome to all
the abundance of my house, and when he went away
I gave him all customary presents. I gave him seven
talents of fine gold, and a cup of solid silver with flowers
chased upon it. I gave him twelve light cloaks, and as
many pieces of tapestry; I also gave him twelve cloaks
of single fold, twelve rugs, twelve fair mantles, and an
equal number of shirts. To all this I added four good
looking women skilled in all useful arts, and I let him
take his choice."

His father shed tears and answered, " Sir, you have 280
indeed come to the country that you have named, but
it is fallen into the hands of wicked people. All this

wealth of presents has been given to no purpose. If
you could have found your friend here alive in Ithaca,
he would have entertained you hospitably and would
have requited your presents amply when you left him—
as would have been only right considering what you
had already given him. But tell me, and tell me true,
how many years is it since you entertained this guest—
my unhappy son, as ever was? Alas! He has perished
far from his own country; the fishes of the sea have
eaten him, or he has fallen a prey to the birds and wild
beasts of some continent. Neither his mother, nor I his
father, who were his parents, could throw our arms
about him and wrap him in his shroud, nor could his
excellent and richly dowered wife Penelope bewail her
husband as was natural upon his death bed, and close
his eyes according to the offices due to the departed.
But now, tell me truly for I want to know. Who and
whence are you—tell me of your town and parents?
Where is the ship lying that has brought you and your
men to Ithaca? Or were you a passenger on some
other man's ship, and those who brought you here have
gone on their way and left you?"

302 "I will tell you everything," answered Ulysses,
"quite truly. I come from Alybas, where I have a fine
house. I am son of king Apheidas, who is the son of
Polypemon. My own name is Eperitus; heaven drove
me off my course as I was leaving Sicania, and I have
been carried here against my will. As for my ship
it is lying over yonder, off the open country outside
the town, and this is the fifth year since Ulysses left my
country. Poor fellow, yet the omens were good for
him when he left me. The birds all flew on our right
hands, and both he and I rejoiced to see them as we
parted, for we had every hope that we should have
another friendly meeting and exchange presents."

368

A dark cloud of sorrow fell upon Laertes as he list- 315
ened. He filled both hands with the dust from off the
ground and poured it over his grey head, groaning
heavily as he did so. The heart of Ulysses was touched,
and his nostrils quivered as he looked upon his father;
then he sprang towards him, flung his arms about him
and kissed him, saying, " I am he, father, about whom
you are asking–I have returned after having been away
for twenty years. But cease your sighing and lamentation–we have no time to lose, for I should tell you that
I have been killing the suitors in my house, to punish
them for their insolence and crimes."

" If you really are my son Ulysses," replied Laertes, 327
" and have come back again, you must give me such
manifest proof of your identity as shall convince me."

" First observe this scar," answered Ulysses, " which 330
I got from a boar's tusk when I was hunting on Mount
Parnassus. You and my mother had sent me to Autolycus, my mother's father, to receive the presents which
when he was over here he had promised to give me.
Furthermore I will point out to you the trees in the
vineyard which you gave me, and I asked you all about
them as I followed you round the garden. We went
over them all, and you told me their names and what
they all were. You gave me thirteen pear trees, ten
apple trees, and forty fig trees; you also said you would
give me fifty rows of vines; there was corn planted
between each row, and they yield grapes of every kind
when the heat of heaven has been laid heavy upon
them."

Laertes' strength failed him when he heard the con- 345
vincing proofs which his son had given him. He threw
his arms about him, and Ulysses had to support him,
or he would have gone off into a swoon; but as soon
as he came to, and was beginning to recover his senses,

he said, " O father Jove, then you gods are still in Olympus after all, if the suitors have really been punished for their insolence and folly. Nevertheless, I am much afraid that I shall have all the townspeople of Ithaca up here directly, and they will be sending messengers everywhere throughout the cities of the Cephallenians."

356   Ulysses answered, " Take heart and do not trouble yourself about that, but let us go into the house hard by your garden. I have already told Telemachus, Philoetius, and Eumaeus to go on there and get dinner ready as soon as possible."

361   Thus conversing the two made their way towards the house. When they got there they found Telemachus with the stockman and the swineherd cutting up meat and mixing wine with water. Then the old Sicel woman took Laertes inside and washed him and anointed him with oil. She put him on a good cloak, and Minerva came up to him and gave him a more imposing presence, making him taller and stouter than before. When he came back his son was surprised to see him looking so like an immortal, and said to him, " My dear father, some one of the gods has been making you much taller and better-looking."

375   Laertes answered, " Would, by Father Jove, Minerva, and Apollo, that I were the man I was when I ruled among the Cephallenians, and took Nericum, that strong fortress on the foreland. If I were still what I then was and had been in our house yesterday with my armour on, I should have been able to stand by you and help you against the suitors. I should have killed a great many of them, and you would have rejoiced to see it."

383   Thus did they converse; but the others, when they had finished their work and the feast was ready, left off working, and took each his proper place on the benches

and seats. Then they began eating; by and by old
Dolius and his sons left their work and came up, for
their mother, the Sicel woman who looked after Laertes
now that he was growing old, had been to fetch them.
When they saw Ulysses and were certain it was he, they
ſtood there loſt in aſtonishment; but Ulysses scolded
them good-naturedly and said, " Sit down to your
dinner, old man, and never mind about your surprise;
we have been wanting to begin for some time and have
been waiting for you."

Then Dolius put out both his hands and went up to 397
Ulysses. " Sir," said he, seizing his maſter's hand and
kissing it at the wriſt, " we have long been wishing you
home: and now heaven has reſtored you to us after we
had given up hoping. All hail, therefore, and may the
gods prosper you.[1] But tell me, does Penelope already
know of your return, or shall we send some one to tell
her? "

" Old man," answered Ulysses, " she knows already, 407
so you need not trouble about that." On this he took
his seat, and the sons of Dolius gathered round Ulysses
to give him greeting and embrace him one after the
other; then they took their seats in due order near
Dolius their father.

While they were thus busy getting their dinner 412
ready, Rumour went round the town, and noised
abroad the terrible fate that had befallen the suitors; as
soon, therefore, as the people heard of it they gathered

---

[1] We muſt suppose Dolius not yet to know that his son
Melanthius had been tortured, mutilated, and ,left to die by
Ulysses' orders on the preceding day, and that his daughter
Melantho had been hanged. Dolius was probably exceptionally
simple-minded, and his name was ironical. So on Mt. Eryx
I was shown a man who was always called " Senza Malizia " or
" Guileless "–he being held exceptionally cunning.

from every quarter, groaning and hooting before the house of Ulysses. They took the dead away, buried every man his own, and put the bodies of those who came from elsewhere on board the fishing vessels, for the fishermen to take each of them to his own place. They then met angrily in the place of assembly, and when they were got together Eupeithes rose to speak. He was overwhelmed with grief for the death of his son Antinous, who had been the first man killed by Ulysses, so he said, weeping bitterly, " My friend, this man has done the Achaeans great wrong. He took many of our best men away with him in his fleet, and he has lost both ships and men; now, moreover, on his return he has been killing all the foremost men among the Cephallenians. Let us be up and doing before he can get away to Pylos or to Elis where the Epeans rule, or we shall be ashamed of ourselves for ever afterwards. It will be an everlasting disgrace to us if we do not avenge the murder of our sons and brothers. For my own part I should have no more pleasure in life, but had rather die at once. Let us be up, then, and after them, before they can cross over to the mainland."

438 He wept as he spoke and every one pitied him. But Medon and the bard Phemius had now woke up, and came to them from the house of Ulysses. Every one was astonished at seeing them, but they stood in the middle of the assembly, and Medon said, " Hear me, men of Ithaca. Ulysses did not do these things against the will of heaven. I myself saw an immortal god take the form of Mentor and stand beside him. This god appeared, now in front of him encouraging him, and now going furiously about the court and attacking the suitors, whereon they fell thick on one another."

450 On this pale fear laid hold of them, and old Halitherses, son of Mastor, rose to speak, for he was the

only man among them who knew both past and future;
so he spoke to them plainly and in all honesty, saying,

" Men of Ithaca, it is all your own fault that things 454
have turned out as they have; you would not listen to
me, nor yet to Mentor, when we bade you check the
folly of your sons who were doing much wrong in the
wantonness of their hearts—wasting the substance and
dishonouring the wife of a chieftain who they thought
would not return. Now, however, let it be as I say,
and do as I tell you. Do not go out against Ulysses,
or you may find that you have been drawing down evil
on your own heads."

This was what he said, and more than half raised a 463
loud shout, and at once left the assembly. But the rest
stayed where they were, for the speech of Halitherses
displeased them, and they sided with Eupeithes; they
therefore hurried off for their armour, and when they
had armed themselves, they met together in front of the
city, and Eupeithes led them on in their folly. He
thought he was going to avenge the murder of his son,
whereas in truth he was never to return, but was
himself to perish in his attempt.

Then Minerva said to Jove, " Father, son of Saturn, 472
king of kings, answer me this question—What do you
propose to do? Will you set them fighting still further,
or will you make peace between them? "

And Jove answered, " My child, why should you 477
ask me? Was it not by your own arrangement that
Ulysses came home and took his revenge upon the
suitors? Do whatever you like, but I will tell you what
I think will be the most reasonable arrangement. Now
that Ulysses is revenged, let them swear to a solemn
covenant, in virtue of which he shall continue to rule,
while we cause the others to forgive and forget the
massacre of their sons and brothers. Let them then all

become friends as heretofore, and let peace and plenty reign."

487   This was what Minerva was already eager to bring about, so down she darted from off the topmost summits of Olympus.

489   Now when Laertes and the others had done dinner, Ulysses began by saying, " Some of you go out and see if they are not getting close up to us." So one of Dolius's sons went as he was bid. Standing on the threshold he could see them all quite near, and said to Ulysses, " Here they are, let us put on our armour at once."

496   They put on their armour as fast as they could—that is to say Ulysses, his three men, and the six sons of Dolius. Laertes also and Dolius did the same—warriors by necessity in spite of their grey hair. When they had all put on their armour, they opened the gate and sallied forth, Ulysses leading the way.

502   Then Jove's daughter Minerva came up to them, having assumed the form and voice of Mentor. Ulysses was glad when he saw her, and said to his son Telemachus, " Telemachus, now that you are about to fight in an engagement, which will show every man's mettle, be sure not to disgrace your ancestors, who were eminent for their strength and courage all the world over."

510   " You say truly, my dear father," answered Telemachus, " and you shall see, if you will, that I am in no mind to disgrace your family."

513   Laertes was delighted when he heard this. " Good heavens," he exclaimed, " what a day I am enjoying: I do indeed rejoice at it. My son and grandson are vying with one another in the matter of valour."

516   On this Minerva came close up to him and said, " Son of Arceisius—best friend I have in the world—

374

pray to the blue-eyed damsel, and to Jove her father;
then poise your spear and hurl it."

As she spoke she infused fresh vigour into him, and ₅₂₀
when he had prayed to her he poised his spear and
hurled it. He hit Eupeithes' helmet, and the spear
went right through it, for the helmet stayed it not, and
his armour rang rattling round him as he fell heavily to
the ground. Meantime Ulysses and his son fell upon
the front line of the foe and smote them with their
swords and spears; indeed, they would have killed
every one of them, and prevented them from ever
getting home again, only Minerva raised her voice
aloud, and made every one pause. " Men of Ithaca,"
she cried, " cease this dreadful war, and settle the matter
at once without further bloodshed."

On this pale fear seized every one; they were so ₅₃₃
frightened that their arms dropped from their hands
and fell upon the ground at the sound of the goddess's
voice, and they fled back to the city for their lives.
But Ulysses gave a great cry, and gathering himself
together swooped down like a soaring eagle. Then the
son of Saturn sent a thunderbolt of fire that fell just
in front of Minerva, so she said to Ulysses, " Ulysses,
noble son of Laertes, stop this warful strife, or Jove will
be angry with you."

Thus spoke Minerva, and Ulysses obeyed her gladly. ₅₄₅
Then Minerva assumed the form and voice of Mentor,
and presently made a covenant of peace between the
two contending parties.   ₅₄₈

(Reprinted from *The Authoress of the Odyssey*)

THE ONLY POINTS ON WHICH I DIFFER from Mr. Lang are in respect of the inner court, which he sees as a roofed hall, but which I hold to have been open to the sky, except the covered cloister or μέγαρα σκιόεντα, an arrangement which is still very common in Sicilian houses, especially at Trapani and Palermo. I also differ from him in so far as I see no reason to think that the " stone pavement " was raised, and as believing the ὀρσοθύρα to have been at the top of Telemachus's tower, and called " in the wall " because the tower abutted on the wall; or it may have been a window high up in the tower. These are details: substantially my view of the action and scene during the killing of the suitors agrees with Mr. Lang's. I will not give the reasons which compel me to differ from Sir Richard Jebb [1] and Mr. Platt,[2] but will leave my plan of the house and the abridged translation to the judgement of the reader.

A was the body of the house, containing the women's apartments and other rooms. It had an upper story, in which was Penelope's room overlooking the court where the suitors passed the greater part of their time.

It also contained the store room, which seems to have been placed at the far end of the house, perhaps in a basement. The store room could be reached by a passage from a doorway A', and also by back passages from a side entrance A", which I suppose to have been the back door of the house. The women's apartments

[1] See *Journal of Hellenic Studies*, vol. vii, pp. 170-188, and *Introduction to Homer*, 3rd edit., 1888, pp. 57-62, and Appendix, Note 1.
[2] See *Journal of Philology*, vol. xxiv, p. 39, etc.

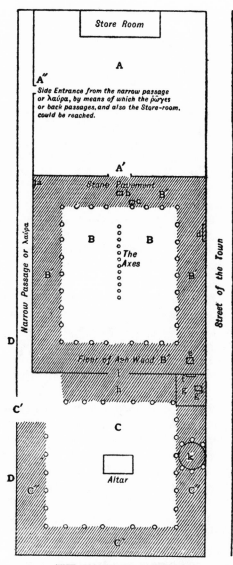

Store Room

A

A″
Side Entrance from the narrow passage
or λαύρα, by means of which the ῥῶγες
or back passages, and also the Store-room,
could be reached.

A′

Stone Pavement

a
b
c
B′

B

B

The
Axes

B″

B‴

B″

Narrow Passage or λαύρα

Street of the Town

d

D

Floor of Ash Wood B‴

e

f
g
g

h

C′

C″

C

Altar

k

D

C″

C‴

C‴

THE HOUSE OF ULYSSES

377

C C

opened on to the passage leading from A' to the store room.

B and B' were the Megaron or Megara, that is to say the inner court, of which B' was a covered cloister with a roof supported by bearing-posts with cross-beams and rafters. The open part of the court had no flooring but the natural soil. Animals seem to have been flayed and dressed here, for Medon, who was certainly in the inner court while the suitors were being killed, concealed himself under a freshly flayed ox (or heifer's) hide (xxii, 363).

B' was called the μέγαρα cκιόεντα or "shaded" part of the court, to distinguish it from that which was open to the sun. The end nearest the house was paved with stones, while that nearest the outer court (and probably the other two sides) were floored with ash. The part of the cloister that was paved with stone does not appear to have been raised above the level of the rest; at one end of the stone pavement there was a door a, opening on to a narrow passage; this door, though mentioned immediately after the ὀρcοθύρα or trap door (xxii, 126), which we shall come to presently, has no connection with it. About the middle of the pavement, during the trial of the axes, there was a seat b, from which Ulysses shot through the axes, and from which he sprang when he began to shoot the suitors; against one of the bearing-posts that supported the roof of the cloister, there was c, a spear stand.

All the four sides of the cloister were filled with small tables at which the suitors dined. A man could hold one of these tables before him as a shield (xxii, 74, 75).

In the cloisters were also,

d, an open hearth, or fire-place, in the wall at right angles to the one which abutted on the house. So, at least, I read τοίχου τοῦ ἑτέρου (xxiii, 90);

Appendix

e, the table at which the wine was mixed in the mixing-bowl as well, of course, as the other tables above mentioned;

f, a door leading into g, the tower in which Telemachus used to sleep [translating ἄγχι παρ' ὀρσοθύρην (xxii, 333) not " near the ὀρσοθύρα " but "near towards the ὀρσοθύρα "].

At the top of this tower there was a trap door g' (ὀρσοθύρα) through which it was possible to get out on to the roof of the tower and raise an alarm, but which afforded neither ingress nor egress—or, as I have said, the ὀρσοθύρα may have been a window.

C was the outer court or αὐλή, approached by C' the main entrance, or πρῶται θύραι, a covered gateway with a room over it. This covered gateway was the αἴθουςη ἐρίδουπος or reverberating portico which we meet with in other Odyssean houses, and with which we are so familiar in Italian and Sicilian houses at the present day. It was surrounded by C", covered sheds, or barns, in which carts, farm implements, and probably some farm produce would be stored. It contained

h, the prodomus, or vestibule in front of the inner court, into which the visitor would pass through

i, the πρόθυρον, or inner gateway (the word πρόθυρον, however, is used also for the outer gateway) and

k, the tholus, or vaulted room, about the exact position of which all we know is that it is described in xxii, 459, 460, as close up against the wall of the outer court. I suspect, but cannot prove it, that this was the room which Ulysses built round his bed (xxiii, 181-204).

D was the τυκτὸν δάπεδον, or level ground, in front of Ulysses' house, on which the suitors amused themselves playing at quoits, or aiming spears at a mark (iv, 625-627).